CATS

A COLLECTION OF STORIES, VERSE AND PROSE

CATS

A COLLECTION OF STORIES, VERSE AND PROSE

Edited by
Mark Bryant

CASTLE BOOKS

Originally published as *The Mammoth Book of Cats*

This edition published in 2002 by
CASTLE BOOKS
A division of Book Sales, Inc.
114 Northfield Avenue
Edison, New Jersey 08837

This edition published by arrangement with and permission of
Carroll & Graf Publishers, Inc.
161 William Street
New York, New York 10038

First published in the UK by Robinson Publishing 1999

First Carroll & Graf edition 1999

Copyright © Mark Bryant 1999

The author's moral right has been asserted.

ISBN: 0-7858-1558-9

Printed in the United States of America

Contents

Preface

Aldous Huxley once said that if you want to be a writer you should keep a pair of cats, preferably Siamese. Judging by the vast number of renowned literary men and women who have owned or been inspired by them throughout history, this would seem to be sound advice. From the finely honed lyrics of Keats and Baudelaire to the madcap waggery of Edward Lear and Lewis Carroll, from Aesop and Chaucer to James Herriot and Ellis Peters, the muse has, as it were, always followed the mews. Whether odes, fables, stories, limericks, songs, nursery rhymes or just plain caterwauls, cats have been a part of our literary heritage for centuries.

This book brings together some of the very best writings about cats of every variety, male and female, young and old. I have tried to make the anthology as balanced as the limitations of length and copyright availability have allowed and it contains work from the pens of both men and women. The material has been gathered from all periods of history, from Ancient Egypt up to the present day, and from all round the world, including contributions from Great Britain, Ireland, the USA, Germany, France, Switzerland and Russia. A wide variety of genres is represented, from humour and horror to romance and fantasy. As well as classic stories and poems, the collection includes extracts from essays, letters, diaries and journals, together with a number of rare and hitherto little-known items, old and new.

I am indebted to the many individuals and institutions who have helped me in my research for this book, not least the staff at the British Library and the Senate House Library, University of London. Particular thanks must also go to Nick Robinson, editors Krystyna Green and Sarah Lavelle, Andrew Tennant at Hewer Text and all the staff at Robinson

Publishing who have worked so hard to turn it into such an attractive volume.

Mark Bryant
London, 1999

THE
FIRESIDE
SPHINX

"Sitting drowsy in the fire-light,
winked and purred the mottled cat."
John Greenleaf Whittier (1807–92)

The Cat

ANONYMOUS

You see the beauty of the world
    Through eyes of unalloyed content,
And in my study chair upcurled,
    Move me to pensive wonderment.

I wish I knew your trick of thought,
    The perfect balance of your ways:
They seem an inspiration, caught
    From other laws in older days.

from the *Spectator*

The Cat by the Fire

LEIGH HUNT (1784–1859)

A blazing fire, a warm rug, candles lit and curtains drawn, the
kettle on for tea (nor do the "first circles" despise the preference
of a kettle to an urn, as the third or fourth may do), and finally,
the cat before you, attracting your attention – it is a scene
which everybody likes unless he has a morbid aversion to cats;
which is not common. There are some nice inquirers, it is true,
who are apt to make uneasy comparisons of cats with dogs – to
say they are not so loving, that they prefer the house to the
man, etc. But agreeably to the good old maxim, that "comparisons are odious", our readers, we hope, will continue to
like what is likable in anything, for its own sake, without trying
to render it unlikable from its inferiority to something else – a
process by which we might ingeniously contrive to put soot
into every dish that is set before us, and to reject one thing after
another, till we were pleased with nothing. Here is a good

fireside, and a cat to it; and it would be our own fault, if, in removing to another house and another fireside, we did not take care that the cat removed with us. Cats cannot look to the moving of goods, as men do. If we would have creatures considerate towards us, we must be so towards them. It is not to be expected of everybody, quadruped or biped, that they should stick to us in spite of our want of merit, like a dog or a benevolent sage. Besides, stories have been told of cats very much to the credit of their benignity; such as their following a master about like a dog, waiting at a gentleman's door to thank him for some obligation overnight, etc. And our readers may remember the history of the famous Godolphin Arabian, upon whose grave a cat that had lived with him in the stable went and stretched itself, and died.

The cat purrs, as if it applauded our consideration – and gently moves its tail. What an odd expression of the power to be irritable and the will to be pleased there is in its face, as it looks up at us! We must own, that we do not prefer a cat in the act of purring, or of looking in that manner. It reminds us of the sort of smile, or *simmer* (*simper* is too weak and fleeting a word) that is apt to be in the faces of irritable people when they are pleased to be in a state of satisfaction. We prefer, for a general expression, the cat in a quiet, unpretending state, and the human countenance with a look indicative of habitual grace and composure, as if it were not necessary to take any violent steps to prove its amiability – the "smile without a smile", as the poet beautifully calls it [...]

Poor Pussy! she looks up at us again [...] and symbolically gives a twist of a yawn and a lick to her whiskers. Now she proceeds to clean herself all over, having a just sense of the demands of her elegant person – beginning judiciously with her paws, and fetching amazing tongues at her hind-hips. Anon, she scratches her neck with a foot of rapid delight, leaning her head towards it, and shutting her eyes, half to accommodate the action of the skin, and half to enjoy the luxury. She then rewards her paws with a few more touches; look at the action of her head and neck, how pleasing it is, the ears pointed forward, and the neck gently arching to and fro. Finally, she gives a sneeze, and another twist of mouth and whiskers, and then, curling her tail towards her front claws, settles herself on her hind quarters, in an attitude of bland meditation.

What does she think of – of her saucer of milk at breakfast? or of the thump she got yesterday in the kitchen for stealing the meat? or of her own meat, the Tartar's dish, noble horse-flesh? or of her friend the cat next door, the most impassioned of serenaders? or of her little ones, some of whom are now large, and all of them gone? Is *that* among her recollections when she looks pensive? Does she taste of the noble prerogative-sorrows of man? [...]

That lapping of the milk out of the saucer is what one's human thirst cannot sympathize with. It seems as if there could be no satisfaction in such a series of atoms of drink. Yet the saucer is soon emptied; and there is a refreshment to one's ears in that sound of plashing with which the action is accompanied, and which seems indicative of a like comfort to Pussy's mouth. Her tongue is thin, and can make a spoon of itself. This, however, is common to other quadrupeds with the cat, and does not, therefore, more particularly belong to our feline consideration. Not so the electricity of its coat, which gives out sparks under the hand; its passion for the herb valerian (did the reader ever see one roll in it? it is a mad sight) and other singular delicacies of nature, among which, perhaps, is to be reckoned its taste for fish, a creature with whose element it has so little to do, that it is supposed even to abhor it; though lately we read somewhere of a swimming cat, that used to fish for itself. And this reminds us of an exquisite anecdote of dear, dogmatic, diseased, thoughtful, surly, charitable Johnson, who would go out of doors himself, and buy oysters for his cat, because his black servant was too proud to do it! Not that we condemn the black, in those enslaving, unliberating days. He had a right to the mistake, though we should have thought better of him had he seen farther, and subjected his pride to affection for such a master. But Johnson's true practical delicacy in the matter is beautiful. Be assured that he thought nothing of "condescension" in it, or of being eccentric. He was singular in some things, because he could not help it. But he hated eccentricity. No: in his best moments he felt himself simply to be a man, and a good man too, though a frail – one that in virtue as well as humility, and in a knowledge of his ignorance as well as his wisdom, was desirous of being a Christian philosopher; and accordingly he went out, and bought food for his hungry cat, because his poor negro was too proud to do it, and there was nobody else in the way whom he had a right to ask. What must anybody that saw him have thought, as he turned up Bolt Court! But doubtless he went as secretly as possible – that is to say, if he considered the thing at all. His friend Garrick could not have done as much! He was too grand, and on the great "stage" of life. Goldsmith could; but he would hardly have thought of it. Beauclerc might; but he would have thought it necessary to excuse it with a jest or a wager, or some such thing. Sir Joshua Reynolds, with his fashionable, fine-lady-painting hand, would certainly have shrunk from it. Burke would have reasoned himself into its propriety, but he would have reasoned himself out again. Gibbon! Imagine its being put into the head of Gibbon!! He and his bag-wig would have started with all the horror of a gentleman-usher; and he would have rung the bell for the cook's-deputy's-under-assistant-errand-boy.

Cats at firesides live luxuriously, and are the picture of comfort; but lest they should not bear their portion of trouble in this world, they have the drawbacks of being liable to be shut out of doors on cold nights, beatings from the "aggravated" cooks, overpettings of children (how should we like to be squeezed and pulled about in that manner by some great patronizing giants?) and last, not least, horrible merciless tramples of unconscious human feet and unfeeling legs of chairs. Elegance, comfort, and security seem the order of the day on all sides, and you are going to sit down to dinner, or to music, or to take tea, when all of a sudden the cat gives a squall as if she was mashed; and you are not sure that the fact is otherwise. Yet she gets in the way again, as before; and dares all the feet and mahogany in the room. Beautiful present sufficingness of a cat's imagination! Confined to the snug circle of her own sides, and the two next inches of rug or carpet.

from *Essays* (*c.* 1870)

Le Chat Noir

GRAHAM TOMSON (1863–1911)

Half loving-kindliness, and half disdain,
Thou comest to my call, serenely suave,
With humming speech and gracious gesture grave,
In salutation courtly and urbane.
Yet must I humble me thy grace to gain,
For wiles may win thee, but no arts enslave,
And nowhere gladly thou abidest, save
Where naught disturbs the concord of thy reign.
Sphinx of my quiet hearth! who deignst to dwell
Friend of my toil, companion of mine ease,
Thine is the lore of Ra and Rameses;
That men forget dost thou remember well,
Beholden still in blinking reveries,
With sombre, sea-green gaze inscrutable.

To a Cat

ALGERNON CHARLES SWINBURNE (1837–1909)

Stately, kindly, lordly friend,
    Condescend
Here to sit by me, and turn
Glorious eyes that smile and burn,
Golden eyes, love's lustrous meed,
On the golden page I read.

All your wondrous wealth of hair,
   Dark and fair,
Silken-shaggy, soft and bright
As the clouds and beams of night,
Pays my reverent hand's caress
Back with friendlier gentleness.

Dogs may fawn on all and some,
   As they come;
You, a friend of loftier mind,
Answer friends alone in kind;
Just your foot upon my hand
Softly bids it understand.

Morning round this silent sweet
   Garden-seat
Sheds its wealth of gathering light,
Thrills the gradual clouds with might,
Changes woodland, orchard, heath,
Lawn, and garden there beneath.

Fair and dim they gleamed below:
   Now they glow
Deep as even your sunbright eyes,
Fair as even the wakening skies.
Can it not or can it be
Now that you give thanks to see?

May not you rejoice as I,
   Seeing the sky
Change to heaven revealed, and bid
Earth reveal the heaven it hid
All night long from stars and moon,
Now the sun sets all in tune?

What within you wakes with day
   Who can say?

All too little may we tell,
Friends who like each other well,
What might haply, if we might,
Bid us read our lives aright.

Wild on woodland ways your sires
    Flashed like fires;
Fair as flame and fierce and fleet
As with wings on wingless feet
Shone and sprang your mother, free,
Bright and brave as wind or sea.

Free and proud and glad as they,
    Here today
Rests or roams their radiant child,
Vanquished not, but reconciled,
Free from curb of aught above
Save the lovely curb of love.

Love through dreams of souls divine
    Fain would shine
Round a dawn whose light and song
Then should right our mutual wrong –
Speak, and seal the love-lit law
Sweet Assisi's seer foresaw.

Dreams were theirs; yet haply may,
    Dawn a day
When such friends and fellows born,
Seeing our earth as fair at morn,
May for wiser love's sake see
More of heaven's deep heart than we.

The Philanthropist and the Happy Cat

SAKI (1870–1916)

Jocantha Bessbury was in the mood to be serenely and graciously happy. Her world was a pleasant place, and it was wearing one of its pleasantest aspects. Gregory had managed to get home for a hurried lunch and a smoke afterwards in the little snuggery; the lunch had been a good one, and there was just time to do justice to the coffee and cigarettes. Both were excellent in their way, and Gregory was, in his way, an excellent husband. Jocantha rather suspected herself of making him a very charming wife; and more than suspected herself of having a first-rate dress-maker.

"I don't suppose a more thoroughly contented personality is to be found in all Chelsea," observed Jocantha in allusion to herself, "except perhaps Attab," she continued, glancing towards the large tabby-marked cat that lay in considerable ease in a corner of the divan. "He lies there, purring and dreaming, shifting his limbs now and then in an ecstasy of cushioned comfort. He seems the incarnation of everything soft and silky and velvety, without a sharp edge in his composition, a dreamer whose philosophy is sleep and let sleep; and then, as evening draws on, he goes out into the garden with a red glint in his eyes and slays a drowsy sparrow."

"As every pair of sparrows hatches out ten or more young ones in the year, while their food supply remains stationary, it is just as well that the Attabs of the community should have that idea of how to pass an amusing afternoon," said Gregory. Having delivered himself of this sage comment he lit another cigarette, bade Jocantha a playfully affectionate goodbye, and departed into the outer world.

"Remember, dinner's a wee bit earlier tonight, as we're going to the Haymarket," she called after him.

Left to herself, Jocantha continued the process of looking at her life with placid, introspective eyes. If she had not everything she wanted in this world, at least she was very well pleased with what she had got. She was very well pleased, for instance, with the snuggery, which contrived somehow to be cosy and dainty and expensive all at once. The porcelain was rare and beautiful, the Chinese enamels took on wonderful tints in the firelight, the rugs and hangings led the eye through sumptuous harmonies of colouring. It was a room in which one might have suitably entertained an ambassador or an archbishop, but it was also a room in which one could cut out pictures for a scrapbook without feeling that one was scandalizing the deities of the place with one's litter. And as with the snuggery, so with the rest of the house, and as with the house, so with the other departments of Jocantha's life; she really had good reason for being one of the most contented women in Chelsea.

From being in a mood of simmering satisfaction with her lot she passed to the phase of being generously commiserating for those thousands around her whose lives and circumstances were dull, cheap, pleasureless, and empty. Work girls, shop assistants, and so forth, the class that have neither the happy-go-lucky freedom of the poor nor the leisured freedom of the rich, came specially within the range of her sympathy. It was sad to think that there were young people who, after a long day's work, had to sit alone in chill, dreary bedrooms because they could not afford the price of a cup of coffee and a sandwich in a restaurant, still less a shilling for a theatre gallery.

Jocantha's mind was still dwelling on this theme when she started forth on an afternoon campaign of desultory shopping; it would be rather a comforting thing, she told herself, if she could do something, on the spur of the moment, to bring a gleam of pleasure and interest into the life of even one or two wistful-hearted, empty-pocketed workers; it would add a good deal to her sense of enjoyment at the theatre that night. She would get two upper-circle tickets for a popular play, make her way into some cheap tea shop, and present the tickets to the first couple of interesting work-girls with whom she could casually drop into conversation. She could explain matters by saying that she was unable to use the tickets herself and did not want them to be wasted, and, on the other hand, did not want the trouble of sending them back. On further reflection she decided that it might be better to get only one ticket and give it to some lonely-looking girl sitting eating her frugal meal by herself; the girl might scrape acquaintance with her next-seat neighbour at the theatre and lay the foundations of a lasting friendship.

With the fairy-godmother impulse strong upon her, Jocantha marched into a ticket agency and selected with immense care an upper-circle seat for *The Yellow Peacock*, a play that was attracting a considerable amount of discussion and criticism. Then she went forth in search of a tea shop and philanthropic adventure, at about the same time that Attab sauntered into the garden with a mind attuned to sparrow stalking. In a corner of an ABC shop she found an unoccupied table, whereat she promptly installed herself, impelled by the fact that at the next table was sitting a young girl, rather plain of feature, with tired, listless eyes and a general air of uncomplaining forlornness. Her dress was of poor material, but aimed at being in the fashion, her hair was pretty, and her complexion bad; she was finishing a modest meal of tea and scones, and she was not very different in her way from thousands of other girls who were finishing, or beginning, or continuing their teas in London tea shops at that exact moment. The odds were enormously in favour of the supposition that she had never seen *The Yellow Peacock*; obviously she supplied excellent material for Jocantha's first experiment in haphazard benefaction.

Jocantha ordered some tea and a muffin, and then turned a friendly scrutiny on her neighbour with a view to catching her eye. At that precise moment the girl's face lit up with sudden pleasure, her eyes sparkled, a flush came into her cheeks, and she looked almost pretty. A young man, whom she greeted with an affectionate "Hullo, Bertie," came up to her table and took his seat in a chair facing her. Jocantha looked hard at the newcomer; he was in appearance a few years younger than herself, very much better looking than Gregory, rather better looking, in fact, than any of the young men of her set. She guessed him to be a well-mannered young clerk in some wholesale warehouse, existing and amusing himself as best he might on a tiny salary, and commanding a holiday of about two weeks in the year. He was aware, of course, of his good looks, but with shy self-consciousness, not blatant complacency. He was obviously on terms of friendly intimacy with the girl he was talking to, probably they were drifting towards a formal engagement. Jocantha pictured the boy's home, in a rather narrow circle, with a tiresome mother who always wanted to know how and where he spent his evenings. He would exchange that humdrum thraldom in due course for a home of his own, dominated by a chronic scarcity of pounds, shillings, and pence, and a dearth of most of the things that made life attractive or comfortable. Jocantha felt extremely sorry for him. She wondered if he had seen *The Yellow Peacock*; the odds were enormously in favour of the supposition that he had not. The girl had finished her tea, and would shortly be going back to her work; when the boy was alone it would be quite easy for Jocantha to say: "My husband has made other arrangements for me this evening; would you care to make use of this ticket, which would otherwise be wasted?" Then she could come there again one afternoon for tea, and, if she saw him, ask him how he liked the play. If he was a nice boy and improved on acquaintance he could be given more theatre tickets and perhaps asked to come one Sunday to tea at Chelsea. Jocantha made up her mind that he would improve on acquaintance, and that Gregory would like him, and that the fairy-godmother business would prove far more entertaining than she had originally anticipated. The boy was distinctly presentable; he knew how to brush his hair, which was possibly an imitative faculty; he knew what colour of tie suited him, which might be intuition; he was exactly the type that Jocantha admired, which of course was accident. Altogether she was rather pleased when the girl looked at the clock and bade a friendly but hurried farewell to her companion. Bertie nodded "Goodbye", gulped down a mouthful of tea, and then produced from his overcoat pocket a paper-covered book bearing the title *Sepoy and Sahib, a Tale of the Great Mutiny*.

The laws of tea-shop etiquette forbid that you should offer

theatre tickets to a stranger without having first caught the stranger's eye. It is even better if you can ask to have a sugar basin passed to you, having previously concealed the fact that you have a large and well-filled sugar basin on your own table; this is not difficult to manage, as the printed menu is generally nearly as large as the table, and can be made to stand on end. Jocantha set to work hopefully; she had a long and rather high-pitched discussion with the waitress concerning alleged defects in an altogether blameless muffin, she made loud and plaintive inquiries about the tube service to some impossibly remote suburb, she talked with brilliant insincerity to the tea-shop kitten, and as a last resort she upset a milk jug and swore at it daintily. Altogether she attracted a good deal of attention, but never for a moment did she attract the attention of the boy with the beautifully brushed hair, who was some thousands of miles away in the baking plains of Hindustan, amid deserted bungalows, seething bazaars, and riotous barrack squares, listening to the throbbing of tomtoms and the distant rattle of musketry.

Jocantha went back to her house in Chelsea, which struck her for the first time as looking dull and overfurnished. She had a resentful conviction that Gregory would be uninteresting at dinner, and that the play would be stupid after dinner. On the whole her frame of mind showed a marked divergence from the purring complacency of Attab, who was again curled up in his corner of the divan with a great peace radiating from every curve of his body.

But then, he had killed his sparrow.

Cat on the Roof

J.V. VON SCHEFFEL (1826–86)

Here I sit, with clearest vision
Gazing on the world and life,
Gazing from my proud position
On that scene of party strife.

Smiling from the tower or steeple,
   Lo, the Cat all scornful stares
At the foolish pigmy people,
   Busied with their trifling cares.

Vain my thoughts – I cannot give them
   Access to my point of sight;
To their ignorance I leave them –
   Verily my loss is slight!

Warped and poor the human spirit,
   Human deeds of small behoof:
Calm, in consciousness of merit,
   Sits the Cat upon the roof.

from "Songs of the Tom-cat Hiddigeigei"
in *The Trumpeter* (1893)

A Cat's Friendship

THÉOPHILE GAUTIER (1811–72)

To gain the friendship of a cat is not an easy thing. It is a philosophic, well-regulated, tranquil animal, a creature of habit and a lover of order and cleanliness. It does not give its affections indiscriminately. It will consent to be your friend if you are worthy of the honour, but it will not be your slave. With all its affection, it preserves its freedom of judgment, and it will not do anything for you which it considers unreasonable; but once it has given its love, what absolute confidence, what fidelity of affection! It will make itself the companion of your hours of work, of loneliness, or of sadness. It will lie the whole evening on your knee, purring and happy in your society, and leaving the company of creatures of its own kind to be with you. In vain the sound of caterwauling reverberates from the house-tops, inviting it to one of those cats' evening parties where essence of red-herring takes the place of tea. It will not be tempted, but continues to keep its vigil with you. If you put it down it climbs up again quickly, with a sort of crooning noise, which is like a gentle reproach. Sometimes, when seated in front of you, it gazes at you with such soft, melting eyes, such a human and caressing look, that you are almost awed, for it seems impossible that reason can be absent from it.

from "The White and Black Dynasties"
in *La Ménagerie Intime* translated by Lady Chance

To Winky

AMY LOWELL (1874–1925)

Cat,
Cat,
What are you?
Son, through a thousand generations, of the black leopards
Padding among the sprigs of young bamboo;
Descendant of many removals from the white panthers
Who crouch by night under the loquat-trees?
You crouch under the orange begonias,
And your eyes are green
With the violence of murder,
Or half-closed and stealthy
Like your sheathed claws.

Slowly, slowly,
You rise and stretch
In a glossiness of beautiful curves,
Of muscles fluctuating under black, glazed hair.

Cat,
You are a strange creature.
You sit on your haunches
And yawn,
But when you leap

I can almost hear the whine
Of a released string,
And I look to see its flaccid shaking
In the place whence you sprang.

You carry your tail as a banner,
Slowly it passes my chair,
But when I look for you, you are on the table
Moving easily among the most delicate porcelains.
Your food is a matter of importance
And you are insistent on having
Your wants attended to,
And yet you will eat a bird and its feathers
Apparently without injury.

In the night, I hear you crying,
But if I try to find you
There are only the shadows of rhododendron leaves
Brushing the ground.
When you come in out of the rain,
All wet and with your tail full of burrs,
You fawn upon me in coils and subtleties;
But once you are dry
You leave me with a gesture of inconceivable impudence,
Conveyed by the vanishing quirk of your tail
As you slide through the open door.

You walk as a king scorning his subjects;
You flirt with me as a concubine in robes of silk.
Cat,
I am afraid of your poisonous beauty,
I have seen you torturing a mouse.
Yet when you lie purring in my lap
I forget everything but how soft you are,
And it is only when I feel your claws open upon my hand
That I remember –

Remember a puma lying out on a branch above my head
Years ago.

Shall I choke you, Cat,
Or kiss you?
Really I do not know.

The Paradise of Cats

EMILE ZOLA (1840–1902)

An aunt bequeathed me an Angora cat, which is certainly the
most stupid animal I know of. This is what my cat related to
me, one winter night, before the warm embers.

I

I was then two years old, and I was certainly the fattest and most
simple cat anyone could have seen. Even at that tender age I
displayed all the presumption of an animal that scorns the
attractions of the fireside. And yet what gratitude I owed to
Providence for having placed me with your aunt! The worthy
woman idolized me. I had a regular bedroom at the bottom of a
cupboard, with a feather pillow and a triple-folded rug. The
food was as good as the bed; no bread or soup, nothing but
meat, good underdone meat.

Well! amidst all these comforts, I had but one wish, but one
dream, to slip out by the half-open window, and run away on
to the tiles. Caresses appeared to me insipid, the softness of my
bed disgusted me, I was so fat that I felt sick, and from morn till
eve I experienced the weariness of being happy.

I must tell you that by straining my neck I had perceived the
opposite roof from the window. That day four cats were
fighting there. With bristling coats and tails in the air, they
were rolling on the blue slates, in the full sun, amidst oaths of
joy. I had never witnessed such an extraordinary sight. From

that moment my convictions were settled. Real happiness was upon that roof, in front of that window which the people of the house so carefully closed. I found the proof of this in the way in which they shut the doors of the cupboards where the meat was hidden.

I made up my mind to fly. I felt sure there were other things in life than underdone meat. There was the unknown, the ideal. One day they forgot to close the kitchen window. I sprang on to a small roof beneath it.

II

How beautiful the roofs were! They were bordered by broad gutters exhaling delicious odours. I followed those gutters in raptures of delight, my feet sinking into fine mud, which was deliciously warm and soft. I fancied I was walking on velvet. And the generous heat of the sun melted my fat.

I will not conceal from you the fact that I was trembling in every limb. My delight was mingled with terror. I remember, particularly, experiencing a terrible shock that almost made me tumble down into the street. Three cats came rolling over from the top of a house towards me, mewing most frightfully, and as I was on the point of fainting away, they called me a silly thing, and said they were mewing for fun. I began mewing to them. It was charming. The jolly fellows had none of my stupid fat. When I slipped on the sheets of zinc heated by the burning sun, they laughed at me. An old tom, who was one of the band, showed me particular friendship. He offered to teach me a thing or two, and I gratefully accepted. Ah! your aunt's cat's-meat was far from my thoughts! I drank in the gutters, and never had sugared milk seemed so sweet to me. Everything appeared nice and beautiful. A she-cat passed by, a charming she-cat, the sight of her gave me a feeling I had never experienced before. Hitherto, I had only seen these exquisite creatures, with such delightfully supple backbones, in my dreams. I and my three companions rushed forward to meet the newcomer. I was in front of the others, and was about to pay my respects to the bewitching thing, when one of my comrades cruelly bit my neck. I cried out with pain.

"Bah!" said the old tom, leading me away; "you will meet with stranger adventures than that."

III

After an hour's walk I felt as hungry as a wolf.

"What do you eat on the roofs?" I inquired of my friend the tom.

"What you can find," he answered shrewdly.

This reply caused me some embarrassment, for though I carefully searched I found nothing. At last I perceived a young work-girl in a garret preparing her lunch. A beautiful chop of a tasty red colour was lying on a table under the window.

"That's the very thing I want," I thought, in all simplicity.

And I sprang on to the table and took the chop. But the work-girl, having seen me, struck me a fearful blow with a broom on the spine, and I fled, uttering a dreadful oath.

"You are fresh from your village, then?" said the tom. "Meat that is on tables is there for the purpose of being longed for at a distance. You must search in the gutters."

I could never understand that kitchen meat did not belong to cats. My stomach was beginning to get seriously angry. The tom put me completely to despair by telling me it would be necessary to wait until night. Then we would go down into the street and turn over the heaps of muck. Wait until night! He said it quietly, like a hardened philosopher. I felt myself fainting at the mere thought of this prolonged fast.

IV

Night came slowly, a foggy night that chilled me to the bones. It soon began to rain, a fine, penetrating rain, driven by sudden gusts of wind. We went down along the glazed roof of a staircase. How ugly the street appeared to me! It was no longer that nice heat, that beautiful sun, those roofs white with light where one rolled about so deliciously. My paws slipped on the greasy stones. I sorrowfully recalled to memory my triple blanket and feather pillow.

We were hardly in the street when my friend the tom began to tremble. He made himself small, very small, and ran stealthily along beside the houses, telling me to follow as rapidly as possible. He rushed in at the first street door he came to, and purred with satisfaction as he sought refuge there. When I questioned him as to the motive of his flight, he answered: "Did you see that man with a basket on his back and a stick with an iron hook at the end?"

"Yes."

"Well! if he had seen us he would have knocked us on the heads and roasted us!"

"Roasted us!" I exclaimed. "Then the street is not ours? One can't eat, but one's eaten!"

V

However, the boxes of kitchen refuse had been emptied before the street doors. I rummaged in the heaps in despair. I came across two or three bare bones that had been lying among the cinders, and I then understood what a succulent dish fresh cat's-meat made. My friend the tom scratched artistically among the muck. He made me run about until morning, inspecting each heap, and without showing the least hurry. I was out in the rain for more than ten hours, shivering in every limb. Cursed street, cursed liberty, and how I regretted my prison!

At dawn the tom, seeing I was staggering, said to me with a strange air: "Have you had enough of it?"

"Oh yes," I answered.

"Do you want to go home?"

"I do, indeed; but how shall I find the house?"

"Come along. This morning, when I saw you come out, I understood that a fat cat like you was not made for the lively delights of liberty. I know your place of abode and will take you to the door."

The worthy tom said this very quietly. When we had arrived, he bid me "Goodbye", without betraying the least emotion.

"No," I exclaimed, "we will not leave each other so. You must accompany me. We will share the same bed and the same food. My mistress is a good woman –"

He would not allow me to finish my sentence.

"Hold your tongue," he said sharply, "you are a simpleton. Your effeminate existence would kill me. Your life of plenty is good for bastard cats. Free cats would never purchase your cat's-meat and feather pillow at the price of a prison. Goodbye."

And he returned up on to the roofs, where I saw his long outline quiver with joy in the rays of the rising sun.

When I got in, your aunt took the whip and gave me a thrashing which I received with profound delight. I tasted in full measure the pleasure of being beaten and being warm. Whilst she was striking me, I thought with rapture of the meat she would give me afterwards.

VI

You see – concluded my cat, stretching itself out in front of the embers – real happiness, paradise, my dear master, consists of being shut up and beaten in a room where there is meat.

I am speaking from the point of view of cats.

Cats

CHARLES BAUDELAIRE (1821–67)

The fervent lover and the sage austere
In their ripe season equally admire
The great soft cats, who, like their masters dear,
Are shivery folk and sit beside the fire.

Friends both of learning and of wantonness,
They hunt where silence and dread shadows are;
Erebus would have yoked them to his car
For funeral coursers had their pride been less.

They take, brooding, the noble attitudes
Of sphinxes stretched in deepest solitudes
That look to slumber in an endless dream:
Their loins are quick with kindlings magical,
And glints of gold, as in a sandy stream,
Vaguely bestar their eyeballs mystical.

translated by D.S. MacColl

The Reticence of Lady Anne

SAKI (1870–1916)

Egbert came into the large, dimly lit drawing-room with the air of a man who is not certain whether he is entering a dovecote or a bomb factory, and is prepared for either eventuality. The little domestic quarrel over the luncheon-table had not been fought to a definite finish, and the question was how far Lady Anne was in a mood to renew or forgo hostilities. Her pose in the armchair by the tea-table was rather elaborately rigid; in the gloom of a December afternoon Egbert's pince-nez did not materially help him to discern the expression of her face.

By way of breaking whatever ice might be floating on the surface he made a remark about a dim religious light. He or Lady Anne was accustomed to make that remark between 4.30 and 6 on winter and late autumn evenings; it was a part of their married life. There was no recognized rejoinder to it, and Lady Anne made none.

Don Tarquinio lay astretch on the Persian rug, basking in the firelight with superb indifference to the possible ill-humour of Lady Anne. His pedigree was as flawlessly Persian as the rug, and his ruff was coming into the glory of its second winter. The page-boy, who had Renaissance tendencies, had christened him Don Tarquinio. Left to themselves, Egbert and Lady Anne would unfailingly have called him Fluff, but they were not obstinate.

Egbert poured himself out some tea. As the silence gave no sign of breaking on Lady Anne's initiative, he braced himself for another Yermak effort.

"My remark at lunch had a purely academic application," he announced; "you seem to put an unnecessarily personal significance into it."

Lady Anne maintained her defensive barrier of silence. The bullfinch lazily filled in the interval with an air from *Iphigénie en Tauride*. Egbert recognized it immediately, because it was the only air the bullfinch whistled, and he had come to them with the reputation for whistling it. Both Egbert and Lady Anne would have preferred something from *The Yeoman of the Guard*, which was their favourite opera. In matters artistic they had a similarity of taste. They leaned towards the honest and explicit in art, a picture, for instance, that told its own story, with generous assistance from its title. A riderless warhorse with harness in obvious disarray, staggering into a courtyard full of pale swooning women, and marginally noted "Bad News", suggested to their minds a distinct interpretation of some military catastrophe. They could see what it was meant to convey, and explain it to friends of duller intelligence.

The silence continued. As a rule Lady Anne's displeasure became articulate and markedly voluble after four minutes of introductory muteness. Egbert seized the milk-jug and poured some of its contents into Don Tarquinio's saucer; as the saucer was already full to the brim an unsightly overflow was the result. Don Tarquinio looked on with a surprised interest that evanesced into elaborate unconsciousness when he was appealed to by Egbert to come and drink up some of the spilt matter. Don Tarquinio was prepared to play many roles in life, but a vacuum carpet-cleaner was not one of them.

"Don't you think we're being rather foolish?" said Egbert cheerfully.

If Lady Anne thought so she didn't say so.

"I daresay the fault has been partly on my side," continued Egbert, with evaporating cheerfulness. "After all, I'm only human, you know. You seem to forget that I'm only human."

He insisted on the point, as if there had been unfounded suggestions that he was built on Satyr lines, with goat continuations where the human left off.

The bullfinch recommenced its air from *Iphigénie en Tauride*. Egbert began to feel depressed. Lady Anne was not drinking her tea. Perhaps she was feeling unwell. But when Lady Anne felt unwell she was not wont to be reticent on the subject. "No one knows what I suffer from indigestion" was one of her favourite statements; but the lack of knowledge can only have been caused by defective listening; the amount of information available on the subject would have supplied material for a monograph.

Evidently Lady Anne was not feeling unwell.

Egbert began to think he was being unreasonably dealt with; naturally he began to make concessions.

"I daresay," he observed, taking as central a position on the hearth-rug as Don Tarquinio could be persuaded to concede him, "I may have been to blame. I am willing, if I can thereby restore things to a happier standpoint, to undertake to lead a better life."

He wondered vaguely how it would be possible. Temptations came to him, in middle age, tentatively and without insistence, like a neglected butcher-boy who asks for a Christmas box in February for no more hopeful reason than that he didn't get one in December. He had no more idea of succumbing to them than he had of purchasing the fish-knives and fur boas that ladies are impelled to sacrifice through the medium of advertisement columns during twelve months of the year. Still, there was something impressive in this unasked-for renunciation of possibly latent enormities.

Lady Anne showed no sign of being impressed.

Egbert looked at her nervously through his glasses. To get the worst of an argument with her was no new experience. To get the worst of a monologue was a humiliating novelty.

"I shall go and dress for dinner," he announced in a voice into which he intended some shade of sternness to creep.

At the door a final access of weakness impelled him to make a further appeal.

"Aren't we being very silly?"

"A fool," was Don Tarquinio's mental comment as the door closed on Egbert's retreat. Then he lifted his velvet forepaws in the air and leapt lightly on to a bookshelf immediately under the bullfinch's cage. It was the first time he had seemed to notice the bird's existence, but he was carrying out a long-formed theory of action with the precision of mature deliberation. The bullfinch, who had fancied himself something of a despot, depressed himself of a sudden into a third of his normal displacement; then he fell to a helpless wing-beating and shrill cheeping. He had cost twenty-seven shillings without the cage, but Lady Anne made no sign of interfering. She had been dead for two hours.

from Reginald in Russia (1910)

Hiddigeigei

J.V. VON SCHEFFEL (1826–86)

Stretched beside the Baron's footstool
Dainty lay the gallant tom-cat,
Hiddigeigei, with the sable
Velvet coat and tail majestic.
Heirloom he, left to the Baron
By his sainted, well-loved lady,
Leanor Montfort du Plessys.
Far in Hungary Hiddigeigei
Saw the light, for he was born there
By a daughter of Angora
To a wild-cat of the Puszta.
To fair Paris, as a kitten,
Was he sent, in sign of homage,

By a brave Hungarian noble,
Who in Debreczin, far distant,
Cherished still, in recollection,
Leanor's clear eyes of azure
And the rats who, like an army,
Overran her father's castle.
Hiddigeigei to the Rhineland
Came with haughty Leanora,
Loyal and trusted. Somewhat lonely
Ran the thread of his existence,
For he hated all communion
With the vulgar German cat-folk.
"Certes," he reflected proudly,
In his feline self-reliance,
"They may have good hearts, these creatures,
And a fund of kindly feeling,
All these native cats untutored,
Aboriginal and common,
In these wilds brought up and nurtured.
But in *style* they're sadly lacking,
They want breeding, manners, finish.
One who gained his spurs at Paris,
Following the chase full boldly
In the salons of Montfaucon,
Cannot, certes, in the country
Look to find congenial spirits,
Fit companions for his leisure."

Dignified, though isolated,
Always dignified and stately,
Dwelt he in the Baron's castle,
Paced its halls with measured footsteps.
Deeply tuneful was his purring,
And, in anger, when indignant
He would arch his supple backbone,
When each hair rose bristling upward,
Gentleness he still would study

To unite with dignity.
But when over roof and gable
He would clamber, agile, daring,
Sallying forth upon a mouse-hunt,
When mysterious in the moonlight
Flashed his emerald eyes and sparkled,
Then, e'en envy must acknowledge,
Hiddigeigei was imposing.

from *The Trumpeter* (1893)

The Well-Dressed Cat

CHAMPFLEURY (1821–89)

The love of dress is very marked in this attractive animal; he is proud of the lustre of his coat, and cannot endure that a hair of it shall lie the wrong way. When the cat has eaten, he passes his tongue several times over both sides of his jaws, and his whiskers, in order to clean them thoroughly; he keeps his coat clean with a prickly tongue which fulfils the office of the curry-comb.

from *The Cat Past and Present*

The College Cat

ALFRED DENIS GODLEY (1856–1925)

Within those halls where student zeal
    Hangs every morn on learning's lips,
Intent to make its daily meal
    Of Tips,

While drones the conscientious Don
    Of Latin Prose, of Human Will,
Of Aristotle and of John
    Stuart Mill,

We mouth with stern didactic air:
    We prate of this, we rant of that:
While slumbers on his favourite chair
    The Cat!

For what is Mill, and what is Prose,
    Compared with warmth, and sleep, and food,
— All which collectively compose
    The Good?

Although thy unreceptive pose
    In presence of eternal Truth
No virtuous example shows
    To youth,

Sleep on, O Cat! serenely through
    My hurricanes of hoarded lore,
Nor seek with agitated mew
    The door:

Thy calm repose I would not mar,
    Nor chase thee forth in angry flight
Protesting loud (though some there are
    Who might),

Because to my reflective mind
    Thou dost from generations gone
Recall a wholly different kind
    Of Don,

Who took his glass, his social cup,
    And having quaffed it, mostly sat
Curled (metaphorically) up
    Like that!

Far from those scenes of daily strife
    And seldom necessary fuss

Wherein consists the most of life
  For us,

When Movements moved, they let them move:
  When Problems raged, they let them rage:
And quite ignored the Spirit of
  The Age.

Of such thou wert the proper mate,
  O peaceful-minded quadruped!
But liv'st with fellows up to date
  Instead –

With men who spend their vital span
  In petty stress and futile storm,
And for a recreation plan
  Reform:

Whom pupils ne'er in quiet leave,
  But throng their rooms in countless hordes:
Who sit from morn to dewy eve
  On Boards:

Who skim but erudition's cream,
  And con by night and cram by day
Such subjects as the likeliest seem
  To pay!

But thou, from cares like these exempt,
  Our follies dost serenely scan,
Professing thus thy just contempt
  For Man:

For well thou knowest, that wished-for goal
  Which still to win we vainly pine,
That calm tranquillity of soul
  Is thine!

To a Cat

HARTLEY COLERIDGE (1796–1849)

Nellie, methinks, 'twixt thee and me
There is a kind of sympathy;
And could we interchange our nature –
If I were cat, thou human creature –
I should, like thee, be no great mouser,
And thou, like me, no great composer;
For, like thy plaintive mews, my muse
With villainous whine doth fate abuse,
Because it hath not made me sleek
As golden down on Cupid's cheek;
And yet thou canst upon the rug lie,
Stretched out like snail, or curled up snugly,
As if thou wert not lean or ugly;
And I, who in poetic flights
Sometimes complain of sleepless nights,
Regardless of the sun in heaven,
Am apt to doze till past eleven –
The world would just the same go round
If I were hanged and thou wert drowned;
There is one difference, 'tis true:
Thou dost not know it, and I do.

The Dreaming Cat

SIR OLIVER LODGE (1851–1940)

Puddy is the oldest of the cats. Mostly she sits by the fireside and
dreams her dreams. I imagine that she has come to agree with
the philosopher that the eye and the ear and the other senses are
full of deceit. More and more her mind dwells on the invisible.

A Modest Cat's Soliloquy

ANONYMOUS

Far down within the damp dark earth
The grimy miner goes
That I on chilly nights may have
A fire to warm my toes;
Brave sailors plough the wintry main
Through peril and mishap,
That I, on Oriental rugs
May take my morning nap.
Out in the distant meadow
Meekly graze the lowing kine,
That milk in endless saucerfuls,
All foaming, may be mine;
The fish that swim the ocean
And the birds that fill the air –
Did I not like to pick their bones,
Pray, think you they'd be there?

A Companion

PIERRE LOTI (1850–1923)

He settles down as close to me as possible, after stretching out his paw towards me two or three times, looking at me as though craving
permission to leap on to my knees. And there he lies, his head daintily resting on my arm, as though to say: "Since you will not have me altogether, permit this at least, for I shall not disturb you if I remain so."

from *Reflets sur la Route Sombre*

The Sphinx

OSCAR WILDE (1854–1900)

In a dim corner of my room for longer than my fancy
  thinks
A beautiful and silent Sphinx has watched me through
  the shifting gloom.

Inviolate and immobile she does not rise she does not
  stir
For silver moons are naught to her and naught to her
  the suns that reel.

Red follows grey across the air, the waves of moonlight ebb and flow
But with the Dawn she does not go and in the night-
  time she is there.

Dawn follows Dawn and Nights grow old and all the
  while this curious cat
Lies couching on the Chinese mat with eyes of satin
  rimmed with gold.

Upon the mat she lies and leers and on the tawny
  throat of her
Flutters the soft and silky fur or ripples to her pointed ears.

Come forth, my lovely seneschal! so somnolent, so
  statuesque!
Come forth you exquisite grotesque! half woman and
  half animal!

Come forth my lovely languorous Sphinx! and put
  your head upon my knee!
And let me stroke your throat and see your body
  spotted like the Lynx!

And let me touch those curving claws of yellow ivory
  and grasp

The tail that like a monstrous Asp coils round your
   heavy velvet paws!

A thousand weary centuries are thine while I have
   hardly seen
Some twenty summers cast their green for Autumn's
   gaudy liveries.

But you can read the Hieroglyphs on the great sand-
   stone obelisks,
And you have talked with Basilisks, and you have
   looked on Hippogriffs.

O tell me, were you standing by when Isis to Osiris
   knelt?
And did you watch the Egyptian melt her union for
   Antony

And drink the jewel-drunken wine and bend her head
   in mimic awe
To see the huge proconsul draw the salted tunny from
   the brine?

And did you mark the Cyprian kiss white Adon on his
   catafalque?
And did you follow Amenalk, the God of
   Heliopolis?

And did you talk with Thoth, and did you hear the
   moon-horned Io weep?
And know the painted kings who sleep beneath the
   wedge-shaped Pyramid?

Lift up your large black satin eyes which are like
   cushions where one sinks!
Fawn at my feet, fantastic Sphinx! and sing me all your
   memories!

Sing to me of the Jewish maid who wandered with
   the Holy Child,

And how you led them through the wild, and how
they slept beneath your shade.

Sing to me of that odorous green eve when crouching
by the marge
You heard from Adrian's gilded barge the laughter of
Antinous

And lapped the stream and fed your drouth and
watched with hot and hungry stare
The ivory body of that rare young slave with his
pomegranate mouth!

Sing to me of the Labyrinth in which the twi-formed
bull was stalled!
Sing to me of the night you crawled across the
temple's granite plinth

When through the purple corridors the screaming
scarlet Ibis flew
In terror, and a horrid dew dripped from the moaning
Mandragores,

And the great torpid crocodile within the tank shed
slimy tears,
And tare the jewels from his ears and staggered back
into the Nile,

And the priests cursed you with shrill psalms as in your
claws you seized their snake
And crept away with it to slake your passion by the
shuddering palms.

Who were your lovers? who were they who wrestled
for you in the dust?
Which was the vessel of your Lust? What Leman had
you, every day?

Did giant Lizards come and crouch before you on the
reedy banks?

Did Gryphons with great metal flanks leap on you in
    your trampled couch?

Did monstrous hippopotami come sidling toward you
    in the mist?
Did gilt-scaled dragons writhe and twist with passion as
    you passed them by?

And from the brick-built Lycian tomb what horrible
    Chimera came
With fearful heads and fearful flame to breed new
    wonders from your womb?

Or had you shameful secret quests and did you harry
    to your home
Some Nereid coiled in amber foam with curious rock
    crystal breasts?

Or did you treading through the froth call to the
    brown Sidonian
For tidings of Leviathan, Leviathan or
    Behemoth?

Or did you when the sun was set climb up the cactus-
    covered slope
To meet your swarthy Ethiop whose body was of
    polished jet?

Or did you while the earthen skiffs dropped down the
    grey Nilotic flats
At twilight and the flickering bats flew round the
    temple's triple glyphs

Steal to the border of the bar and swim across the
    silent lake
And slink into the vault and make the Pyramid your
    lúpanar

Till from each black sarcophagus rose up the painted
    swathèd dead?

Or did you lure unto your bed the ivory-horned
  Tragelaphos?

Or did you love the god of flies who plagued the
  Hebrews and was splashed
With wine unto the waist? or Pasht, who had green
  beryls for her eyes?

Or that young god, the Tyrian, who was more
  amorous than the dove
Of Ashtaroth? or did you love the god of the Assyrian

Whose wings, like strange transparent talc, rose high
  above his hawk-faced head,
Painted with silver and with red and ribbed with rods
  of Oreichalch?

Or did huge Apis from his car leap down and lay
  before your feet
Big blossoms of the honey-sweet and honey-coloured
  nenuphar?

How subtle-secret is your smile! Did you love none
  then? Nay, I know
Great Ammon was your bedfellow! He lay with you
  beside the Nile! [...]

Your lovers are not dead, I know. They will rise up
  and hear your voice
And clash their cymbals and rejoice and run to kiss
  your mouth! And so,

Set wings upon your argosies! Set horses to your ebon car!
Back to your Nile! Or if you are grown sick of dead
  divinities

Follow some roving lion's spoor across the copper-
  coloured plain,
Reach out and hale him by the mane and bid him be
  your paramour!

Couch by his side upon the grass and set your white
teeth in his throat
And when you hear his dying note lash your long
flanks of polished brass

And take a tiger for your mate, whose amber sides are
flecked with black,
And ride upon his gilded back in triumph through the
Theban gate,

And toy with him in amorous jests, and when he
turns, and snarls, and gnaws,
O smite him with your jasper claws! and bruise him
with your agate breasts!

Why are you tarrying? Get hence! I weary of your
sullen ways,
I weary of your steadfast gaze, your somnolent
magnificence.

Your horrible and heavy breath makes the light flicker
in the lamp,
And on my brow I feel the damp and dreadful dews
of night and death.

Your eyes are like fantastic moons that shiver in some
stagnant lake,
Your tongue is like a scarlet snake that dances to
fantastic tunes,

Your pulse makes poisonous melodies, and your black
throat is like the hole
Left by some torch or burning coal on Saracenic
tapestries.

Away! The sulphur-coloured stars are hurrying through
the Western gate!
Away! Or it may be too late to climb their silent silver
cars!

See, the dawn shivers round the grey gilt-dialled
    towers, and the rain
Streams down each diamonded pane and blurs with
    tears the wannish day.

What snake-tressed fury fresh from Hell, with uncouth
    gestures and unclean,
Stole from the poppy-drowsy queen and led you to a
    student's cell?

What songless tongueless ghost of sin crept through
    the curtains of the night,
And saw my taper turning bright, and knocked, and
    bade you enter in?

Are there not others more accursed, whiter with
    leprosies than I?
Are Abana and Pharphar dry that you come here to
    slake your thirst?

Get hence, you loathsome mystery! Hideous animal,
    get hence!
You wake in me each bestial sense, you make me
    what I would not be.

You make my creed a barren sham, you wake foul
    dreams of sensual life,
And Atys with his blood-stained knife were better than
    the thing I am.

False Sphinx! False Sphinx! By reedy Styx old Charon,
    leaning on his oar,
Waits for my coin. Go thou before, and leave me to
    my crucifix,

Whose pallid burden, sick with pain, watches the
    world with wearied eyes,
And weeps for every soul that dies, and weeps for
    every soul in vain.

CATLINGS
AND
KITTENS

"A kitten is in the animal world what a
rosebud is in a garden."
Robert Southey (1774–1843)

In the Image of the Lion

HEINRICH HEINE (1797–1856)

Wild beasts he created later,
Lions with their paws so furious;
In the image of the lion
Made he kittens small and curious.

from *Songs of Creation* translated by E.A. Bowring

The Tail of a Kitten

H.D. THOREAU (1817–62)

A kitten is so flexible that she is almost double; the hind parts
are equivalent to another kitten with which the fore part plays.
She does not discover that her tail belongs to her till you tread
upon it.

How eloquent she can be with her tail! Its sudden swellings
and vibrations! She jumps into a chair and then stands on her
hind legs to look out the window; looks steadily at objects far
and near, first turning her gaze to this side then to that, for she
loves to look out a window as much as any gossip. Ever and
anon she bends back her ears to hear what is going on within
the room, and all the while her eloquent tail is reporting the
progress and success of her survey by speaking gestures which
betray her interest in what she sees.

Then what a delicate hint she can give with her tail! passing
perhaps underneath, as you sit at table, and letting the tip of her
tail just touch your legs, as much as to say, I am here and ready
for that milk or meat, though she may not be so forward as to
look round at you when she emerges.

from *Journal*, 15 February 1861

The Kitten

JOANNA BAILLIE (1762–1851)

Wanton droll, whose harmless play
Beguiles the rustic's closing day,
When, drawn the evening fire about,
Sit aged crone and thoughtless lout,
And child upon his three-foot stool,
Waiting until his supper cool,
And maid, whose cheek outblooms the rose,
As bright the blazing faggot glows,
Who, bending to the friendly light,
Plies her task with busy sleight;
Come, show thy tricks and sportive graces,
Thus circled round with merry faces!

Backward coil'd and crouching low,
With glaring eyeballs watch thy foe,
The housewife's spindle whirling round,
Or thread or straw that on the ground
Its shadow throws, by urchin sly
Held out to lure thy roving eye;
Then stealing onward, fiercely spring
Upon the tempting faithless thing.
Now, wheeling round with bootless skill,
Thy bo-peep tail provokes thee still,
As still beyond thy curving side
Its jetty tip is seen to glide;
Till from thy centre starting far,
Thou sidelong veerst with rump in air
Erected stiff, and gait awry,
Like madam in her tantrums high;
Though ne'er a madam of them all,
Whose silken kirtle sweeps the hall,
More varied trick and whim displays
To catch the admiring stranger's gaze.

Doth power in measured verses dwell,
All thy vagaries wild to tell?
Ah no! the start, the jet, the bound,
The giddy scamper round and round,
With leap and toss and high curvet,
And many a whirling somerset,
(Permitted by the modern muse
Expression technical to use)
These mock the deftest rhymester's skill,
But poor in art, though rich in will.

The featest tumbler, stage bedight,
To thee is but a clumsy wight,
Who every limb and sinew strains
To do what costs thee little pains;
For which, I trow, the gaping crowd
Requite him oft with plaudits loud.

But, stopp'd the while thy wanton play,
Applauses too thy pains repay:
For then, beneath some urchin's hand
With modest pride thou tak'st thy stand,
While many a stroke of kindness glides
Along thy back and tabby sides.
Dilated swells thy glossy fur,
And loudly croons thy busy purr,
As, timing well the equal sound,
Thy clutching feet bepat the ground,
And all their harmless claws disclose
Like prickles of an early rose,
While softly from thy whisker'd cheek
Thy half-closed eyes peer, mild and meek.

But not alone by cottage fire
Do rustics rude thy feats admire.
The learned sage, whose thoughts explore
The widest range of human lore,

Or with unfetter'd fancy fly
Through airy heights of poesy,
Pausing smiles with alter'd air
To see thee climb his elbow-chair,
Or, struggling on the mat below,
Hold warfare with his slipper'd toe.
The widow'd dame or lonely maid,
Who, in the still but cheerless shade
Of home unsocial, spends her age,
And rarely turns a letter'd page,
Upon her hearth for thee lets fall
The rounded cork or paper ball,
Nor chides thee on thy wicked watch,
The ends of ravell'd skein to catch,
But lets thee have thy wayward will,
Perplexing oft her better skill.

E'en he, whose mind of gloomy bent,
In lonely tower or prison pent,
Reviews the coil of former days,
And loathes the world and all its ways.
What time the lamp's unsteady gleam
Hath roused him from his moody dream,
Feels, as thou gambol'st round his seat,
His heart of pride less fiercely beat,
And smiles, a link in thee to find,
That joins it still to living kind.

Whence hast thou then, thou witless puss!
The magic power to charm us thus?
Is it that in thy glaring eye
And rapid movements, we descry –
Whilst we at ease, secure from ill,
The chimney corner snugly fill –
A lion darting on his prey,
A tiger at his ruthless play?
Or is it that in thee we trace,

With all thy varied wanton grace,
An emblem, view'd with kindred eye,
Of tricky, restless infancy?
Ah! many a lightly sportive child,
Who hath like thee our wits beguiled,
To dull and sober manhood grown,
With strange recoil our hearts disown.

And so, poor kit! must thou endure,
When thou becom'st a cat demure,
Full many a cuff and angry word,
Chased roughly from the tempting board.
But yet, for that thou hast, I ween,
So oft our favour'd playmate been,
Soft be the change which thou shalt prove!
When time hath spoil'd thee of our love,
Still be thou deem'd by housewife fat
A comely, careful, mousing cat,
Whose dish is, for the public good,
Replenish'd oft with savoury food,
Nor, when thy span of life is past,
Be thou to pond or dung-hill cast,
But, gently borne on goodman's spade,
Beneath the decent sod be laid;
And children show with glistening eyes
The place where poor old pussy lies.

from *Dramatic and Poetical Works* (1851)

The Master's Cat

MAMIE DICKENS

On account of our birds, cats were not allowed in the house;
but from a friend in London I received a present of a white
kitten – Williamina – and she and her numerous offspring had a
happy home at "Gad's Hill". She became a favourite with all

47

the household, and showed particular devotion to my father. I remember on one occasion when she had presented us with a family of kittens, she selected a corner of father's study for their home. She brought them one by one from the kitchen and deposited them in her chosen corner. My father called to me to remove them, saying that he could not allow the kittens to remain in his room. I did so, but Williamina brought them back again, one by one. Again they were removed. The third time, instead of putting them in the corner, she placed them all, and herself beside them, at my father's feet, and gave him such an imploring glance that he could resist no longer, and they were allowed to remain. As the kittens grew older they became more and more frolicsome, swarming up the curtains, playing about on the writing table and scampering behind the bookshelves. But they were never complained of and lived happily in the study until the time came for finding them other homes. One of these kittens was kept, who, as he was quite deaf, was left unnamed, and became known by the servants as "the master's cat", because of his devotion to my father. He was always with him, and used to follow him about the garden like a dog, and sit with him while he wrote. One evening we were all, except father, going to a ball, and when we started, left "the master" and his cat in the drawing-room together. "The master" was reading at a small table, on which a lighted candle was placed. Suddenly the candle went out. My father, who was much interested in his book, relighted the candle, stroked the cat, who was looking at him pathetically he noticed, and continued his reading. A few minutes later, as the light became dim, he looked up just in time to see puss deliberately put out the candle with his paw, and then look appealingly towards him. This second and unmistakable hint was not disregarded, and puss was given the petting he craved. Father was full of this anecdote when all met at breakfast the next morning.

from *My Father As I Recall Him* (1897)

The Cruel Boy and the Kittens

ANONYMOUS

What! go to see the kittens drowned,
On purpose, in the yard!
I did not think there could be found
A little heart so hard.

Poor kittens! no more pretty play
With pussy's wagging tail:
Oh! I'd go far enough away
Before I'd see the pail.

Poor things! the little child that can
Be pleased to go and see,
Most likely when he grows a man,
A cruel man will be.

And many a wicked thing he'll do,
Because his heart is hard;
A great deal worse than killing you,
Poor kittens, in the yard.

from *Rhymes for the Nursery* (new edition, 1839)

Tittums

JEROME K. JEROME (1859–1927)

He came in this morning in his usual style, which he appears to
have founded on that of an American cyclone, and the first
thing he did was to sweep my coffee cup off the table with his
tail, sending the contents full into the middle of my waistcoat.

I rose from my chair, hurriedly, and remarking, "———,"
approached him at a rapid rate. He preceded me in the
direction of the door. At the door, he met Eliza, coming in

49

with eggs. Eliza observed, "Ugh!" and sat down on the floor, the eggs took up different positions about the carpet, where they spread themselves out, and Gustavus Adolphus left the room. I called after him, strongly advising him to go straight downstairs, and not let me see him again for the next hour or so; and he, seeming to agree with me, dodged the coal-scoop, and went; while I returned, dried myself, and finished breakfast. I made sure that he had gone into the yard, but when I looked into the passage ten minutes later, he was sitting at the top of the stairs. I ordered him down at once, but he only barked and jumped about, so I went to see what was the matter.

It was Tittums. She was sitting on the top stair but one, and wouldn't let him pass.

Tittums is our kitten. She is about the size of a penny roll. Her back was up, and she was swearing like a medical student.

She does swear fearfully. I do a little that way myself sometimes, but I am a mere amateur compared with her. To tell you the truth – mind, this is strictly between ourselves, please; I shouldn't like your wife to know I said it, the womenfolk don't understand these things; but between you and me, you know, I think it does a man good to swear. Swearing is the safety-valve through which the bad temper, that might otherwise do serious internal injury to his mental mechanism, escapes in harmless vapouring. When a man has said: "Bless you, my dear, sweet sir. What the sun, moon and stars made you so careless (if I may be permitted the expression) as to allow your light and delicate foot to descend upon my corn with so much force? Is it that you are physically incapable of comprehending the direction in which you are proceeding? you nice, clever young man – you!" or words to that effect, he feels better. Swearing has the same soothing effect upon our angry passions that smashing the furniture or slamming the doors is so well known to exercise; added to which it is much cheaper. Swearing clears a man out like a pen'orth of gunpowder does the wash-house chimney. An occasional explosion is good for both. I rather distrust a man who never swears, or savagely kicks the footstool, or pokes the fire with unnecessary violence. Without some outlet, the anger caused by the ever-occurring troubles of life is apt to rankle and fester within. The petty annoyance, instead of being thrown from us, sits down beside us, and becomes a sorrow; and the little offence is brooded over till, in the hotbed of rumination, it grows into a great injury, under whose poisonous shadow springs up hatred and revenge.

Swearing relieves the feelings, that is what swearing does. I explained this to my aunt on one occasion, but it didn't answer with her. She said I had no business to have such feelings.

That is what I told Tittums. I told her she ought to be ashamed of herself, brought up in a Christian family as she was, too. I don't so much mind hearing an old cat swear, but I can't bear to see a mere kitten give way to it. It seems sad in one so young.

I put Tittums in my pocket, and returned to my desk. I forgot her for the moment, and when I looked I found that she had squirmed out of my pocket on to the table, and was trying to swallow the pen; then she put her leg into the ink-pot and upset it; then she licked her leg; then she swore again – at *me* this time.

I put her down on the floor, and there Tim began rowing with her. I do wish Tim would mind his own business. It was no concern of his what she had been doing. Besides, he is not a saint himself. He is only a two-year-old fox terrier, and he interferes with everything, and gives himself the airs of a grey-headed Scotch collie.

Tittums' mother has come in, and Tim has got his nose scratched, for which I am remarkably glad. I have put them all three out in the passage, where they are fighting at the present moment. I'm in a mess with the ink, and in a thundering bad temper; and if anything more in the cat or dog line comes fooling about me this morning, it had better bring its own funeral contractor with it.

from "On Cats and Dogs" in *Idle Thoughts of an Idle Fellow* (1886)

The Colubriad

WILLIAM COWPER (1731–1800)

Close by the threshold of a door nail'd fast
Three kittens sat: each kitten look'd aghast.
I, passing swift and inattentive by,
At the three kittens cast a careless eye;
Not much concern'd to know what they did there,
Not deeming kittens worth a poet's care.
But presently a loud and furious hiss
Caused me to stop, and to exclaim – what's this?
When, lo! upon the threshold met my view,
With head erect, and eyes of fiery hue,
A viper, long as Count de Grasse's queue.
Forth from his head his forkèd tongue he throws,
Darting it full against a kitten's nose;
Who having never seen in field or house
The like, sat still and silent, as a mouse:
Only, projecting with attention due
Her whisker'd face, she ask'd him – who are you?

On to the hall went I, with pace not slow,
But swift as lightning, for a long Dutch hoe;
With which well arm'd I hasten'd to the spot,
To find the viper. But I found him not,
And, turning up the leaves and shrubs around,
Found only, that he was not to be found.
But still the kittens, sitting as before
Sat watching close the bottom of the door.
I hope – said I – the villain I would kill
Has slipt between the door and the door's sill;
And if I make dispatch, and follow hard,
No doubt but I shall find him in the yard –
For long ere now it should have been rehears'd,
'Twas in the garden that I found him first.
E'en there I found him; there the full-grown cat

His head with velvet paw did gently pat,
As curious as the kittens erst had been
To learn what this phenomenon might mean.
Fill'd with heroic ardour at the sight,
And fearing every moment he might bite,
And rob our household of our only cat
That was of age to combat with a rat,
With outstretch'd hoe I slew him at the door,
And taught him NEVER TO COME THERE NO MORE.

Who Was to Blame?

ANTON CHEKHOV (1860–1904)

As my uncle Pyotr Demyanitch, a lean, bilious collegiate councillor, exceedingly like a stale smoked fish with a stick through it, was getting ready to go to the high school, where he taught Latin, he noticed that the corner of his grammar was nibbled by mice.

"I say, Praskovya," he said, going into the kitchen and addressing the cook, "how is it we have got mice here? Upon my word! yesterday my top hat was nibbled, today they have disfigured my Latin grammar . . . at this rate they will soon begin eating my clothes!"

"What can I do? I did not bring them in!" answered Praskovya.

"We must do something! You had better get a cat, hadn't you?"

"I've got a cat, but what good is it?"

And Praskovya pointed to the corner where a white kitten, thin as a match, lay curled up asleep beside a broom.

"Why is it no good?" asked Pyotr Demyanitch.

"It's young yet, and foolish. It's not two months old yet."

"H'm . . . then it must be trained. It had much better be learning instead of lying there."

Saying this, Pyotr Demyanitch sighed with a careworn air

and went out of the kitchen. The kitten raised his head, looked lazily after him, and shut his eyes again.

The kitten lay awake thinking. Of what? Unacquainted with real life, having no store of accumulated impressions, his mental processes could only be instinctive, and he could but picture life in accordance with the conceptions that he had inherited, together with his flesh and blood, from his ancestors, the tigers (*vide* Darwin). His thoughts were of the nature of day-dreams. His feline imagination pictured something like the Arabian desert, over which flitted shadows closely resembling Praskovya, the stove, the broom. In the midst of the shadows there suddenly appeared a saucer of milk; the saucer began to grow paws, it began moving and displayed a tendency to run; the kitten made a bound, and with a thrill of bloodthirsty sensuality thrust his claws into it. When the saucer had vanished into obscurity a piece of meat appeared, dropped by Praskovya; the meat ran away with a cowardly squeak, but the kitten made a bound and got his claws into it. Everything that rose before the imagination of the young dreamer had for its starting-point leaps, claws, and teeth. The soul of another is darkness, and a cat's soul more than most, but how near the visions just described are to the truth may be seen from the following fact: under the influence of his day-dreams the kitten suddenly leaped up, looked with flashing eyes at Praskovya, ruffled up his coat, and making one bound, thrust his claws into the cook's skirt. Obviously he was born a mouse catcher, a worthy son of his bloodthirsty ancestors. Fate had destined him to be the terror of cellars, store-rooms and cornbins, and had it not been for education . . . we will not anticipate, however.

On his way home from the high school, Pyotr Demyanitch went into a general shop and bought a mouse-trap for fifteen kopecks. At dinner he fixed a little bit of his rissole on the hook, and set the trap under the sofa, where there were heaps of the pupils' old exercise-books, which Praskovya used for various domestic purposes. At six o'clock in the evening, when the worthy Latin master was sitting at the table correcting his pupils' exercises, there was a sudden "klop!" so loud that my uncle started and dropped his pen. He went at once to the sofa and took out the trap. A neat little mouse, the size of a thimble, was sniffing the wires and trembling with fear.

"Aha," muttered Pyotr Demyanitch, and he looked at the mouse malignantly, as though he were about to give him a bad mark. "You are caught, wretch! Wait a bit! I'll teach you to eat my grammar!"

Having gloated over his victim, Pyotr Demyanitch put the mouse-trap on the floor and called: "Praskovya, there's a mouse caught! Bring the kitten here!"

"I'm coming," responded Praskovya, and a minute later she came in with the descendant of tigers in her arms.

"Capital!" said Pyotr Demyanitch, rubbing his hands. "We will give him a lesson. Put him down opposite the mouse-trap . . . that's it. Let him sniff it and look at it. That's it . . ."

The kitten looked wonderingly at my uncle, at his armchair, sniffed the mouse-trap in bewilderment, then, frightened probably by the glaring lamplight and the attention directed to him, made a dash and ran in terror to the door.

"Stop!" shouted my uncle, seizing him by the tail, "stop, you rascal! He's afraid of a mouse, the idiot! Look! It's a mouse! Look! Well? Look, I tell you!"

Pyotr Demyanitch took the kitten by the scruff of the neck and pushed him with his nose against the mouse-trap.

"Look, you carrion! Take him and hold him, Praskovya. Hold him opposite the door of the trap. When I let the mouse out, you let him go instantly. Do you hear? Instantly let go! Now!"

My uncle assumed a mysterious expression and lifted the door of the trap. The mouse came out irresolutely, sniffed the air, and flew like an arrow under the sofa. The kitten on being released darted under the table with his tail in the air.

"It has got away! got away!" cried Pyotr Demyanitch, looking ferocious. "Where is he, the scoundrel? Under the table? You wait . . ."

My uncle dragged the kitten from under the table and shook him in the air.

"Wretched little beast," he muttered, smacking him on the ear. "Take that, take that! Will you shirk it next time? Wr-r-r-etch . . ."

Next day Praskovya heard again the summons.

"Praskovya, there is a mouse caught! Bring the kitten here!"

After the outrage of the previous day the kitten had taken refuge under the stove and had not come out all night. When Praskovya pulled him out and, carrying him by the scruff of the neck into the study, set him down before the mouse-trap, he trembled all over and mewed piteously.

"Come, let him feel at home first," Pyotr Demyanitch commanded. "Let him look and sniff. Look and learn! Stop, plague take you!" he shouted, noticing that the kitten was backing away from the mouse-trap. "I'll thrash you! Hold him by the ear! That's it [...] Well now, set him down before the trap [...]"

My uncle slowly lifted the door of the trap . . . the mouse whisked under the very nose of the kitten, flung itself against Praskovya's hand and fled under the cupboard; the kitten, feeling himself free, took a desperate bound and retreated under the sofa.

"He's let another mouse go!" bawled Pyotr Demyanitch. "Do you call that a cat? Nasty little beast! Thrash him! Thrash him by the mouse-trap!"

When the third mouse had been caught, the kitten shivered all over at the sight of the mouse-trap and its inmate, and scratched Praskovya's hand. After the fourth mouse my uncle flew into a rage, kicked the kitten, and said: "Take the nasty thing away! Get rid of it! Chuck it away! It's no earthly use!"

A year passed, the thin, frail kitten had turned into a solid and sagacious tom-cat. One day he was on his way by the back yards to an amatory interview. He had just reached his destination when he suddenly heard a rustle, and thereupon caught sight of a mouse which ran from a water-trough towards a stable; my hero's hair stood on end, he arched his back, hissed, and trembling all over, took to ignominious flight.

Alas! sometimes I feel myself in the ludicrous position of the flying cat. Like the kitten, I had in my day the honour of being taught Latin by my uncle. Now, whenever I chance to see some work of classical antiquity, instead of being moved to eager enthusiasm, I begin recalling, *ut consecutivum*, the irregular verbs, the sallow grey face of my uncle, the ablative absolute . . . I turn pale, my hair stands up on my head, and, like the cat, I take to ignominious flight.

translated by Constance Garnett

Familiarity Dangerous

VINCENT BOURNE (1695–1747)

As in her ancient mistress' lap,
  The youthful tabby lay,
They gave each other many a tap,
  Alike dispos'd to play.

But strife ensues. Puss waxes warm,
  And with protruded claws
Ploughs all the length of Lydia's arm,
  Mere wantonness the cause.

At once, resentful of the deed,
  She shakes her to the ground
With many a threat, that she shall bleed
  With still a deeper wound.

But, Lydia, bid thy fury rest!
  It was a venial stroke;
For she, that will with kittens jest,
  Should bear a kitten's joke.

translated by William Cowper

Four Little Kittens

H.D. THOREAU (1817–62)

Four little kittens just born; lay like stuffed skins of kittens in a heap, with pink feet; so flimsy and helpless they lie, yet blind, without any stiffness or ability to stand. [...]

The kitten can already spit at a fortnight old, and it can mew from the first, though it often makes the motion of mewing without uttering any sound.

The cat about to bring forth seeks out some dark and secret place for the purpose, not frequented by other cats.

The kittens' ears are at first nearly concealed in the fur, and at a fortnight old they are mere broad-based triangles with a side foremost. But the old cat is ears for them at present, and comes running hastily to their aid when she hears them mew and licks them into contentment again. Even at three weeks the kitten cannot fairly walk, but only creeps feebly with outspread legs. But thenceforth its ears visibly though gradually lift and sharpen themselves.

At three weeks old the kitten begins to walk in a staggering and creeping manner and even to play a little with its mother, and, if you put your ear close, you may hear it purr. It is remarkable that it will not wander far from the dark corner where the cat has left it, but will instinctively find its way back to it, probably by the sense of touch, and will rest nowhere else. Also it is careful not to venture too near the edge of a precipice, and its claws are ever extended to save itself in such places. It washes itself somewhat, and assumes many of the attitudes of an old cat at this age. By the disproportionate size of its feet and head and legs now it reminds you [of] a lion.

I saw it scratch its ear today, probably for the first time; yet it lifted one of its hind legs and scratched its ear as effectually as an old cat does. So this is instinctive, and you may say that, when a kitten's ear first itches, Providence comes to the rescue and lifts its hind leg for it. You would say that this little creature was as perfectly protected by its instinct in its infancy as an old man can be by his wisdom. I observed when she first noticed the figures on the carpet, and also put up her paws to touch or play with surfaces a foot off. By the same instinct that they find the mother's teat before they can see they scratch their ears and guard against falling.

from *Journal*, 29 September 1861

K was a Kitten

ANONYMOUS

K, was a Kitten,
   Who jump'd at a cork,
And learn'd to eat mice
   Without plate, knife, or fork.

And L, was a Lady,
   Who made him so wise;
But he tore her long train,
   And she cried out her eyes.

from *The Alphabet of Goody Two Shoes* (1808)

A Little Pickle

LEIGH HUNT (1784–1859)

She is a sprightly cat, hardly past her youth; so, happening to move the fringe of the rug a little with our foot, she darts out a paw, and begins plucking it and enquiring into the matter, as if it were a challenge to play, or something lively enough to be eaten. What a graceful action of that foot of hers, between delicacy and petulance – combining something of a thrust out, a beat, and a scratch. There seems even something of a little bit of fear in it, as if just enough to provoke her courage, and give her the excitement of a sense of hazard. We remember being much amused with seeing a kitten manifestly making a series of experiments upon the patience of its mother – trying how far the latter would put up with positive bites and thumps. The kitten ran at her every moment, gave her a knock or a bite of the tail; and then ran back again, to recommence the assault. The mother sat looking at her, as if betwixt tolerance and admiration, to see how far the spirit of the family was inherited or improved by her sprightly offspring. At length, however, the "little Pickle" presumed too far, and the mother, lifting up her paw, and meeting her at the very nick of the moment, gave her one of the most unsophisticated boxes of the ear we ever beheld. It sent her rolling half over the room, and made her come to a most ludicrous pause, with the oddest little look of premature and wincing meditation.

from "The Cat by the Fire" in *Essays* (*c.* 1887)

The Kitten and the Falling Leaves

WILLIAM WORDSWORTH (1770–1850)

That way look, my Infant, lo!
What a pretty baby show!
See, the Kitten on the Wall,
Sporting with the leaves that fall,
Wither'd leaves, one, two, and three,
From the lofty Elder-tree!
Through the calm and frosty air
Of this morning bright and fair.
Eddying round and round they sink
Softly, slowly: one might think,
From the motions that are made,
Every little leaf convey'd
Sylph or Faery hither tending,
To this lower world descending,
Each invisible and mute,
In his wavering parachute.

But the Kitten, how she starts,
– Crouches, stretches, paws, and darts;

First at one and then its fellow
Just as light and just as yellow;
There are many now – now one –
Now they stop; and there are none –
What intenseness of desire
In her upward eye of fire!
With a tiger-leap half way
Now she meets the coming prey,
Lets it go as fast, and then
Has it in her power again:
Now she works with three or four,
Like an Indian Conjuror;
Quick as he in feats of art,
Far beyond in joy of heart.
Were her antics play'd in the eye
Of a thousand Standers-by,
Clapping hands with shout and stare,
What would little Tabby care
For the plaudits of the Crowd?
Over happy to be proud,
Over wealthy in the treasure
Of her own exceeding pleasure!

'Tis a pretty Baby-treat;
Nor, I deem, for me unmeet:
Here, for neither Babe or me,
Other Playmate can I see.
Of the countless, living things,
That with stir of feet and wings,
(In the sun or under shade
Upon bough or grassy blade)

And with busy revellings,
Chirp and song, and murmurings,
Made this Orchard's narrow space,
And this Vale so blithe a place;
Multitudes are swept away

Never more to breathe the day:
Some are sleeping; some in Bands
Travell'd into distant Lands;
Others slunk to moor and wood,
Far from human neighbourhood,
And, among the Kinds that keep
With us closer fellowship,
With us openly abide,
All have laid their mirth aside.

– Where is he that giddy Sprite,
Blue-cap, with his colours bright,
Who was blest as bird could be,
Feeding in the apple-tree,
Made such wanton spoil and rout,
Turning blossoms inside out,
Hung with head towards the ground,
Flutter'd, perch'd; into a round
Bound himself, and then unbound;
Lithest, gaudiest Harlequin,
Prettiest Tumbler ever seen,
Light of heart, and light of limb,
What is now become of Him?
Lambs, that through the mountains went
Frisking, bleating merriment,
When the year was in its prime,
They are sober'd by this time.
If you look to vale or hill,
If you listen, all is still,
Save a little neighbouring Rill;
That from out the rocky ground
Strikes a solitary sound.
Vainly glitters hill and plain,
And the air is calm in vain;
Vainly Morning spreads the lure
Of a sky serene and pure;

Creature none can she decoy
Into open sign of joy:
Is it that they have a fear
Of the dreary season near?
Or that other pleasures be
Sweeter even than gaiety?

Yet, whate'er enjoyments dwell
In the impenetrable cell
Of the silent heart which Nature
Furnishes to every Creature,
Whatsoe'er we feel and know
Too sedate for outward show,
Such a light of gladness breaks,
Pretty Kitten! from thy freaks,
Spreads with such a living grace
O'er my little Laura's face;
Yes, the sight so stirs and charms
Thee, Baby, laughing in my arms,
That almost I could repine
That your transports are not mine,
That I do not wholly fare
Even as ye do, thoughtless Pair!
And I will have my careless season
Spite of melancholy reason,
Will walk through life in such a way
That, when time brings on decay,
Now and then I may possess
Hours of perfect gladsomeness.
– Pleas'd by any random toy;
By a Kitten's busy joy,
Or an infant's laughing eye
Sharing in the ecstasy,
I would fare like that or this,
Find my wisdom in my bliss;
Keep the sprightly soul awake,
And have faculties to take

Even from things by sorrow wrought
Matter for a jocund thought;
Spite of care, and spite of grief,
To gambol with Life's falling Leaf.

Youth and Age

JEROME K. JEROME (1859–1927)

Ah me! life sadly changes us all. The world seems a vast horrible grinding machine, into which what is fresh and bright and pure is pushed at one end, to come out old and crabbed and wrinkled at the other.

Look even at Pussy Sobersides, with her dull sleepy glance, her grave slow walk, and dignified, prudish airs; who could ever think that once she was the blue-eyed, whirling, scampering, head-over-heels, mad little firework that we call a kitten.

What marvellous vitality a kitten has. It is really something very beautiful the way life bubbles over in the little creatures. They rush about, and mew, and spring; dance on their hind legs, embrace everything with their front ones, roll over and over and over, lie on their backs and kick. They don't know what to do with themselves, they are so full of life.

from "On Cats and Dogs" in *Idle Thoughts
of an Idle Fellow* (1886)

Two Little Kittens

ANONYMOUS (c. 1879)

Two little kittens, one stormy night,
Began to quarrel, and then to fight;

One had a mouse, the other had none,
And that's the way the quarrel began.

"I'll have that mouse," said the biggest cat;
"You'll have that mouse? We'll see about that!"
"I *will* have that mouse," said the eldest son;
"You *shan't* have the mouse," said the little one.

I told you before 'twas a stormy night
When these two little kittens began to fight;
The old woman seized her sweeping broom,
And swept the two kittens right out of the room.

The ground was covered with frost and snow,
And the two little kittens had nowhere to go;
So they laid them down on the mat at the door,
While the old woman finished sweeping the floor.

Then they crept in, as quiet as mice,
All wet with the snow, and as cold as ice,
For they found it was better, that stormy night,
To lie down and sleep than to quarrel and fight.

A Lost Kitten

H.D. THOREAU (1817–62)

When yesterday Sophia and I were rowing past Mr Prichard's
land, where the river is bordered by a row of elms and low
willows, at 6 p.m., we heard a singular note of distress as it were
from a catbird – a loud, vibrating, catbird sort of note, as if the
catbird's mew were imitated by a smart vibrating spring. Blackbirds and others were flitting about, apparently attracted by it. At
first, thinking it was merely some peevish catbird or red-wing, I
was disregarding it, but on second thought turned the bows to
the shore, looking into the trees as well as over the shore, thinking

some bird might be in distress, caught by a snake or in a forked twig. The hovering birds dispersed at my approach; the note of distress sounded louder and nearer as I approached the shore covered with low osiers. The sound came from the ground, not from the trees. I saw a little black animal making haste to meet the boat under the osiers. A young muskrat? A mink? No, it was a little dot of a kitten. It was scarcely six inches long from the face to the base – or I might as well say the tip – of the tail, for the latter was a short, sharp pyramid, perfectly perpendicular but not swelled in the least. It was a very handsome and very precocious kitten, in perfectly good condition, its breadth being considerably more than one third of its length. Leaving its mewing, it came scrambling over the stones as fast as its weak legs would permit, straight to me. I took it up and dropped it into the boat, but while I was pushing off it ran the length of the boat to Sophia, who held it while we rowed homeward. Evidently it had not been weaned – was smaller than we remembered that kittens ever were – almost infinitely small; yet it had hailed a boat, its life being in danger, and saved itself. Its performance, considering its age and amount of experience, was more wonderful than that of any young mathematician or musician that I have read of. Various were the conjectures as to how the kitten came there, a quarter of a mile from a house. The possible solutions were finally reduced to three: first, it must either have been born there, or, secondly, carried there by its mother, or, thirdly, by human hands. In the first case, it had possibly brothers and sisters, one or both, and its mother had left them to go a-hunting on her own account and might be expected back. In the second, she might equally be expected to return. At any rate, not having thought of all this till we got home, we found that we had got ourselves into a scrape; for this kitten, though exceedingly interesting, required one nurse to attend it constantly for the present, and, of course, another to spell the first; and, beside, we had already a cat wellnigh grown, who manifested such a disposition towards the young stranger that we had no doubt it would have torn it in pieces in a moment if left alone with it. As nobody made up his or her mind to have it drowned, and still less to drown it – having once looked into its innocent extremely pale blue eyes (as of milk thrice skimmed) and had his finger or his chin sucked by it, while, its eyes being shut, its little paws played a soothing tune – it was resolved to keep it till it could be suitably disposed of. It rested nowhere, in no lap, under no covert, but still faintly cried for its mother and its accustomed supper. It ran towards every sound or movement of a human being, and whoever crossed the room it was sure to follow at a rapid pace. It had all the ways of a cat of the maturest years; could purr divinely and raised its back to rub all boots and shoes. When it raised its foot to scratch its ear, which by the way it never hit, it was sure to fall over and roll on the floor. It climbed straight up the sitter, faintly mewing all the way, and sucked his chin. In vain, at first, its head was bent down into saucers of milk which its eyes did not see, and its chin was wetted. But soon it learned to suck a finger that had been dipped in it, and better still a rag; and then at last it slept and rested. The street was explored in vain to find its owner, and at length an Irish family took it into their cradle. Soon after we learned that a neighbour who had heard the mewing of kittens in the partition had sent for a carpenter, taken off a board, and found two the very day at noon that we sailed. That same hour it was first brought to the light a coarse Irish cook had volunteered to drown it, had carried it to the river, and without bag or sinker had cast it in! It saved itself and hailed a boat! What an eventful life! What a precocious kitten! We feared it owed its first plump condition to the water. How strong and effective the instinct of self-preservation!

from *Journal*, 22 May 1853

The Kitten

ANONYMOUS

I sprang to life with playful, merry face,
The prettiest kitten of my pretty race;
My mother purr'd her joys with fond surprise,
And watch'd with anxious care my opening eyes.

The History of the Seven Young Cats

EDWARD LEAR (1812–88)

The Seven Young Cats set off on their travels with great delight and rapacity. But, on coming to the top of a high hill, they perceived at a long distance off a Clangle-Wangle (or, as it is more properly written, Clangel-Wangel), and in spite of the warning they had had, they ran straight up to it.

(Now the Clangle-Wangle is a most dangerous and delusive beast, and by no means commonly to be met with. They live in the water as well as on land, using their long tail as a sail when in the former element. Their speed is extreme, but their habits of life are domestic and superfluous, and their general demeanour pensive and pellucid. On summer evenings they may sometimes be observed near the Lake Pipple-popple, standing on their heads and humming their national melodies: they subsist entirely on vegetables, excepting when they eat veal, or mutton, or pork, or beef, or fish, or saltpetre.)

The moment the Clangle-Wangle saw the Seven Young Cats approach, he ran away; and as he ran straight on for four months, and the Cats, though they continued to run, could never overtake him, they all gradually *died* of fatigue and of exhaustion, and never afterwards recovered.

And this was the end of the Seven Young Cats.

Choosing Their Names

THOMAS HOOD (1799–1845)

Our old cat has kittens three –
What do you think their names should be?
Pepperpot, Sootikin, Scratchaway-there,
Was there ever a kitten with these to compare?
And we call their old mother – now, what do you think?
Tabitha Long-claws Tiddley-wink!

One is tabby with emerald eyes,
   And a tail that's long and slender,
And into a temper she quickly flies
   If you ever by chance offend her.
     I think we shall call her this –
     I think we shall call her that –
Now, don't you think that Pepperpot
   Is a nice name for a cat?

One is black with a frill of white,
   And her feet are all white fur,
If you stroke her she carries her tail upright
   And quickly begins to purr.
     I think we shall call her this –
     I think we shall call her that –
Now, don't you think that Sootikin
   Is a nice name for a cat?

One is a tortoiseshell yellow and black,
   With plenty of white about him;
If you tease him, at once he sets up his back,
   He's a quarrelsome one, ne'er doubt him.
     I think we shall call him this –
     I think we shall call him that –
Now, don't you think that Scratchaway
   Is a nice name for a cat?

A Young Cat From Clifford's Inn

SAMUEL BUTLER (1835–1902)

No, I will not have any Persian cat; it is undertaking too much
responsibility. I must have a cat whom I find homeless, wandering about the court, and to whom, therefore, I am under no
obligation. There is a Clifford's Inn euphemism about cats which
the laundresses use quite gravely: they say people come to this

place "to lose their cats". They mean that, when they have a cat they don't want to kill and don't know how to get rid of, they bring it here, drop it inside the railings of our grass-plot, and go away under the impression that they have been "losing" their cat. Well, this happens very frequently and I have already selected a dirty little drunken wretch of a kitten to be successor to my poor old cat. I don't suppose it drinks anything stronger than milk and water but then, you know, so much milk and water must be bad for a kitten that age – at any rate it looks as if it drank; but it gives me the impression of being affectionate, intelligent, and fond of mice, and I believe, if it had a home, it would become more respectable; at any rate I will see how it works.

from a letter to his sister

The Kitten and the Cat

ANONYMOUS

Domestic and fond, see
  The kitten and the cat;
Clear houses of vermin,
  The mouse and the rat;
They live in contentment,
  And keep you in peace,
Or these foes in number,
  Would greatly increase.

Tom Quartz

THEODORE ROOSEVELT (1858–1919)

Tom Quartz is certainly the cunningest kitten I have ever seen. He is always playing pranks on Jack and I get very nervous lest Jack should grow too irritated. The other evening they were both in the library – Jack sleeping before the fire – Tom Quartz scampering about, an exceedingly playful little creature – which is about what he is. He would race across the floor, then jump upon the curtain or play with the tassel. Suddenly he spied Jack and galloped up to him. Jack, looking exceedingly sullen and shame-faced, jumped out of the way and got upon the sofa and around the table, and Tom Quartz instantly jumped upon him again. Jack suddenly shifted to the other sofa, where Tom Quartz again went after him. Then Jack started for the door, while Tom made a rapid turn under the sofa and around the table and just as Jack reached the door leaped on his hind-quarters. Jack bounded forward and away and the two went tandem out of the room – Jack not co-operating at all; and about five minutes afterwards Tom Quartz stalked solemnly back.

Another evening, the next Speaker of the House, Mr Cannon, an exceedingly solemn, elderly gentleman with chin whiskers, who certainly does not look to be of playful nature, came to call upon me. He is a great friend of mine, and we sat talking over what our policies for the session should be until about eleven o'clock and when he went away I accompanied him to the head of the stairs. He had gone about halfway down when Tom Quartz strolled by, his tail erect and very fluffy. He spied Mr Cannon going down the stairs, jumped to the conclusion that he was a playmate escaping, and raced after him, suddenly grasping him by the leg the way he does Archie and Quentin when they play hide and seek with him; then loosening his hold he tore downstairs ahead of Mr Cannon, who eyed him with an iron calm and not one particle of surprise . . .

from a letter to his daughter, 6 January 1903

Old Mother Mitten and Her Funny Kitten

ANONYMOUS (c. 1825)

Old mother Mitten
And her pretty kitten,
Took supper, one night rather late;

But they sat down to tea,
And the dog came to see
Pussy cut the meat up on her plate.

The dog and the cat
Were having a chat,
When Pussy cried out with a mew:

"Dear old mother Mitten,
Just look at your kitten,
She's going to drink mead with you."

When the supper was over,
The kitten moreover,
Did stand on the top of her head.

So the dog he declares,
They must sleep in their chairs,
And none of them get into bed.

So when they awoke,
Miss Pussy first spoke,
And to the old Lady said she:

"My dear if you please,
Take this bread and cheese,
And I'll give you a hot cup of tea."

At the table there sat,
The dog and the cat,
With cards they were trying to play;

But the dog's beard is long,
Which the cat thinks is wrong,
And soon she is shaving poor Tray.

Having shaved Mr Tray,
She hastens away,
And dresses herself for a walk;

And when she came in,
Told where she had been,
To have with the neighbours a talk.

Says granny indeed,
"I believe you're agreed,
To marry Miss Puss, Mr Tray";

The dog made a bow,
And the cat she said mow,
And I think they got married that day.

from *The Pretty Primer* (*c.* 1825)

A Rescued Kitten

GERARD MANLEY HOPKINS (1844–89)

Rescued a little kitten that was perched in the sill of the round window at the sink over the gasjet and dared not jump down. I heard her mew a piteous long time till I could bear it no longer; but I make a note of it because of her gratitude after I had taken her down, which made her follow me about and at each turn of the stairs as I went down leading her to the kitchen ran back a few steps up and try to get up to lick me through the banisters from the flight above.

from his *Diary*

Kitten

HEINRICH HEINE (1797–1856)

Kitten! O my pretty kitten!
    Why delightest thou to do ill?
Sadly is my poor heart smitten
    By thy tiger-talons cruel.

from *Clarissa* translated by E.A. Bowring

Kitten Overboard

HENRY FIELDING (1707–54)

Thursday, July 11th 1754. A most tragical incident fell out this day at sea. While the ship was under sail, but making as will appear no great way, a kitten, one of four of the feline inhabitants of the cabin, fell from the window into the water: an alarm was immediately given to the captain, who was then upon deck, and received it with the utmost concern and many bitter oaths. He immediately gave orders to the steersman in favour of the poor thing, as he called it; the sails were instantly slackened, and all hands, as the phrase is, employed to recover the poor animal. I was, I own, extremely surprised at all this; less indeed at the captain's extreme tenderness than at his conceiving any possibility of success; for if puss had had nine thousand instead of nine lives, I concluded they had been all lost. The boatswain, however, had more sanguine hopes, for having stripped himself of his jacket, breeches and shirt, he leaped boldly into the water, and to my great astonishment, in a few minutes returned to the ship, bearing the motionless animal in his mouth. Nor was this, I observed, a matter of such great difficulty as it appeared to my ignorance, and possibly may seem to that of my fresh-water reader. The kitten was now exposed to air and sun on the deck, where its life, of which it retained no symptoms, was despaired of by all.

The captain's humanity, if I may so call it, did not so totally destroy his philosophy as to make him yield himself up to affliction on this melancholy occasion. Having felt his loss like a man, he resolved to shew he could bear it like one; and, having declared he had rather have lost a cask of rum or brandy, betook himself to threshing at backgammon with the Portuguese friar, in which innocent amusement they passed about two-thirds of their time.

But as I have, perhaps, a little too wantonly endeavoured to raise the tender passions of my readers in this narrative, I should think myself unpardonable if I concluded it without giving them the satisfaction of hearing that the kitten at last recovered, to the great joy of the good captain, but to the great disappointment of some of the sailors, who asserted that the drowning cat was the very surest way of raising a favourable wind; a supposition of which, though we have heard several plausible accounts, we will not presume to assign the true original reason.

Wednesday. He even extended his humanity, if I may so call it, to animals, and even his cats and kittens had large shares in his affection. An instance of which we saw this evening, when the cat, which had shewn it could not be drowned, was found suffocated under a feather-bed in the cabin. I will not endeavour to describe his lamentations with more prolixity than barely by saying they were grievous, and seemed to have some mixture of the Irish howl in them.

from *Journal of a Voyage to Lisbon* (1755)

Observations on Kittens

VARIOUS

No matter how much cats fight, there always seem to be plenty of kittens.

Abraham Lincoln

A kitten is chiefly remarkable for rushing like mad at nothing whatever, and generally stopping before it gets there.

Anonymous

Do you see that kitten chasing so prettily her own tail? If you could look with her eyes, you might see her surrounded with hundreds of figures performing complex dramas, with tragic and comic issues, long conversations, many characters, many ups and downs of fate.

Ralph Waldo Emerson

The Black Kitten

LEWIS CARROLL (1832–98)

One thing was certain, that the *white* kitten had had nothing to do with it: it was the black kitten's fault entirely. For the white kitten had been having its face washed by the old cat for the last quarter of an hour (and bearing it pretty well, considering); so you see that it *couldn't* have had any hand in the mischief.

The way Dinah washed her children's faces was this: first she held the poor thing down by its ear with one paw, and then with the other paw she rubbed its face all over, the wrong way, beginning at the nose: and just now, as I said, she was hard at work on the white kitten, which was lying quite still and trying to purr – no doubt feeling that it was all meant for its good.

But the black kitten had been finished with earlier in the afternoon, and so, while Alice was sitting curled up in a corner of the great armchair, half talking to herself and half asleep, the kitten had been having a grand game of romps with the ball of worsted Alice had been trying to wind up, and had been rolling it up and down till it had all come undone again; and there it was, spread over the hearth-rug, all knots and tangles, with the kitten running after its own tail in the middle.

"Oh, you wicked, wicked little thing!" cried Alice, catching up the kitten, and giving it a little kiss to make it understand that it was in disgrace. "Really, Dinah ought to have taught you better manners! You *ought*, Dinah, you know you ought!" she added, looking reproachfully at the old cat, and speaking in as cross a voice as she could manage – and then she scrambled back into the armchair, taking the kitten and the worsted with her, and began winding up the ball again. But she didn't get on very fast, as she was talking all the time, sometimes to the kitten, and sometimes to herself. Kitty sat very demurely on her knee, pretending to watch the progress of the winding, and now and then putting out one paw and gently touching the ball, as if it would be glad to help if it might.

"Do you know what tomorrow is, Kitty?" Alice began.

"You'd have guessed if you'd been up in the window with me – only Dinah was making you tidy, so you couldn't. I was watching the boys getting in sticks for the bonfire – and it wants plenty of sticks, Kitty! Only it got so cold, and it snowed so, they had to leave off. Never mind, Kitty, we'll go and see the bonfire tomorrow." Here Alice wound two or three turns of the worsted round the kitten's neck, just to see how it would look: this led to a scramble, in which the ball rolled down upon the floor, and yards and yards of it got unwound again.

"Do you know, I was so angry, Kitty," Alice went on, as soon as they were comfortably settled again, "when I saw all the mischief you had been doing, I was very nearly opening the window, and putting you out into the snow! And you'd have deserved it, you little mischievous darling! What have you got to say for yourself? Now don't interrupt me!" she went on, holding up one finger. "I'm going to tell you all your faults. Number one: you squeaked twice while Dinah was washing your face this morning. Now you can't deny it, Kitty: I heard you! What's that you say?" (pretending that the kitten was speaking). "Her paw went into your eye? Well, that's *your* fault, for keeping your eyes open – if you'd shut them tight up, it wouldn't have happened. Now don't make any more excuses, but listen! Number two: you pulled Snowdrop away by the tail just as I had put down the saucer of milk before her! What, you were thirsty, were you? How do you know she wasn't thirsty too? Now for number three: you unwound every bit of the worsted while I wasn't looking!

"That's three faults, Kitty, and you've not been punished for any of them yet. You know I'm saving up all your punishments for Wednesday week – suppose they had saved up all *my* punishments?" she went on, talking more to herself than the kitten. "What *would* they do at the end of a year? I should be sent to prison, I suppose, when the day came. Or – let me see – suppose each punishment was to be going without a dinner: then, when the miserable day came, I should have to go without fifty dinners at once! Well, I shouldn't mind *that* much! I'd far rather go without them than eat them!

"Do you hear the snow against the window-panes, Kitty? How nice and soft it sounds! Just as if someone was kissing the window all over outside. I wonder if the snow *loves* the trees and fields, that it kisses them so gently? And then it covers them up snug, you know, with a white quilt; and perhaps it says, 'Go to sleep, darlings, till the summer comes again.' And when they wake up in the summer, Kitty, they dress themselves all in green, and dance about – whenever the wind blows – oh, that's very pretty!" cried Alice, dropping the ball of worsted to clap her hands. "And I do so *wish* it was true! I'm sure the woods look sleepy in the autumn, when the leaves are getting brown.

"Kitty, can you play chess? Now, don't smile, my dear, I'm asking it seriously. Because, when we were playing just now, you watched just as if you understood it: and when I said 'Check!' you purred! Well, it *was* a nice check, Kitty, and really I might have won, if it hadn't been for that nasty Knight, that came wriggling down among my pieces. Kitty, dear, let's pretend –" And here I wish I could tell you half the things Alice used to say, beginning with her favourite phrase "Let's pretend". She had had quite a long argument with her sister only the day before – all because Alice had begun with "Let's pretend we're kings and queens"; and her sister, who liked being very exact, had argued that they couldn't, because there were only two of them, and Alice had been reduced at last to say, "Well, *you* can be one of them, then, and *I'll* be all the rest." And once she had really frightened her old nurse by shouting suddenly in her ear, "Nurse! Do let's pretend that I'm a hungry hyæna, and you're a bone!"

But this is taking us away from Alice's speech to the kitten. "Let's pretend that you're the Red Queen, Kitty! Do you know, I think if you sat up and folded your arms, you'd look exactly like her. Now do try, there's a dear!" And Alice got the Red Queen off the table, and set it up before the kitten as a model for it to imitate: however, the thing didn't succeed, principally, Alice said, because the kitten wouldn't fold its arms properly. So, to punish it, she held it up to the Looking Glass, that it might see how sulky it was, "– and if you're not good directly," she added, "I'll put you through into Looking Glass House. How would you like *that*?

"Now, if you'll only attend, Kitty, and not talk so much, I'll tell you all my ideas about Looking Glass House. First, there's the room you can see through the glass – that's just the same as our drawing-room, only the things go the other way. I can see all of it when I get upon a chair – all but the bit just behind the fireplace. Oh! I do so wish I could see *that* bit! I want so much to know whether they've a fire in the winter: you never *can* tell, you know, unless our fire smokes, and then smoke comes up in that room too – but that may be only pretence, just to make it look as if they had a fire. Well then, the books are something like our books, only the words go the wrong way; I know *that*, because I've held up one of our books to the glass, and then they hold up one in the other room.

"How would you like to live in Looking Glass House, Kitty? I wonder if they'd give you milk in there? Perhaps Looking Glass milk isn't good to drink – but oh, Kitty! now we come to the passage. You can just see a little *peep* of the passage in Looking Glass House, if you leave the door of our drawing-room wide open: and it's very like our passage as far as you can see, only you know it may be quite different on beyond. Oh, Kitty! how nice it would be if we could only get through into Looking Glass House! I'm sure it's got, oh! such beautiful things in it! Let's pretend there's a way of getting through into it somehow, Kitty. Let's pretend the glass has got all soft like gauze, so that we can get through. Why, it's turning into a sort of mist now, I declare! It'll be easy enough to get through –" She was up on the chimney-piece while she said this, though she hardly knew how she had got there. And certainly the glass *was* beginning to melt away, just like a bright silvery mist.

In another moment Alice was through the glass, and had jumped lightly down into the Looking Glass room. The very first thing she did was to look whether there was a fire in the fireplace, and she was quite pleased to find that there was a real one, blazing away as brightly as the one she had left behind. "So I shall be as warm here as I was in the old room," thought Alice:

"warmer, in fact, because there'll be no one here to scold me away from the fire. Oh, what fun it'll be, when they see me through the glass in here, and can't get at me!" [...]

[*After her adventures in the Looking-Glass world, Alice awakes to find it has all been a dream.*]

"Your Red Majesty shouldn't purr so loud," Alice said, rubbing her eyes, and addressing the kitten, respectfully, yet with some severity. "You woke me out of oh! such a nice dream! And you've been along with me, Kitty – all through the Looking Glass world. Did you know it, dear?"

It is a very inconvenient habit of kittens (Alice had once made the remark) that, whatever you say to them, they *always* purr. "If they would only purr for 'yes', and mew for 'no', or any rule of that sort," she had said, "so that one could keep up a conversation! But how *can* you talk with a person if they *always* say the same thing?"

On this occasion the kitten only purred: and it was impossible to guess whether it meant "yes" or "no".

So Alice hunted among the chessmen on the table till she had found the Red Queen: then she went down on her knees on the hearthrug, and put the kitten and the Queen to look at each other. "Now, Kitty!" she cried, clapping her hands triumphantly. "Confess that was what you turned into!"

("But it wouldn't look at it," she said, when she was explaining the thing afterwards to her sister: "it turned away its head, and pretended not to see it: but it looked a *little* ashamed of itself, so I think it *must* have been the Red Queen.")

"Sit up a little more stiffly, dear!" Alice cried with a merry laugh. "And curtsey while you're thinking what to – what to purr. It saves time, remember!" And she caught it up and gave it one little kiss "just in honour of its having been a Red Queen".

"Snowdrop, my pet!" she went on, looking over her shoulder at the white kitten, which was still patiently undergoing its toilet, "when *will* Dinah have finished with your White Majesty, I wonder? That must be the reason you were so untidy in my dream. Dinah! Do you know that you're scrubbing a White Queen? Really, it's most disrespectful of you!

"And what did *Dinah* turn to, I wonder?" she prattled on, as she settled comfortably down, with one elbow on the rug, and her chin in her hand, to watch the kittens. "Tell me, Dinah, did you turn to Humpty Dumpty? I *think* you did – however, you'd better not mention it to your friends just yet, for I'm not sure.

"By the way, Kitty, if only you'd been really with me in my dream, there was one thing you *would* have enjoyed – I had such a quantity of poetry said to me, all about fishes! Tomorrow morning you shall have a real treat. All the time you're eating your breakfast, I'll repeat 'The Walrus and the Carpenter' to you; and then you can make believe it's oysters, my dear!

"Now, Kitty, let's consider who it was that dreamed it all. This is a serious question, my dear, and you should *not* go on licking your paw like that – as if Dinah hadn't washed you this morning! You see, Kitty, it *must* have been either me or the Red King. He was part of my dream, of course – but then I was part of his dream, too! *Was* it the Red King, Kitty? You were his wife, my dear, so you ought to know – oh, Kitty, *do* help to settle it! I'm sure your paw can wait!" But the provoking kitten only began on the other paw, and pretended it hadn't heard the question.

from *Through the Looking Glass*
and What Alice Found There (1871)

The Kitten and the Billiard-Table

MARK TWAIN (1835–1910)

If I can find a photograph of my "Tammany" and her kittens, I will enclose it in this. One of them likes to be crammed into a corner-pocket of the billiard-table – which he fits as snugly as does a finger in a glove – and then he watches the game (and obstructs it) by the hour, and spoils many a shot by putting out his paw and changing the direction of a passing ball. Whenever a ball is in his arms, or so close to him that it cannot be played upon without risk of hurting him, the player is privileged to remove it to any one of the three spots that chances to be vacant.

from *Letters*

A Kitten's Castle

H.D. THOREAU (1817–62)

It is amusing to observe how a kitten regards the attic, kitchen, or shed where it was bred as its castle to resort to in time of danger. It loves best to sleep on some elevated place, as a shelf or chair, and for many months does not venture far from the back door where it first saw the light. Two rods is a great range for it, but so far it is tempted, when the dew is off, by the motions of grasshoppers and crickets and other such small game, sufficiently novel and surprising to it. They frequently have a wheezing cough, which some refer to grasshoppers' wings across their windpipes. The kitten has been eating grasshoppers.

If some member of the household with whom they are familiar – their mistress or master – goes forth into the garden, they are then encouraged to take a wider range, and for a short season explore the more distant bean and cabbage rows, or, if several of the family go forth at once -- as it were a reconnaissance in force – the kitten does a transient scout duty outside, but yet on the slightest alarm they are seen bounding back with great leaps over the grass towards the castle, where they stand panting on the doorstep, with their small lower jaws fallen, until they fill up with courage again. A cat looks down with complacency on the strange dog from the corn-barn window.

The kitten when it is two or three months old is full of play. Ever and anon she takes up her plaything in her mouth and carries it to another place – a distant corner of the room or some other nook, as under a rocker – or perchance drops it at your feet, seeming to delight in the mere carriage of it, as if it were her prey – tiger-like. In proportion to her animal spirits are her quick motions and sudden whirlings about on the carpet or in the air. She may make a great show of scratching and biting, but let her have your hand and she will presently lick it instead.

They are so naturally stealthy, skulking and creeping about, affecting holes and darkness, that they will enter a shed rather by some hole under the door-sill than go over the sill through the open door.

Though able to bear cold, few creatures love warmth more or sooner find out where the fire is. The cat, whether she comes home wet or dry, directly squeezes herself under the cooking-stove, and stews her brain there, if permitted. If the cat is in the kitchen, she is most likely to be found under the stove.

from *Journal*, 14 May 1861

TIGER!
TIGER!

"God made the cat that man might have the
pleasure of caressing the tiger."
Ferdinand Méry

The Cat and the Partridge

DAMOCHARIS THE GRAMMARIAN (*c.* AD550)

Your master grieved as though you'd savaged *him*,
When you devoured his partridge, wicked cat.
The hounds which tore Actæon limb from limb,
Fierce man-eaters, did hardly worse than that.
And now so set on partridge is your soul,
The mice can dance and rob your dainty bowl.

from *Anthologia Palatina,* Book VII,
No. 206 translated by W. Bedell Stanford

A Trout-Catching Tabby

W.H. HUDSON (1841–1922)

One of the shepherd's most interesting memories of his Dove-ton period was of a cat they possessed, which was greatly admired. He was a very large, handsome, finely marked tabby, with a thick coat, and always appeared very well nourished but never wanted to be fed. He was a nice-tempered, friendly animal, and whenever he came in he appeared pleased at seeing the inmates of the house, and would go from one to another, rubbing his sides against their legs and purring aloud with satisfaction. Then they would give him food, and he would take a morsel or two or lap up as much milk as would fill a teaspoon and leave the rest. He was not hungry, and it always appeared, they said, as if he smelt at or tasted the food they put down for him just to please them. Everybody in the village admired their cat for his great size, his beauty, and gentle, friendly disposition, but how he fed himself was a mystery to all, since no one had ever detected him trying to catch anything out of doors. In that part of the Wylye valley there were no woods for him to hunt in; they also noticed that when, out of doors, the small birds, anxious and angered at his presence, would flit, uttering their cries, close to him, he paid no attention. The only thing they discovered about his outdoor life by watching him was that he had the habit of going to the railway track, then recently constructed, from Westbury to Salisbury, which ran near their cottage, and would there seat himself on one of the rails and remain for a long time gazing fixedly before him as if he found it a pleasure to keep his eyes on the long, glittering metal line.

At the back of the cottage there was a piece of waste ground extending to the river, with a small, old, ruinous barn standing on it a few yards from the bank. Between the barn and the stream the ground was overgrown with rank weeds, and here one day Caleb came by chance upon his cat eating something among the weeds – a good-sized, fresh-caught trout! On examining the ground he found it littered with the heads, fins, and portions of backbones of the trout their cat had been feeding on every day since they had been in possession of him. They did not destroy their favourite, nor tell any one of their discovery, but they watched him and found that it was his habit to bring a trout every day to that spot, but how he caught his fish was never known.

Eventually their cat came to a tragic end, as all Wylye anglers will be pleased to hear. He was found on the railway track, at the spot where he had the habit of sitting, crushed as flat as a pancake. It was thought that while sitting on the rail in his usual way he had become so absorbed at the sight of the straight, shining line that the noise and vibration of the approaching train failed to arouse him in time to save himself. It seemed strange to them that a creature so very much alive and quick to escape danger should have met its death in this way; and what added to the wonder was that another cat of the village was found on the line crushed by a train shortly afterwards. Probably the sight of the shining rail gazed at too long and fixedly had produced a hypnotic effect on the animal's brain and made it powerless to escape.

from *A Shepherd's Life* (1910)

Who is This Cat?

ANONYMOUS (c. 3000BC)

I am the Cat which fought hard by the Acacia Tree in Heliopolis on the night when the foes of the Setting Sun were destroyed.

Who is this Cat?

This male Cat is the Sun-god Ra himself and he was called Mau because of the speech of the God Sa concerning him: He is like unto that which he hath made, therefore did the name Ra become Mau. Others, however, say that the male cat is Shu, the God of the Air, who made over the possessions of the Earth-god Geb to Osiris.

As concerning the fight which took place near the Acacia Tree in Heliopolis these words refer to the slaughter of the children of rebellion, when righteous retribution was meted out to them for the evil they had done. As concerning the night of the battle these words refer to the invasion of the eastern portion of the heavens by the children of rebellion, where upon a great battle arose in heaven and in all the earth.

from *The Book of the Dead* (before 3000BC)

The Cat and the Old Rat

JEAN DE LA FONTAINE (1621–95)

A story-writer of our sort
Historifies, in short,
Of one that may be reckon'd
A Rodilard the Second –
The Alexander of the cats,
The Attila, the scourge of rats,
Whose fierce and whisker'd head
Among the latter spread,
A league around, its dread;
Who seem'd, indeed, determined

The world should be unvermined.
The planks with props more false than slim,
The tempting heaps of poison'd meal,
The traps of wire and traps of steel,
Were only play compared with him.
At length, so sadly were they scared,
The rats and mice no longer dared
To show their thievish faces
Outside their hiding-places,
Thus shunning all pursuit; whereat
Our crafty General Cat
Contrived to hang himself, as dead,
Beside the wall with downward head,
Resisting gravitation's laws
By clinging with his hinder claws
To some small bit of string.
The rats esteem'd the thing
A judgment for some naughty deed,
Some thievish snatch,
Or ugly scratch;
And thought their foe had got his meed
By being hung indeed.
With hope elated all
Of laughing at his funeral,
They thrust their noses out in air;
And now to show their heads they dare;
Now dodging back, now venturing more.
At last upon the larder's store
They fall to filching, as of yore.
A scanty feast enjoy'd these shallows;
Down dropp'd the hung one from his gallows,
And of the hindmost caught.
"Some other tricks to me are known,"
Said he, while tearing bone from bone,
"By long experience taught;
The point is settled, free from doubt,
That from your holes you shall come out."

His threat as good as prophecy
Was proved by Mr Mildandsly;
For, putting on a mealy robe,
He squatted in an open tub,
And held his purring and his breath;
Out came the vermin to their death.
On this occasion, one old stager,
A rat as grey as any badger,
Who had in battle lost his tail,
Abstained from smelling at the meal;
And cried, far off, "Ah! General Cat,
I much suspect a heap like that;
Your meal is not the thing, perhaps,
For one who knows somewhat of traps;
Should you a sack of meal become,
I'd let you be, and stay at home."

Well said, I think, and prudently,
By one who knew distrust to be
The parent of security.

from *The Fables* (1842) translated by Elizur Wright

Jim Wolf and the Cats

MARK TWAIN (1835–1910)

It was back in those far-distant days – 1848 or '49 – that Jim Wolf
came to us. He was from a hamlet thirty or forty miles back in the
country, and he brought all his native sweetnesses and gentlenesses
and simplicities with him. He was approaching seventeen, a grave
and slender lad, trustful, honest, honourable, a creature to love and
cling to. And he was incredibly bashful. He was with us a good
while, but he could never conquer that peculiarity; he could not
be at ease in the presence of any woman, not even in my good and
gentle mother's; and as to speaking to any girl, it was wholly
impossible. He sat perfectly still, one day – there were ladies

chatting in the room – while a wasp up his leg stabbed him cruelly a dozen times; and all the sign he gave was a slight wince for each stab and the tear of torture in his eye. He was too bashful to move.

It is to this kind that untoward things happen. My sister gave a "candy-pull" on a winter's night. I was too young to be of the company, and Jim was too diffident. I was sent up to bed early, and Jim followed of his own motion. His room was in the new part of the house and his window looked out on the roof of the L annexe. That roof was six inches deep in snow, and the snow had an ice crust upon it which was as slick as glass. Out of the comb of the roof projected a short chimney, a common resort for sentimental cats on moonlight nights – and this was a moonlight night. Down at the eaves, below the chimney, a canopy of dead vines spread away to some posts, making a cosy shelter, and after an hour or two the rollicking crowd of young ladies and gentlemen grouped themselves in its shade, with their saucers of liquid and piping-hot candy disposed about them on the frozen ground to cool. There was joyous chaffing and joking and laughter – peal upon peal of it.

About this time a couple of old, disreputable tomcats got up on the chimney and started a heated argument about something; also about this time I gave up trying to get to sleep and went visiting to Jim's room. He was awake and fuming about the cats and their intolerable yowling. I asked him, mockingly, why he didn't climb out and drive them away. He was nettled, and said overboldly that for two cents he *would*.

It was a rash remark and was probably repented of before it was fairly out of his mouth. But it was too late – he was committed. I knew him; and I knew he would rather break his neck than back down, if I egged him on judiciously.

"Oh, of course you would! Who's doubting it?"

It galled him, and he burst out, with sharp irritation, "Maybe *you* doubt it!"

"I? Oh no! I shouldn't think of such a thing. You are always doing wonderful things, with your mouth."

He was in a passion now. He snatched on his yarn socks and began to raise the window, saying in a voice quivering with anger: "*You* think I dasn't – you do! Think what you blame please. *I* don't care what you think. I'll show you!"

The window made him rage; it wouldn't stay up.

I said, "Never mind, I'll hold it."

Indeed, I would have done anything to help. I was only a boy and was already in a radiant heaven of anticipation. He climbed carefully out, clung to the window sill until his feet were safely placed, then began to pick his perilous way on all-fours along the glassy comb, a foot and a hand on each side of it. I believe I enjoy it now as much as I did then; yet it is nearly fifty years ago. The frosty breeze flapped his short shirt about his lean legs; the crystal roof shone like polished marble in the intense glory of the moon; the unconscious cats sat erect upon the chimney, alertly watching each other, lashing their tails and pouring out their hollow grievances; and slowly and cautiously Jim crept on, flapping as he went, the gay and frolicsome young creatures under the vine canopy unaware, and outraging these solemnities with their misplaced laughter. Every time Jim slipped I had a hope; but always on he crept and disappointed it. At last he was within reaching distance. He paused, raised himself carefully up, measured his distance deliberately, then made a frantic grab at the nearest cat – and missed it. Of course he lost his balance. His heels flew up, he struck on his back, and like a rocket he darted down the roof feet first, crashed through the dead vines, and landed in a sitting position in fourteen saucers of red-hot candy, in the midst of all that party – and dressed as *he* was – this lad who could not look a girl in the face with his clothes on. There was a wild scramble and a storm of shrieks, and Jim fled up the stairs, dripping broken crockery all the way.

from *Autobiography* (1924)

On Mrs Reynolds' Cat

JOHN KEATS (1795–1821)

Cat! who hast pass'd thy grand climacteric,
  How many mice and rats hast in thy days

93

Destroy'd? – How many titbits stolen? Gaze
With those bright languid segments green, and prick
Those velvet ears – but pr'ythee do not stick
Thy latent talons in me – and upraise
Thy gentle mew – and tell me all thy frays
Of fish and mice, and rats and tender chick.
Nay, look not down, nor lick thy dainty wrists –
For all the wheezy asthma, and for all
Thy tail's tip is nick'd off – and though the fists
Of many a maid have given thee many a maul,
Still is that fur as soft as when the lists
In youth thou enter'dst on glass bottled wall.

The Poacher Cat

w.h. hudson (1841–1922)

It is a well-known habit of some hunting, or poaching, cats to bring their captives to their master or mistress. I have met with scores – I might say with hundreds – of such cases. I remember an old gaucho, a neighbour of mine in South America, who used to boast that he usually had a spotted tinamou – the partridge of the pampas – for his dinner every day, brought in by his cat. Even in England, where partridges are not so abundant or easily taken, there are clever partridge-hunting cats. I remember one, a very fine white cat, owned by a woodman I once lodged with in Savernake Forest, who was in the habit of bringing in a partridge and would place it on the kitchen floor and keep guard over it until the woodman's wife came to take it up and put it away for the Sunday's dinner. A lady friend told me of a cat at a farmhouse where she was staying during the summer months, which became attached to her and was constantly bringing her young rabbits. They were never injured but held firmly by the skin of the neck. The lady would take the rabbit gently into her hands and deposit it on her lap, and cover it over with a handkerchief or a cloth, and pussy, seeing it safe in her power, would then go away. The lady would then walk away to a distance from the house to liberate the little trembler, devoutly wishing that this too affectionate cat would get over the delusion that such gifts were acceptable to her. One day pussy came trotting into the drawing-room with a stoat in her mouth, and depositing it on the carpet by the side of her chair immediately turned round and hastily left the room. The stoat was dead, not being a creature that could easily be carried about alive, and pussy, having other matters to attend to, did not think it necessary to wait to see her present taken up and carefully deposited in her mistress's lap.

Cases of this kind are exceedingly common, and the simple explanation is, that the cat is not quite so unsocial a creature as some naturalists would have us believe. We may say that in this respect he compares badly with elephants, whales, pigs, seals, cattle, apes, wolves, dogs, and other large-brained social mammals; but he does not live wholly for himself. He is able to take thought for other cats and for his human companion – master hardly seems the right word in the case of such an animal – who is doubtless to him only a very big cat that walks erect on his hind-legs.

from *A Shepherd's Life* (1910)

Pangur Bán

ANONYMOUS (9th century)

I and Pangur Bán, my cat,
'Tis a like task we are at;
Hunting mice is his delight,
Hunting words I sit all night.

Better far than praise of men
'Tis to sit with book and pen;
Pangur bears me no ill-will,
He too plies his simple skill.

'Tis a merry thing to see
At our tasks how glad are we,
When at home we sit and find
Entertainment to our mind.

Oftentimes a mouse will stray
In the hero Pangur's way;
Oftentimes my keen thought set
Takes a meaning in its net.

'Gainst the wall he sets his eye
Full and fierce and sharp and sly;
'Gainst the wall of knowledge I
All my little wisdom try.

When a mouse darts from its den,
Oh how glad is Pangur then!
Oh what gladness do I prove
When I solve the doubts I love!

So in peace our tasks we ply,
Pangur Bán, my cat, and I;
In our arts we find our bliss,
I have mine and he has his.

Practice every day has made
Pangur perfect in his trade;
I get wisdom day and night
Turning darkness into light.

translated by Robin Flower

Six Little Mice

ANONYMOUS

Six little mice sat down to spin;
Pussy passed by and she peeped in.

"What are you doing, my little men?"
"Weaving coats for gentlemen."
"Shall I come in and cut off your threads?"
"No, no, Mistress Pussy, you'd bite off our heads."
"Oh, no, I'll not; I'll help you to spin."
"That may be so, but you can't come in."
Says Puss: "You look so wondrous wise,
I like your whiskers and bright black eyes;
Your house is the nicest house I see,
I think there is room for you and for me."
The mice were so pleased that they opened the door,
And Pussy soon had them all dead on the floor.

Whittington and His Cat

ANONYMOUS (c. 1825)

Who has not heard of Whittington,
Thrice Lord Mayor of London Town?

In former times (for long ago
Lived Whittington, as records show),
Poor country lads were often told
That London streets were paved with gold.
One day, as Dick upon the grass
Reclined, a waggon chanced to pass
To London bound: this thought occurr'd –
I'll see if all is true I've heard:
So jumping up, away he ran,
And walk'd beside the waggon-man.

Judge Richard's feelings of surprise,
When London really met his eyes!
Not yet by sad experience taught,
His mind was fix'd in pleasing thought.

97

His friend the waggoner pass'd on;
Poor Whittington was left alone;
That night was houseless. In the morn,
The youthful wanderer rose forlorn:
Exhausted, spiritless, and faint,
The poor lad utter'd no complaint;
But, weeping, stretch'd himself before
A wealthy Merchant's open door.
The portly Cook, who lived at ease
And slighted Richard's miseries,
Bade him depart, with angry face,
And seek another resting place.
Just at this moment to his home
The worthy master chanced to come:
"Why lie you there, my lad?" said he,
"Labour you do not like, I see."

"I never would," was Dick's reply,
"Thus idly on your door-steps lie,
Could I but work obtain. I'm weak,
And vainly for employment seek."
"Get up, poor fellow; let me see —
Go, help them in the scullery."

Soon as the morning sun arose,
Dick quickly to the kitchen goes
To ply his task; and though the Cook
Oft greeted him with sullen look,
He still determined to obey,
And sought to please her every way.
Yet still she scolded, still would try
To make him from her service fly;
Nay more, she sometimes took a broom,
And beat poor Richard round the room;
But Whittington, as Christian should,
Always requited ill with good.

Within the room where Richard slept,
The rats and mice a revel kept;
And nightly as he lay in bed,
They ran across his face and head:
Among such plagues the attempt was vain
Refreshing sleep or rest to gain.
Yet patient Dick did not repine,
He made his master's slippers shine.
The Merchant's eye his labour traced:
And finding kindness rightly placed,
Sent him a penny by the maid –
Industry always is repaid.
With this poor Richard bought a Cat,
Dire enemy to mouse and rat.
Puss went to work that very night,
And put the rats and mice to flight.

The Merchant had an only child,
A daughter affable and mild,
From whom poor Richard learn'd to read.
Slowly indeed did he proceed;
But those who readily pursue
The proper path, may wonders do.
Just like the snail, which seldom fails
To reach the top of garden-rails,
Because with diligence its race
Continues till it gains the place.

The Merchant summon'd to the hall
His clerks and servants, one and all,
Told of his Ship, and then explain'd
How wealth was by her cargo gain'd;
To fill the white and spreading sail,
His Captain waited for a gale;
Then ask'd if each would like to send
Something which might to profit tend.

All but young Richard heard with joy
This kind proposal; he, poor boy!
Stood mute and mournful. "Why so sad?
Hast nothing for a venture, lad?"
"No, Sir," in downcast tone he said,
"Only a Cat, Sir, overhead."
"Well, bring the Cat, my lad; let's see
How fortunate poor Puss may be."

Dick wept his tabby friend to lose;
His grief served others to amuse.
All ask'd him if his famous Cat
Would catch a fine gold mouse or rat?
Or whether for enough 'twould sell
To buy a stick to beat him well?
At last poor Richard's temper fail'd,
And anger for a time prevail'd:
For all he did or tried to do,
Still worse and worse Cook's conduct grew.

Darkness had scarcely pass'd away,
On the morning of All-Hallows day,
When from the house he turn'd to go
With heavy heart and footsteps slow.
His future path unknown, he sigh'd;
For all was new and yet untried.
To Holloway he walk'd, when, lo!
He heard the merry bells of Bow:
In Richard's ear they seem'd to chime
This uncouth, strange, and simple rhyme:
"Turn again, Whittington,
Thrice Lord Mayor of London."
Mayor of London! – can there be
Such honour yet design'd for me?
To London Dick return'd before
His tyrant oped the kitchen door.

The Merchant's ship, by weather toss'd,
Was driven on the Barbary coast.
The Monarch of that distant land
Had hourly visits from a band
Of puny thieves – even rats and mice,
Who ate up all things sweet and nice.
The Captain offer'd Dicky's Cat,
Which snapp'd up every mouse and rat.
"Now," said the King, "cost what it may,
That creature must not go away,
But for the Cat I'll give you more
Than for the rest of all your store."
And so he did; and bags of gold
Upon the carpet they behold.
Which quickly to the ship convey'd,
Most nobly for poor Pussy paid.

The Captain back to England came,
The herald of Dick's wealth and fame.

I need not say, to all he'd send
To share his wealth, to all a friend.
The cross Cook even was not forgot,
Now Heaven had so improved his lot;
And numbers bless'd the happy hour
Which gave poor Richard wealth and power.
The Merchant wishing Richard joy,
Said, "May you, simple honest boy,
Be happy! May you ever be
Famed for your strict integrity!"

Sheriff of London he was made,
And in his new career display'd
Manners so mild yet dignified,
So free from forwardness and pride,
That all the Corporation said
He must an Alderman be made.

In this high office praise he earn'd,
And shortly after was return'd
Lord Mayor of London: then he told
What once he thought the bells foretold.

He thrice the Civic honour gain'd,
And each time general praise obtain'd.
When the heroic Henry came
Fresh from the well-fought field of fame,
In City chronicles we find,
With Whittington the Monarch dined.

The gentle Emma now became
A blooming bride to grace his name,
To bless his fireside hours, and share
The honours of the great Lord Mayor.

Let every Child who reads this tale,
Remember Virtue cannot fail
To be beloved: that Wealth cannot
Confer true glory on our lot;
And that respect and love outweigh
The idle pleasures of a day:
That none on poverty should frown,
Nor on an honest man look down,
Since every virtue may adorn
The being whom you treat with scorn,
And none to wealth or rank can say,
"Ye cannot, shall not flee away."

To make his glory yet more bright,
Our Whittington was dubb'd a Knight.
Sir Richard fully understood
The pure delight of doing good;
Rejoiced to succour the oppress'd,
And aid the humble and distress'd.
A life in constant virtue spent,
Became his proudest monument.

A Cat's Vocation

J.V. VON SCHEFFEL (1826–86)

Clear is Hiddigeigei's conscience,
 Strict his walk, his conduct wise;
Yet when neighbour cats are flirting,
 He, indulgent, shuts his eyes.

Lo, he lives for his vocation,
 For the slaughter of the mouse:
Yet he is not wroth though others
 Live for singing and carouse.

Hiddigeigei speaks, the Ancient:
 "Pluck the fruits before they fall;
Should the years of famine follow
 Memory's joys will never pall."

from "Songs of the Tom-cat Hiddigeigei"
in *The Trumpeters* (1893)

The Trial of Mysouff

ALEXANDRE DUMAS (1802–70)

We left Mysouff gloating over the mangled remains of his
feathered victims, and his capture presented little difficulty. By
merely shutting the door of the aviary we had the culprit at the
disposition of justice.

The only question was to decide his fate. Michel voted to
shoot him straight away. I opposed such a step, which seemed
too violent altogether.

I proposed to wait for the coming Sunday and have Mysouff
brought to trial before the friends who always visited me on
that day.

In addition to the regular weekly habitués of the house, we

could invite others specially for the occasion. This was accordingly done, and judgment postponed till the fateful Sunday.

Meantime Mysouff remained a prisoner on the very scene of his crime. Michel removed the last vestiges of the dead birds on which he was feeding without a touch of compunction. He was put on a diet of bread and water, Michel constituting himself his gaoler.

When Sunday came, both the ordinary weekly habitués and the specially invited guests having turned up in force, the necessary quorum for a jury was more than provided.

Michel was nominated Procureur-Général, and Nogent Saint-Laurent official Counsel for the Defence.

I am bound to say the minds of the jury were manifestly predisposed against the prisoner, and that after the Public Prosecutor's speech, a sentence of death seemed a practical certainty.

But the clever advocate to whom poor Mysouff's defence had been entrusted, taking the accusation in the most serious way and calling all his eloquence into play, insisted on the animal's innocent intentions contrasted with the mischievousness of the monkeys, on the absence of initiation on the part of the four-footed as compared with two-handed vertebrates. He demonstrated how, closely approximating to men as they did, the latter were bound to be full of criminal promptings. He showed Mysouff incapable by himself of meditating such a crime. He showed him sleeping the sleep of the just; then suddenly awakened from his harmless slumbers by the odious apes that had long been watching the aviary intent on committing murder. He described Mysouff, still only half awake, stretching his paws, purring softly the while, opening his little pink mouth and showing his pretty tongue; listening, and shaking his ears – a plain sign that he rejected the odious proposal his tempters dared to make; at first refusing all participation in the foul deed (the speaker asserted positively that his client had begun by refusing); then, young and easily led astray, demoralized moreover by the cook, who instead of giving him his innocent bread and milk and bowl of broth according to orders, had excited his carnivorous appetite by feeding him on scraps of meat, the remains of bullocks' hearts and mutton bones; gradually degenerating more from weakness of character and feebleness to resist temptation than from actual greediness and cruelty; following, even now only part awake, with half-shut eyes and staggering steps, the wretched apes, the true instigators of the crime. Then he took the accused in his arms, displayed his paws, drew attention to their shape and form, appealed to the anatomists, calling upon them to say if, with such paws, an animal could open a locked aviary. Finally he borrowed from Michel himself his famous *Dictionary of Natural History*, he opened it at the article "Cat" – *domestic cat, brindled cat*; he demonstrated that Mysouff, albeit not of the brindled sort, was not a whit less interesting for having a white coat – the token of his innocence. Then, to wind up, he struck a resounding blow on the book.

"Cat!" he exclaimed vehemently, "cat! . . . yes, I will read you what Buffon, the great Buffon, who always wrote in lace ruffles, what he wrote on the knees of Mother Nature, concerning the cat –

" 'The cat,' M. de Buffon tells us, 'is but a faithless domestic pet, one we only keep out of necessity, to keep down other household enemies even more annoying, and which we cannot otherwise get rid of . . . ; true,' continues the illustrious Naturalist, 'true, the cat, and still more the kitten, has pretty ways, it has at the same time an inborn love of mischief, a treacherous disposition, a natural perversity, which age only increases and training only succeeds in partially concealing.'

"Well," pursued the orator, after concluding this description of his client, "what need I say more? . . . Did Mysouff, I ask you, did poor Mysouff present himself here with a false certificate of character signed, it may be, by Lacépède or Geoffroy Saint-Hilaire, to weigh in the balance against Buffon's indictment? No, he scorned to do so. It was the cook herself who went and fetched him from M. Acoyer's, who hunted him out from behind a heap of firewood where he had taken refuge, who then invented a fictitious tale to enlist her master's sympathies of how she had found the creature mewing piteously in the cellar. Was any attempt made to give him an idea of the wickedness he was guilty of in killing these unfortunate birds, these poor little creatures – greatly to be pitied, of course, yet which, when all is said and done – the quails in particular – were liable to be sacrificed at any moment to satisfy man's hunger, and now find themselves happily delivered from the agonies of terror they must daily have experienced every time they saw the cook come near their cage? . . . In a word, gentlemen, I appeal to your sense of fairness; we have invented a new word to excuse crime among ourselves, as featherless bipeds, endowed with free will, to wit *monomania*; when, thanks to the word, we have saved the lives of the greatest criminals, shall we not admit that the unfortunate and interesting Mysouff yielded not merely to his natural instincts but also to extraneous suggestions? . . . I have done, gentlemen. I claim for my client the benefit of extenuating circumstances."

Shouts of enthusiasm greeted this flight of eloquence, which was purely extempore. The jury gave their verdict whilst still under the impression of the great advocate's address, and Mysouff was declared guilty of complicity in the assassination of the doves and quails, also of the wrynecks, widow-birds, Indian sparrows, and other rare birds, but with extenuating circumstances. He was merely condemned to five years of incarceration with the apes.

from *My Pets* (1867) translated by Alfred Allinson

The White Cat

SIR PHILIP SIDNEY (1554–86)

I have (and long shall have) a white great nimble cat,
A king upon a mouse, a strong foe to the rat,
Fine eares, long taile he hath, with Lions curbed clawe,
Which oft he lifteth up, and stayes his lifted pawe,
Deepe musing to himselfe, which after-mewing showes,
Till with lickt blood, his eye of fire espie his foes.

from *Second Eclogues of Arcadia*

The Zombi

ROBERT SOUTHEY (1774–1843)

Now to a more important subject. You were duly apprised towards the end of the year of Othello's death. Since that lamented event this house was cat-less, till on Saturday, March 24, Mrs Calvert, knowing how grievously we were annoyed by rats, offered me what she described as a fine full-grown black cat, who was moreover a tom. She gave him an excellent character in all points but one, which was that he was a most expert pigeon-catcher; and as they had a pigeon-house, the propensity rendered it necessary to pass sentence upon him either of transportation or of death. Moved by compassion (his colour and his tomship also being taken into consideration), I consented to give him an asylum, and on the evening of that day here he came in a sack.

You, Grosvenor, who are a *philogalist*, and therefore understand more of cat nature than has been ever attained by the most profound naturalists, know how difficult it is to reconcile a cat to a new domicile. When the sack was opened, the kitchen door, which led into the passage, was open also, and the cat disappeared; not indeed like a flash of lightning, but as fast as one – that is to say, for all purposes of a simile. There was no chance of his making his way back to the pigeon-house. He might have done this had he been carried thrice the distance in any other direction; but in this there was either a river to cross, or a part of the town to pass, both of which were such obstacles to his travels that we were quite sure all on this side of them was to him *terra incognita*. Food, therefore, was placed where he would be likely to find it in the night; and at the unanimous desire of the children, I took upon myself the charge of providing him with a name, for it is not proper that a cat should remain without one. Taking into consideration his complexion, as well as his sex, my first thought was to call him Henrique Diaz, a name which poor Koster would have approved, had he been living to have heard it; but it presently occurred to me that the Zombi would be an appellation equally appropriate and more dignified. The Zombi, therefore, he was named.

It was soon ascertained that the Zombi had taken possession of poor Wilsey's cellar, which being filled with pea-sticks afforded him a secure hiding-place; the kitchen also of that part of the house being forsaken, he was in perfect quiet. Food was laid for him every day, and the children waited impatiently for the time when the Zombi would become acquainted with the house, and suffer them to become acquainted with him. Once or twice in the evening he was seen out of doors, and it was known that he reconnoitred the premises in the night; but in obstinate retirement he continued from Saturday till Saturday, seven days and nights, notwithstanding all kind words were used to bring him out, as if he had been determined to live and die a hermit.

But between four and five o'clock on the Sunday morning, all who had ears to hear were awakened by such screams as if the Zombi had been caught in a rat-trap, or had met with some other excruciating accident. You, Mr Bedford, understand cats, and know very well that a cat-*solo* is a very different thing from a *duet*; and that no person versed in their tongue can mistake their expression of pain for anything else. The creature seemed to be in agonies. A light was procured, that it might be relieved if that were possible. Upon searching the house, the Zombi was seen at the top of Wilsey's stairs, from whence he disappeared, retreating to his stronghold in the cellar; nor could any traces be discovered of any hurt that could have befallen him, nor has it since appeared that he had received any, so that the cause of this nocturnal disturbance remains an impenetrable mystery.

Various have been our attempts to explain it. Some of the women who measure the power of rats by their own fears, would have it that he was bitten by a rat, or by an association of rats; but to this I indignantly replied that in that case the ground would have been strewn with their bodies, and that it would have been the rats' cry, not the Zombi's, that would have been heard. Dismissing, therefore, that impossible supposition, I submit to your consideration, in the form of queries, the various possibilities which have occurred to me – all unsatisfactory, I confess –

requesting you to assist me in my endeavour to find out the mystery of this wonderful history, as it may truly be called. You will be pleased to bear in mind that the Zombi was the only cat concerned in the transaction: of that I am perfectly certain

Now then, Grosvenor –
1. Had he seen the devil?
2. Was he making love to himself?
3. Was he engaged in single combat with himself?
4. Was he attempting to raise the devil by invocation?
5. Had he heard me sing, and was he attempting (vainly) to imitate it?

These queries, you will perceive, all proceed upon the supposition that it was the Zombi who made the noise. But I have further to ask –
6. Was it the devil?
7. Was it Jeffery?
8. Were either of these personages tormenting the Zombi?

I have only to add that from that time to this he continues in the same obstinate retirement, and to assure you that

I remain, Mr Bedford. With the highest consideration,
Yours as ever,
Robert Southey

PS. One further query occurs while I am writing. Sunday having been the first of the month –
9. Was he making April fools of us? R.S.

from a letter to Grosvenor C. Bedford, 3 April 1821,
in *Selections from the Letters of Robert Southey* (1856)

The Auld Seceder Cat

ANONYMOUS

There was a Presbyterian cat
Went forth to catch her prey;
She brought a mouse intill the house,
Upon the Sabbath day.

The minister, offended
With such an act profane,
Laid down his book, the cat he took,
And bound her with a chain.

Thou vile malicious creature,
Thou murderer, said he,
Oh do you think to bring to Hell
My holy wife and me?
But be thou well assured,
That blood for blood shall pay,
For taking of the mouse's life
Upon the Sabbath Day.

Then he took doun his Bible,
And fervently he prayed,
That the great sin the cat had done
Might not on him be laid.
Then forth to exe-cu-ti-on,
Poor Baudrons she was drawn,
And on a tree they hanged her hie,
And then they sang a psalm.

Barbaric Cats

CHARLES DICKENS (1812–70)

As the dogs of shy neighbourhoods usually betray a slinking consciousness of being in poor circumstances – for the most part manifested in an aspect of anxiety, an awkwardness in their play, and a misgiving that somebody is going to harness them to something, to pick up a living – so the cats of shy neighbourhoods exhibit a strong tendency to relapse into barbarism. Not only are they made selfishly ferocious by ruminating on the surplus population around them, and on the densely crowded state of all the avenues to cat's meat; not only is there a moral and politico-economical haggardness in them, traceable to these reflections; but they evince a physical deterioration. Their linen is not clean, and is wretchedly got up; their black turns rusty, like old mourning; they wear very indifferent fur; and take to the shabbiest cotton velvet, instead of silk velvet. I am on terms of recognition with several small streets of cats, about the Obelisk in Saint George's Fields, and also in the vicinity of Clerkenwell-green, and also in the back settlements of Drury-lane. In appearance, they are very like the women among whom they live. They seem to turn out of their unwholesome beds into the street, without any preparation. They leave their young families to stagger about the gutters, unassisted, while they frouzily quarrel and swear and scratch and spit, at street corners. In particular, I remark that when they are about to increase their families (an event of frequent recurrence) the resemblance is strongly expressed in a certain dusty dowdiness, down-at-heel self-neglect, and general giving up of things. I cannot honestly report that I have ever seen a feline matron of this class washing her face when in an interesting condition.

from *The Uncommercial Traveller* (1860)

The Carlish Cat

JOHN SKELTON (*c*. 1460–1529)

[...] When I remember again
How my Philip was slain,
Never half the pain
Was between you twain,
Pyramus and Thisbe,
As then befell to me.
I wept and I wailéd,
The teares down hailéd,
But nothing it availéd
To call Philip again,
Whom Gib, our cat, hath slain.

Gib, I say, our cat
Worrowéd her on that
Which I lovéd best.
It cannot be exprest
My sorrowful heaviness,
But all without redress!
For within that stound,
Half slumbering, in a sound
I fell downe to the ground [...]

That vengeance I ask and cry,
By way of exclamation,
On all the whole nation
Of cattes wild and tame:
God send them sorrow and shame!
That cat specially
That slew so cruelly
My little pretty sparrow
That I brought up at Carrow.

O cat of carlish kind,
The fiend was in thy mind
When thou my bird untwined!
I would thou hadst been blind!
The léopards savágе,
The lions in their rage
Might catch thee in their paws,
And gnaw thee in their jaws!
The serpents of Libany
Might sting thee venomously!
The dragons with their tongues
Might poison thy liver and lungs!
The manticors of the mountains
Might feed them on thy brains!

Melanchaetes, that hound
That pluckéd Actaeon to the ground,

Gave him his mortal wound,
Changéd to a deer,
The story doth appear,
Was changéd to an hart:
So thou, foul cat that thou art,
The selfsame hound
Might thee confound,
That his own lorde bote,
Might bite asunder thy throat!

Of Ind the greedy grypes
Might tear out all thy tripes!
Of Arcady the bears
Might pluck away thine ears!
The wild wolf Lycaon
Bite asunder thy backbone!
Of Etna the burning hill,
That day and night burneth still,
Set in thy tail a blaze
That all the world may gaze
And wonder upon thee,
From Ocean the great sea
Unto the Isles of Orcady,
From Tilbury Ferry
To the plain of Salisbury!
So traitorously my bird to kill
That never ought thee evil will!

Was never bird in cage
More gentle of coráge
In doing his homáge
Unto his sovereign.
Alas, I say again,
Death hath departed us twain!
The false cat hath thee slain:
Farewell, Philip, adew!
Our Lord, thy soul rescue!

Farewell, without restore,
Farewell, for evermore! [...]

from *Philip Sparrow*

An Humble Petition Presented to Madame Helvétius by Her Cats

BENJAMIN FRANKLIN (1706–90)

We shall not endeavour to defend ourselves equally from devouring as many sparrows, blackbirds, and thrushes, as we can possibly catch. But here we have to plead in extenuation, that our most cruel enemies, your Abbés themselves, are incessantly complaining of the ravages made by these birds among the cherries and other fruit. The Sieur Abbé Morellet, in particular, is always thundering the most violent anathemas against the blackbirds and thrushes, for plundering your vines, which they do with as little mercy as he himself. To us, however, most illustrious Lady, it appears that the grapes may just as well be eaten by *blackbirds* as by *Abbés*, and that our warfare against the winged plunderers will be fruitless, if you encourage other biped and featherless pilferers, who make ten times more havoc.

We know that we are also accused of eating nightingales, who never plunder, and sing, as they say, most enchantingly. It is indeed possible that we may now and then have gratified our palates with a delicious morsel in this way, but we can assure you that it was in utter ignorance of your affection for the species; and that, resembling sparrows in their plumage, we, who make no pretensions to being connoisseurs in music, could not distinguish the song of the one from that of the other, and therefore supposed ourselves regaling only on sparrows. A cat belonging to M. Piccini has assured us, that they who only know how to *mew*, cannot be any judges of the art of singing; and on this we rest for our justification. However, we will henceforward exert our utmost endeavours to distinguish the

Gluckists, who are, as we are informed, the sparrows, from the *Piccinists*, who are the nightingales. We only intreat of you to pardon the inadvertence into which we may possibly fall, if, in roving after nests, we may sometimes fall upon a brood of *Piccinists*, who, being then destitute of plumage, and not having learnt to sing, will have no mark by which to distinguish them.

The Rat-Catcher and Cats

JOHN GAY (1685–1732)

The rats by night such mischief did,
Betty was every morning chid.
They undermined whole sides of bacon,
Her cheese was sapp'd, her tarts were taken.
Her pasties fenced with thickest paste,
Were all demolish'd, and laid waste.
She cursed the Cat for want of duty,
Who left her foes a constant booty.
   An engineer, of noted skill,
Engaged to stop the growing ill.
   From room to room he now surveys
Their haunts, their works, their secret ways;
Finds where they 'scape and ambuscade,
And whence the nightly sally's made,
   And envious Cat, from place to place,
Unseen attends his silent pace.
She saw that if his trade went on,
The purring race must be undone;
So, secretly removes his baits,
And ev'ry stratagem defeats.
   Again he sets the poison'd toils,
And Puss again the labour foils.
What foe (to frustrate my designs)
My schemes thus nightly countermines?
Incensed, he cries, this very hour

The wretch shall bleed beneath my power.
　So said, a pond'rous trap he brought,
And in the fact poor Puss was caught.
　Smuggler, says he, thou shalt be made
A victim to our loss of trade.
　The captive Cat, with piteous mews,
For pardon, life, and freedom sues.
　A sister of the science spare;
One int'rest is our common care.
　What insolence! the man replied;
Shall cats with us the game divide?
Were all you interloping band
Extinguish'd or expell'd the land,
We Rat-catchers might raise our fees,
Sole guardians of a nation's cheese!
　A Cat, who saw the lifted knife,
Thus spoke, and saved her sister's life:
　In ev'ry age and clime we see,
Two of a trade can ne'er agree.
Each hates his neighbour for encroaching;
Squire stigmatizes squire for poaching;
Beauties with beauties are in arms,
And scandal pelts each other's charms;
Kings, too, their neighbour kings dethrone,
In hope to make the world their own,
But let us limit out desires,
Not war like beauties, kings, and squires!
For though we both one prey pursue,
There's game enough for us and you.

A Cat

EDWARD THOMAS (1878–1917)

She had a name among the children:
But no one loved though someone owned

Her, locked her out of doors at bedtime.
And had her kittens duly drowned.

In spring, nevertheless, this cat
Ate blackbirds, thrushes, nightingales,
And birds of bright voice, and plume, and flight,
As well as scraps from neighbours' pails.

I loathed and hated her for this;
One speckle on a thrush's breast
Was worth a million such: and yet
She lived long till God gave her rest.

The Savage Beneath the Skin

H.D. THOREAU (1817–62)

Only skin deep lies the feral nature of the cat, unchanged still. I
just had the misfortune to rock on to our cat's leg, as she was
lying playfully spread out under my chair. Imagine the sound
that arose, and which was excusable; but what will you say to
the fierce growls and flashing eyes with which she met me for a
quarter of an hour thereafter? No tiger in its jungle could have
been savager.

from *Journal*, 15 February 1861

A Fable of the Widow and Her Cat

JONATHAN SWIFT (1667–1745)

A widow kept a favourite cat.
  At first a gentle creature;
But when he was grown sleek and fat,
With many a mouse, and many a rat,
  He soon disclosed his nature.

The fox and he were friends of old,
    Nor could they now be parted;
They nightly slunk to rob the fold,
Devoured the lambs, the fleeces sold,
    And puss grew lion-hearted.

He scratched her maid, he stole the cream,
    He tore her best laced pinner;
Nor Chanticleer upon the beam,
Nor chick, nor duckling 'scapes, when Grim
    Invites the fox to dinner.

The dame full wisely did decree,
    For fear he should dispatch more,
That the false wretch should worried be:
But in a saucy manner he
    Thus speeched it like a Lechmere.

"Must I, against all right and law,
    Like pole-cat vile be treated?
I! who so long with tooth and claw
Have kept domestic mice in awe,
    And foreign foes defeated!

"Your golden pippins, and your pies,
    How oft have I defended?
'Tis true, the pinner which you prize
I tore in frolic; to your eyes
    I never harm intended.

"I am a cat of honour —" "Stay,"
    Quoth she, "no longer parley;
Whate'er you did in battle slay,
By law of arms become your prey,
    I hope you won it fairly.

"Of this, we'll grant you stand acquit,
    But not of your outrages:

Tell me, perfidious! was it fit
To make my cream a *perquisite*,
    And steal to mend your wages!

"So flagrant is thy insolence,
    So vile thy breach of trust is;
That longer with thee to dispense,
Were want of power, or want of sense:
    Here, Towser! – Do him justice."

Cats on the Roof

H.D. THOREAU (1817–62)

At the Pilgrim House, though it was not crowded, they put me into a small attic chamber which had two double beds in it, and only one window, high in a corner, twenty and a half inches by twenty-five and a half, in the alcove when it was swung open, and it required a chair to look out conveniently. Fortunately it was not a cold night and the window could be kept open, though at the risk of being visited by the cats, which appear to swarm on the roofs of Provincetown like the mosquitoes on the summits of its hills. I have spent four memorable nights there in as many different years, and have added considerable thereby to my knowledge of the natural history of the cat and the bedbug. Sleep was out of the question. A night in one of the attics of Provincetown! to say nothing of what is to be learned in entomology. It would be worth the while to send a professor there, one who was also skilled in entomology. Such is your *Pilgerruhe* or Pilgrims'-Rest. Every now and then one of these animals on its travels leaped from a neighbouring roof on to mine, with such a noise as if a six-pounder had fallen within two feet of my head – the discharge of a catapult – a twelve-pounder discharged by a catapult – and then followed such a scrambling as banished sleep for a long season, while I watched lest they came in at the open window. A kind of foretaste, methought, of the infernal regions. I didn't wonder they gave quit-claim deeds of their land here. My experience is that you fare best at private houses. The barroom may be defined a place to spit.

> "Soon as the evening shades prevail,
> The *cats take* up the wondrous tale."

At still midnight, when, half awake, half asleep, you seem to be weltering in your own blood on a battlefield, you hear the stealthy tread of padded feet belonging to some animal of the cat tribe, perambulating the roof within a few inches of your head.

from *Journal*, 21 June 1857

Cat and Mouse

GEOFFREY CHAUCER (*c.* 1343–1400)

Lat take a cat, and fostre hym wel with milk
And tendre flessh, and make his couche of silk,
And lat hym seen a mous go by the wal,
Anon he weyveth milk, and flessh, and al,
And every deyntee that is in that hous,
Swich appetit he hath to ete a mous.
Lo, heere hath lust his dominacioun,
And appetit fleemeth discrecioun.

from *Canterbury Tales* (*c.* 1387)

The Kilkenny Cats

ANONYMOUS

There once were two cats of Kilkenny
Each thought there was one cat too many;

So they fought and they fit,
And they scratched and they bit,
Till, excepting their nails
And the tips of their tails,
Instead of two cats there weren't any.

The Devout Cat

I.L. PERETZ

Once upon a time there were three little singing birds in a
house, but all three were devoured by the cat. It was not an
ordinary cat, but a really, really devout cat. It was not in vain
that it was arrayed in a white robe of immaculate purity, and
that its eyes reflected the heavens.

It was a pious cat, a cat that scrupulously performed all its
ablutions. Ten times a day would this cat wash itself; and as for
food, it devoured it very quietly, lying curled up in an obscure
corner. It fed all the day on a modest milk diet and only in the
evening did it partake of a bit of meat, the kosher meat of some
mouse. And then again this cat, unlike those of a grosser nature,
did not hurry over its food, or gorge itself like a glutton, but ate
slowly, whilst playing with its victim. "Why not let the little
mouse live another few minutes?" thought the devout cat. "Let
the poor mite dance a little while, tremble, and make its
confession; a really pious cat never hurries."

When the first singing bird was brought into the house, the
cat at once felt great pity for the bird and its heart grew
constricted.

"Such a beautiful, tiny thing," sighed the compassionate cat,
"and to think that such a nice little bird will never enjoy
celestial bliss." For, of course, the cat was fully convinced that a
little bird like that could not deserve heaven. "First of all a bird
washes itself in a vulgar way, plunging its whole body into a
basin of water. Then, again, the very fact that it is put in a cage
proves it to be a very wicked animal. In spite of its still being

very young, gentle, and kind, this bird is already showing an inclination towards violence rather than law and order. And what about its song? Its song, to say the least, is full of effrontery, and its manner of looking straight up to heaven is quite disrespectful. And think of all its efforts to break the cage and fly out into the impious world, into the free air; think also of its look turned to the open window. Have you ever seen a cat shut up in a cage? Has a pious cat ever ventured to whistle with such effrontery? The pity of it," sighed the tender-hearted and devout cat, "for, after all, it is a living being, possessed of a precious soul, a spark from above."

Tears welled up in the eyes of the pious and devout cat.

"All its misfortune is due to the fact of its possessing such a beautiful sinful body, a body attracted to terrestrial pleasures and joys, over which the spirit of temptation has so much sway. How can you expect such a gentle little bird to be able to resist the terrible spirit of temptation? And the longer the poor thing lives," thought the devout cat, "the greater the number of sins it will commit, and the more terrible its punishment in the hereafter."

A sacred fire enflamed the heart of the devout cat. Jumping upon the table where stood the cage with the little bird, it . . . The feathers were soon scattered over the room.

Blows rained upon the cat, but it accepted its punishment with humility, as behoves a devout cat. Sighing piously, it began to mew, to groan in pious resignation, reciting a pitiable *mea culpa*. In future the cat will not commit such an error, for being a reasonable cat, it understood why it had been beaten. Henceforth it will never deserve such blows.

"I have been beaten," reasoned the devout cat, "because I have scattered the feathers all over the room, and also because I have left traces of blood all over the white and embroidered tablecloth. When executing such sentences, one ought to proceed with kindness, with gentleness, and piety; one must never scatter the feathers nor spill a drop of blood."

When the second bird was bought and brought into the house, the pious cat acted quite differently. This time it strangled the little bird gently and delicately, and swallowed it whole, body and feathers. Nevertheless the cat was soundly thrashed.

This time the cat understood that it was not at all a question of either feathers or traces of blood left on the tablecloth. The secret of its punishment lay in the fact that it was a sin to kill. On the contrary, one must love and forgive. It is not by means of punishments and tortures that we can reform and save a world steeped in sin. What is required of us is to lead the sinful creatures upon the path of virtue, preach morals to them, and appeal to their hearts.

A repentant canary can soar to lofty summits in heaven, unattainable even for a devout cat. And the heart of the cat swelled with joy. Over were the old, hard, cruel, and wicked days. Over was the shedding of blood. Pity, was the watchword, pity, and once more pity. And it was a cat full of pity that approached the third canary.

"Don't be afraid," said the cat in the most gentle voice that ever issued from a cat's throat. "It is true thou art steeped in sin, but I will do thee no harm, for my heart is full of pity for thee.

"I will not even open thy cage, I will even refrain from touching thee.

"Thou art silent? Excellent. It is better to be silent than to sing impudently.

"Thou art trembling? It is better still. Tremble, my child, but not on account of me!

"May it please God that thou shouldst remain thus gently pure and trembling.

"As for me, I will help thee to tremble. From the depth of my pious soul I will breathe upon thee the spirit of calmness, of gentleness and piety. May my pious breath instill into thy body profound faith, may divine fear penetrate into thy little bones, and may remorse and repentance fill thy little heart."

It was now only that the devout cat understood how sweet forgiveness was, what holy joy one may derive from the action of breathing into others the spirit of piety and of virtue. And the heart of the most pious and devout of white cats swelled for joy and happiness. But, alas, the canary could not breathe in the atmosphere of the cat. It was stifled.

Sad Memories

c.s. CALVERLEY (1831–84)

They tell me I am beautiful: they praise my silken hair,
My little feet that silently slip on from stair to stair:
They praise my pretty trustful face and innocent grey
    eye;
Fond hands caress me oftentimes, yet would that I
    might die!

Why was I born to be abhorred of man and bird and
    beast?
The bullfinch marks me stealing by, and straight his
    song hath ceased;
The shrewmouse eyes me shudderingly, then flees;
    and, worse than that,
The housedog he flees after me – why was I born a
    cat?

Men prize the heartless hound who quits dry-eyed his
    native land;
Who wags a mercenary tail and licks a tyrant hand.
The leal true cat they prize not, that if e'er compelled
    to roam
Still flies, when let out of the bag, precipitately home.

They call me cruel. Do I know if mouse or song-bird
    feels?
I only know they make me light and salutary meals:
And if, as 'tis my nature to, ere I devour I tease 'em,
Why should a low-bred gardener's boy pursue me
    with a besom?

Should china fall or chandeliers, or anything but stocks –
Nay stocks, when they're in flowerpots – the cat
   expects hard knocks:
Should ever anything be missed – milk, coals,
   umbrellas, brandy –
The cat's pitched into with a boot or anything that's
   handy.

"I remember, I remember", how one night I
   "fleeted by",
And gained the blessed tiles and gazed into the cold
   clear sky.
"I remember, I remember, how my little lovers came";
And there, beneath the crescent moon, played many a
   little game.

They fought – by good St Catharine, 'twas a fearsome
   sight to see
The coal-black crest, the glowering orbs, of one
   gigantic He.
Like bow by some tall bowman bent at Hastings or
   Poitiers,
His huge back curved, till none observed a vestige of
   his ears:

He stood, an ebon crescent, flouting that ivory moon;
Then raised the pibroch of his race, the Song without
   a Tune;
Gleamed his white teeth, his mammoth tail waved
   darkly to and fro,
As with one complex yell he burst, all claws, upon the
   foe.

It thrills me now, that final Miaow – that weird
   unearthly din:
Lone maidens heard it far away, and leaped out of
   their skin.

A potboy from his den o'erhead peeped with a scared
  wan face;
Then sent a random brickbat down, which knocked
  me into space,

Nine days I fell, or thereabouts: and, had we not nine
  lives,
I wis I ne'er had seen again thy sausage-shop, St Ives!
Had I, as some cats have, nine tails, how gladly I
  would lick
The hand, and person generally, of him who heaved
  that brick!

For me they fill the milkbowl up, and cull the choice
  sardine:
But ah! I nevermore shall be the cat I once have been!
The memories of that fatal night they haunt me even
  now:
In dreams I see that rampant He, and tremble at that
  Miaow.

Calvin the Hunter

CHARLES DUDLEY WARNER (1829–1900)

I think he was genuinely fond of birds, but, so far as I know, he
usually confined himself to one a day; he never killed, as some
sportsmen do, for the sake of killing, but only as civilized people
do – from necessity. He was intimate with the flying squirrels
who dwelt in the chestnut trees – too intimate, for almost every
day in the summer he would bring in one, until he nearly
discouraged them. He was, indeed, a superb hunter, and would
have been a devastating one if his bump of destructiveness had
not been offset by a bump of moderation. There was very little
of the brutality of the lower animals about him; I don't think he
enjoyed rats for themselves, but he knew his business, and for the

first few months of his residence with us he waged an awful campaign against the horde, and after that his simple presence was sufficient to deter them from coming on the premises. Mice amused him, but he usually considered them too small game to be taken seriously; I have seen him play for an hour with a mouse, and then let him go with a royal condescension. In this whole matter of "getting a living", Calvin was a great contrast to the rapacity of the age in which he lived.

from "Calvin, the Cat" in *My Summer in a Garden* (1882)

An Ode to Eight Cats
Belonging to Israel Mendez, a Jew

PETER PINDAR (1738–1819)

SCENE, *the Street in a Country Town.*
The TIME, *Midnight – The Poet at his Chamber Window,
in his Shirt.*

Singers of Israel, O ye singers sweet,
    Who, with your gentle mouths from ear to ear,
Pour forth rich symphonies from street to street,
    And to the sleepless wretch the night endear!

Lo! in my shirt, on you these eyes I fix,
Admiring much the quaintness of your tricks:
    Your friskings, crawlings, squalls, I much approve:
Your spittings, pawings, high-rais'd rumps,
Swell'd tails, and merry-andrew jumps,
    With the wild minstrelsy of rapt'rous love.

How sweetly roll your gooseb'rry eyes,
As loud you tune your am'rous cries,
    And, loving, scratch each other black and blue!
No boys in wantonness now bang your backs;

No curs, nor fiercer mastiffs, tear your flax;
But all the moon-light world seems made for you.

Singers of Israel, ye no parsons want
    To tie the matrimonial cord;
Ye call the matrimonial service, cant –
    Like our first parents, take each other's word:
On no one ceremony pleas'd to fix –
To jump not even o'er two sticks.

You want no furniture, alas!
    Spit, spoon, dish, frying-pan, nor ladle;
No iron, pewter, copper, tin, nor brass;
    No nurses, wet not dry, nor cradle,
(Which custom, for our *Christian* babes, enjoins)
To rock the staring offspring of your loins.

Nor of the lawyers have you need,
    Ye males, before you seek your bed,
To settle pin-money on Madam:
    No fears of cuckoldom, heav'n bless ye,
    Are ever harbour'd to distress ye,
Tormenting people, since the days of Adam.

No schools ye want for fine behaving;
    No powdering, painting, washing, shaving:
No nightcaps snug – no trouble in undressing
    Before ye seek your strawy nest,
    Pleas'd in each other's arms to rest,
To feast on luscious Love, Heav'n's greatest blessing.

Good gods! ye sweet love-chanting rams!
    How nimble are ye with your hams
To mount a house, to scale a chimney-top;
    And, peeping down that chimney's hole,
    Pour, in a tuneful cry, th' impassion'd soul,
Inviting Miss Grimalkin to come up:

Who, sweet obliging female, far from coy,
Answers your invitation note with joy;
   And, scorning 'midst the ashes more to mope,
Lo! borne on Love's all-daring wing,
She mounteth with a pickle-herring spring,
   Without th'assistance of a rope.

Dear mousing tribe, my limbs are waxing cold –
   Singers of Israel sweet, adieu, adieu!
I do suppose you need not now be told
   How much I wish that I was one of *you*.

Gip

W.H. HUDSON (1841–1922)

It is rather an odd coincidence that in the village inn where I am
writing a portion of this book, including the present chapter,
there should be three cats, unlike one another in appearance
and habits as three animals of different and widely separated
species. [...] All three were strays, which the landlady, who has a
tender heart, took in when they were starving, and made pets
of; and all are beautiful. One has Persian blood in him; a long-
haired, black and brown animal with gold-coloured eyes;
playful as a kitten, incessantly active, fond of going for a walk
with some inmate of the house, and when no one – cat or
human being – will have any more of him you will see him in
the garden stalking a fly, or lying on his back on the ground
under a beech-tree striking with his claws or catching at
something invisible in the air – motes in the sunbeam. The
second is a large black cat with white collar and muzzle and sea-
green eyes, and is of an indolent, luxurious disposition, lying
coiled up by the hour on the most comfortable cushion it can
find. The last is Gip, a magnificent creature, a third bigger than
an average-sized cat – as large and powerfully built as the British
wild cat, a tabby with opaline eyes, which show a pale green

colour in some lights. These singular eyes, when I first saw this animal, almost startled me with their wild, savage expression; nor was it a mere deceptive appearance, as I soon found. I never looked at this animal without finding these panther or lynx eyes fixed with a fierce intensity on me, and no sooner would I look towards him than he would crouch down, flatten his ears, and continue to watch my every movement as if apprehending a sudden attack on his life. It was many days before he allowed me to come near him without bounding away and vanishing, and not for two or three weeks would he suffer me to put a hand on him.

But the native wildness and suspicion in him could never be wholly overcome; it continued to show itself on occasions even after I had known him for months and had won his confidence, and when it seemed that, in his wild-cat, conditional way, he had accepted my friendship. He became lame, having injured one of his forelegs while hunting, and as the weather was cold he was pleased to spend his inactive and suffering time on the hearth-rug in my sitting-room. I found that rubbing warm, melted butter on his injured leg appeared to give him relief, and after the massaging and buttering he would lick the leg vigorously for ten or fifteen minutes, occasionally purring with satisfaction. Yet if I made any sudden movement, or rustled the paper in my hand, he would instantly spring up from his cushion at my feet and dart away to the door to make his escape; then, finding the door closed, he would sit down, recover his domesticity, and return to my feet.

Yet this cat had been taken in as a kitten and had already lived some two or three years in the house, seeing many people and fed regularly with the others every day. It is not, however, very rare to meet with a cat of this disposition – the cat pure and simple, as nature made it, without that little tameness on the surface, or veneer of domesticity which life with man has laid on it.

Gip is the most inveterate rat-killer I have ever known. He is never seen hunting other creatures, not even mice, although it is probable that he does kill and devour them on the spot, but he has the habit of bringing in the rats he captures; and as a day seldom passes on which he is not seen with one, and as sometimes two or three are brought in during the night, he cannot destroy fewer than three hundred to four hundred rats in the year.

Let anyone who knows the destructive powers of the rat consider what that means in an agricultural village, and what an advantage it is to the farmers to have their rick-yards and barns policed day and night by such an animal. For the whole village is his hunting-ground. His owner says that he is "worth his weight in gold". I should say that he is worth much more; that the equivalent in cash of his weight in purest gold, though he is big and heavy, would not be more than the value of the grain and other foodstuffs he saves from destruction in a single year.

He invariably brings in his rats alive to release and play with them in an old, stone-paved yard, and after a little play he kills them, and if they are full-grown he leaves them; but when young he devours them or allows the other cats to have them.

Gip has a somewhat remarkable history. The village has always been a favourite resort of gypsies, and it happened that once when a party of gypsies had gone away it was discovered that they had left a litter of six kittens behind, and it greatly troubled the village mind to know what was to be done with them. "Why didn't we drown them? Oh, no, we couldn't do that," they said, "they were several weeks old and past the time for drowning." However, someone who kept ferrets turned up and kindly said he would take them to give to his ferrets, and everybody was satisfied to have the matter disposed of in that way. But it was a rather disgusting way, for although it seems quite natural to give little living rodents to ferrets to be sucked of their warm blood, it goes against one's feelings to cast young cats to the pink-eyed beast; for the cat is a carnivorous creature, too, and not only so but is infinitely more beautiful and intelligent than the ferret and higher in the organic scale. However, these ideas did not prevail in the village, and the six kittens were taken; but they proved to be exceedingly vigorous and fierce for kittens, as if they knew what was going to be done to them: they fought and scratched, and eventually two, the biggest and fiercest of them, succeeded in making their escape, and by and by one of them was found on the premises at the inn – a refuge for all creatures in distress – which thereupon became its home.

Gypsies, I was told, are fond of keeping cats, and their cats are supposed to be the best ratters. As this was news to me I inquired of some gypsies in the neighbourhood, and they told me that it was true – they loved cats. They love lurchers, too, and no doubt they find cats with a genius for hunting very profitable pets. But how curiously varied hunting cats are in their tastes! You seldom find two quite alike. I have described one that was an accomplished trout-catcher, in spite of the ancient Gaelic proverb and universal saying that the cat loves fish but fears to wet its feet; also another who is exclusively a rat-killer.

from *A Shepherd's Life* (1910)

The Cat

A.C. BENSON (1862–1925)

On some grave business, soft and slow
Along the garden paths you go
   With bold and burning eyes,
Or stand with twitching tail to mark
What starts and rustles in the dark
   Among the peonies.

The dusty cockchafer that springs
Upon the dusk with shirring wings,
   The beetle glossy-horned,
The rabbit pattering through the fern
May frisk unheeded by your stern
   Preoccupation scorned.

You go, and when the morning dawns
O'er blowing trees and dewy lawns
   Dim-veiled with gossamer,
When cheery birds are on the wing,
You creep, a wild and wicked thing,
   With stained and starting fur.

You all day long beside the fire
Retrace in dreams your dark desire
   And mournfully complain
In grave displeasure if I raise
Your languid form to pet or praise,
   And so to sleep again.

The gentle hound that near me lies
Looks up with true and tender eyes
   And waits my generous mirth.
You do not woo me, but demand
A gift from my unwilling hand,
   A tribute to your worth.

You loved me when the fire was warm,
But now I stretch a fondling arm,
   You eye me and depart.
Cold eye, sleek skin and velvet paws,
You win my indolent applause,
   You do not win my heart.

Tigers in Miniature

LEIGH HUNT (1784–1859)

Furthermore (in order to get rid at once of all that may be
objected to poor Pussy, as boys at school get down their bad
dumpling as fast as possible before the meat comes), we own we
have an objection to the way in which a cat sports with a mouse

before she kills it, tossing and jerking it about like a ball, and letting it go, in order to pounce upon it with the greater relish. And yet what right have we to apply human measures of cruelty to the inferior reflectability of a cat? Perhaps she has no idea of the mouse's being alive, in the sense that we have; most likely she looks upon it as a pleasant movable toy, made to be eaten – a sort of lively pudding, that oddly jumps hither and thither. It would be hard to beat into the head of a country squire of the old class that there is any cruelty in hunting a hare; and most assuredly it would be still harder to beat mouse-sparing into the head of a cat. You might read the most pungent essay on the subject into her ear, and she would only sneeze at it.

As to the unnatural cruelties, which we sometimes read of, committed by cats upon their offspring, they are exceptions to the common and beautiful rules of nature, and accordingly we have nothing to do with them. They are traceable to some unnatural circumstances of breeding or position. Enormities as monstrous are to be found among human beings, and argue nothing against the general character of the species. Even dogs are not always immaculate; and sages have made slips. Dr Franklin cut off his son with a shilling for differing with him in politics.

But cats resemble tigers! They are tigers in miniature? Well – and very pretty miniatures they are. And what has the tiger himself done, that he has not a right to eat his dinner as well as Jones? A tiger treats a man much as a cat does a mouse, granted; but we have no reason to suppose that he is aware of the man's sufferings, or means anything but to satisfy his hunger; and what have the butcher and poulterer been about meanwhile? The tiger, it is true, lays about him a little superfluously sometimes, when he gets into a sheep-fold, and kills more than he eats; but does not the Squire or the Marquis do pretty much like him in the month of September? Nay, do we not hear of venerable judges, that would not hurt a fly, going about in that refreshing month, seeking whom they may lame? See the effect of habit and education! And you can educate the tiger in no other way than by attending to his stomach. Fill that, and he will want no men to eat, probably not even to lame. On the other hand, deprive Jones of his dinner for a day or two, and see what a state he will be in, especially if he is by nature irascible. Nay, keep him from it for half an hour, and observe the tiger propensities of his stomach and fingers – how worthy of killing he thinks the cook, and what boxes of the ear he feels inclined to give the footboy.

Animals, by the nature of things, in their present state, dispose of one another into their respective stomachs, without ill-will on any side. They keep down the several populations of their neighbours, till time may come when superfluous popu-lation of any kind need not exist, and predatory appearances may vanish from the earth, as the wolves have done from England. But whether they may or not is not a question by a hundred times so important to moral inquirers as into the possibilities of human education and the nonsense of ill-will. Show the nonentity of that, and we may all get our dinners as jovially as we can, sure of these three undoubted facts – that life is long, death short, and the world beautiful.

from "The Cat by the Fire" in *Essays* (1887)

The Lover

GEORGE TURBERVILLE (*c.* 1544–*c.* 1597)

If I might alter kind,
What, think you, I would bee?
Nor Fish, nor Foule, nor Fle, nor Frog,
Nor Squirril on the Tree;
The Fish the Hooke, the Foule
The lymed Twig doth catch,
The Fle the Finger, and the Frog
The Bustard doth dispatch.

The Squirril thinking nought,
That feately cracks the Nut,

The greedie Goshawke wanting pray
In dread of Death doth put;
But scorning all these kindes,
I would become a Cat,
To combat with the creeping Mouse,
And scratch the screeking Rat.

I would be present, aye,
And at my ladie's call;
To gard her from the fearfull mouse,
In Parlour and in Hall;
In Kitchen, for his Lyfe,
He should not shew his head;
The Peare in Poke should lie untoucht
When shee were gone to Bed.
The Mouse should stand in Feare,
So should the squeaking Rat;
And this would I do if I were
Converted to a Cat.

The Lover, whose mistresse feared a mouse, declareth that
he would become a Cat if he might have his desire

The Law of the Cat

ANONYMOUS (10th century)

The Vendotian (or North Wales) Code

The worth of a cat and her teithi is this:

1. The worth of a kitten from the night it is kittened until it shall open its eyes is a legal penny.
2. And from that time, until it shall kill mice, two legal pence.
3. And after it shall kill mice, four legal pence; and so it always remains.
4. Her teithi are, to see, to hear, to kill mice, to have her claws entire, to rear and not to devour her kittens; and if she be

bought, and be deficient in any one of those teithi, let one-third of her worth be returned.

The Gwentian (or South-east) Code

1. Whoever shall kill a cat that guards a house and a barn of the king, or shall take it stealthily, it is to be held with its head to the ground and its tail up, the ground being swept, and then clean wheat is to be poured about it, until the tip of its tail be hidden; and that is its worth.
2. A common cat is four legal pence in value.
3. The teithi of a cat are, that it be perfect of ear, perfect of eye, perfect of teeth, perfect of tail, perfect of claw and without marks of fire; and that it will kill mice well; and that it shall not devour its kittens; and that it be not caterwauling on every new moon . . .
5. A pound is the worth of a pet animal of the king.

from *The Codes Enacted by Howel the Good, King of All Wales*

Grimalkin

JOHN PHILIPS (1676–1709)

Grimalkin to Domestick Vermin sworn
An everlasting Foe, with watchful Eye
Lies nightly brooding o'er a chinky Gap
Protending her fell Claws, to thoughtless Mice
Sure Ruin.

from *The Splendid Shilling* (1705)

Cats and Men

THOMAS FLATMAN (1637–88)

Men ride many miles,
Cats tread many tiles,

Both hazard their necks in the fray;
Only Cats, when they fall
From a house or a wall,
Keep their feet, mount their tails, and away!

from *An Appeal to Cats in the Business of Love*

The Yellow Terror

W.L. ALDEN

"Speaking of cats," said Captain Foster, "I'm free to say that I don't like 'em. I don't care to be looked down on by any person, whether he be man or cat. I know I ain't the President of the United States, nor yet a millionaire, nor yet the Boss of New York, but all the same I calculate that I'm a man, and entitled to be treated as such. Now, I never knew a cat yet that didn't look down on me, same as cats do on everybody. A cat considers that men are just dirt under his or her paws, as the case may be. I can't see what it is that makes a cat believe that he is so everlastingly superior to all the men that have ever lived, but there's no denying the fact that such is his belief, and he acts accordingly. There was a professor here one day, lecturing on all sorts of animals, and I asked him if he could explain this aggravating conduct of cats. He said that it was because cats used to be gods, thousands of years ago in the land of Egypt; but I didn't believe him. Egypt is a Scripture country, and consequently we ought not to believe anything about it that we don't read in the Bible. Show me anywhere in the Bible that Egyptian cats are mentioned as having practised as gods, and I'll believe it. Till you show it to me, I'll take the liberty of disbelieving any worldly statements that professors or anybody else may make about Egypt.

"The most notorious cat I ever met was old Captain Smedley's Yellow Terror. His real legal name was just plain Tom: but being yellow, and being a holy terror in many respects, it got to be the fashion among his acquaintances to call

him "The Yellow Terror", He was a tremendous big cat, and
he had been with Captain Smedley for five years before I saw
him.

"Smedley was one of the best men I ever knew. I'll admit
that he was a middling hard man on his sailors, so that his ship
got the reputation of being a slaughter-house, which it didn't
really deserve. And there is no denying that he was a very
religious man, which was another thing which made him
unpopular with the men. I'm a religious man myself, even
when I'm at sea, but I never held with serving out religion to a
crew, and making them swallow it with belaying pins. That's
what old Smedley used to do. He was in command of the
barque *Medford*, out of Boston, when I knew him. I mean the
city of Boston in Massachusetts, and not the little town that
folks over in England call Boston: and I must say that I can't see
why they should copy the names of our cities, no matter how
celebrated they may be. Well! The *Medford* used to sail from
Boston to London with grain, where she discharged her cargo
and loaded again for China. On the outward passage we used to
stop at Madeira, and the Cape, and generally Bangkok, and so
on to Canton, where we filled up with tea, and then sailed for
home direct.

"Now this here Yellow Terror had been on the ship's books
for upwards of five years when I first met him. Smedley had him
regularly shipped, and signed his name to the ship articles, and
held a pen in his paw while he made a cross. [...] You see, in
those days the underwriters wouldn't let a ship go to sea without
a cat, so as to keep the rats from getting at the cargo. I don't
know what a land cat may do, but there ain't a seafaring cat that
would look at a rat. What with the steward, and the cook and
the men forrard, being always ready to give the ship's cat a bite,
the cat in generally full from kelson to deck, and wouldn't take
the trouble to speak to a rat, unless one was to bite her tail. But,
then, underwriters never know anything about what goes on at
sea, and it's a shame that a sailorman should be compelled to give
in to their ideas. The Yellow Terror had the general idea that the
Medford was his private yacht, and that all hands were there to

wait on him. And Smedley sort of confirmed him in that idea, by treating him with more respect than he treated his owners, when he was ashore. I don't blame the cat, and after I got to know what sort of a person the cat really was, I can't say as I blamed Smedley to any great extent.

"Tom, which I think I told you was the cat's real name, was far and away the best fighter of all cats in Europe, Asia, Africa and America. Whenever we sighted land he would get himself up in his best fur, spending hours brushing and polishing it, and biting his claws so as to make sure that they were as sharp as they could be made. As soon as the ship was made fast to the quay, or anchored in the harbour, the Yellow Terror went ashore to look for trouble. He always got it too, though he had such a reputation as a fighter, that whenever he showed himself, every cat that recognized him broke for cover. Why, the gatekeeper at the London Docks – I mean the one at the Shadwell entrance – told me that he always knew when the *Medford* was warping into dock, by the stream of cats that went out of the gate, as if a pack of hounds were after them. You see that as soon as the *Medford* was reported, and word passed among the cats belonging to the ships in dock that the Yellow Terror had arrived, they judged that it was time for them to go ashore, and stop till the *Medford* should sail. Whitechapel used to be regularly overflowed with cats, and the newspapers used to have letters from scientific chaps trying to account for what they called the wave of cats that had spread over East London.

"I remember that once we laid alongside of a Russian brig, down in the basin by Old Gravel Lane. There was a tremendous big black cat sitting on the poop, and as soon as he caught sight of our Tom, he sang out to him, remarking that he was able and ready to wipe the deck up with him at any time. We all understood that the Russian was a new arrival who hadn't ever heard of the Yellow Terror, and we knew that he was, as the good book says, rushing on his fate. Tom was sitting on the rail near the mizzen rigging when the Russian made his remarks, and he didn't seem to hear them. But presently we saw him going slowly aloft till he reached our crossjack yard.

He laid out on the yard arm till he was near enough to jump on to the mainyard of the Russian, and the first thing that the Russian cat knew Tom landed square on his back. The fight didn't last more than one round, and at the end of that, the remains of the Russian cat sneaked behind a water cask, and the Yellow Terror came back by the way of the crossjack yard and went on fur brushing, as if nothing had happened.

"When Tom went ashore in a foreign port he generally stopped ashore till we sailed. A few hours before we cast off hawsers, Tom would come aboard. He always knew when we were going to sail, and he never once got left. I remember one time when we were just getting up anchor in Cape Town harbour, and we all reckoned that this time we should have to sail without Tom, he having evidently stopped ashore just a little too long. But presently alongside comes a boat, with Tom lying back at full length in the sternsheets, for all the world like a drunken sailor who has been delaying the ship, and is proud of it. The boatman said that Tom had come down to the pier and jumped into his boat, knowing that the man would row him off to the ship, and calculating that Smedley would be glad to pay the damage. It's my belief that if Tom hadn't found a boatman, he would have chartered the government launch. He had the cheek to do that or anything else.

"Fighting was really Tom's only vice; and it could hardly be called a vice, seeing as he always licked the other cat, and hardly ever came out of a fight with a torn ear or a black eye. Smedley always said that Tom was religious. I used to think that was rubbish; but after I had been with Tom for a couple of voyages I began to believe what Smedley said about him. Every Sunday when the weather permitted, Smedley used to hold service on the quarter-deck. He was a Methodist, and when it came to ladling out Scripture, or singing a hymn, he could give odds to almost any preacher. All hands, except the man at the wheel, and the lookout, were required to attend service on Sunday morning, which naturally caused considerable grumbling, as the watch below considered they had a right to sleep in peace, instead of being dragged aft for service. But they had to knock under, and what they considered even worse, they had to sing, for the old man kept a bright lookout while the singing was going on, and if he caught any man malingering and not doing his full part of the singing he would have a few words to say to that man with a belaying pin, or a rope's end, after the service was over.

"Now Tom never failed to attend service, and to do his level best to help. He would sit somewhere near the old man and pay attention to what was going on better than I've seen some folks do in first-class churches ashore. When the men sang, Tom would start in and let out a yell here and there, which showed that he meant well even if he had never been to a singing-school, and didn't exactly understand singing according to Gunter. First along, I thought that it was all an accident that the cat came to service, and I calculated that his yelling during the singing meant that he didn't like it. But after a while I had to admit that Tom enjoyed the Sunday service as much as the Captain himself, and I agreed with Smedley that the cat was a thorough-going Methodist.

"Now after I'd been with Smedley for about six years, he got married all of a sudden. I didn't blame him, for in the first place it wasn't any of my business; and, in the next place, I hold that a ship's captain ought to have a wife, and the underwriters would be a sight wiser if they insisted that all captains should be married, instead of insisting that all ships should carry cats. You see that if a ship's captain has a wife, he is naturally anxious to get back to her, and have his best clothes mended, and his food cooked to suit him. Consequently he wants to make good passages and he don't want to run the risk of drowning himself, or of getting into trouble with his owners, and losing his berth. You'll find, if you look into it, that married captains live longer, and get on better than unmarried men, as it stands to reason that they ought to do.

"But it happened that the woman Smedley married was an Agonyostic, which is a sort of person that doesn't believe in anything, except the multiplication table, and such-like human vanities. She didn't lose any time in getting Smedley round to her way of thinking, and instead of being the religious man he used to be, he chucked the whole thing, and used to argue with me by the hour at a time, to prove that religion was a waste of time, and that he hadn't any soul, and had never been created, but had just descended from a family of seafaring monkeys. It made me sick to hear a respectable sailorman talking such rubbish, but of course, seeing as he was my commanding officer, I had to be careful about contradicting him. I wouldn't ever yield an inch to his arguments, and I told him as respectfully as I could, that he was making the biggest mistake of his life. 'Why, look at the cat,' I used to say, 'he's got sense enough to be religious, and if you was to tell him that he was descended from a monkey, he'd consider himself insulted.' But it wasn't any use. Smedley was full of his new agonyostical theories, and the more I disagreed with him, the more set he was in his way.

"Of course he knocked off holding Sunday morning services; and the men ought to have been delighted, considering how they used to grumble at having to come aft and sing hymns, when they wanted to be below. But there is no accounting for sailors. They were actually disappointed when Sunday came and there wasn't any service. They said that we should have an unlucky voyage, and that the old man, now that he had got a rich wife, didn't consider sailors good enough to come aft on the quarter-deck, and take a hand in singing. Smedley didn't care for their opinion, but he was some considerable worried about the Yellow Terror. Tom missed the Sunday morning service, and he said so as plain as he could. Every Sunday, for three or four weeks, he came on deck, and took his usual seat near the captain, and waited for the service to begin. When he found out that there was no use in waiting for it, he showed that he disapproved of Smedley's conduct in the strongest way. He gave up being intimate with the old man, and once when Smedley tried to pat him, and be friendly, he swore at him, and bit him on the leg – not in an angry way, you understand, but just to show his disapproval of Smedley's irreligious conduct.

"When we got to London, Tom never once went ashore,

and he hadn't a single fight. He seemed to have lost all interest in worldly things. He'd sit on the poop in a melancholy sort of way, never minding how his fur looked, and never so much as answering if a strange cat sang out to him. After we left London he kept below most of the time, and finally, about the time that we were crossing the line, he took to his bed, as you might say, and got to be as thin and weak as if he had been living in the forecastle of a lime-juicer. And he was that melancholy that you couldn't get him to take an interest in anything. Smedley got to be so anxious about him that he read up in his medical book to try and find out what was the matter with him; and finally made up his mind that the cat had a first-class disease with a big name something like spinal menagerie. That was some little satisfaction to Smedley, but it didn't benefit the cat any; for nothing that Smedley could do would induce Tom to take medicine. He wouldn't so much as sniff at salts, and when Smedley tried to poultice his neck, he considered himself insulted, and roused up enough to take a piece out of the old man's ear.

"About that time we touched at Funchal, and Smedley sent ashore to lay in another tom-cat, thinking that perhaps a fight would brace Tom up a little. But when the new cat was put down alongside of Tom, and swore at him in the most impudent sort of way, Tom just turned over on his other side, and pretended to go asleep. After that we all felt that the Yellow Terror was done for. Smedley sent the new cat ashore again, and told me that Tom was booked for the other world, and that there wouldn't be any more luck for us on that voyage.

"I went down to see the cat, and though he was thin and weak, I couldn't see any signs of serious disease about him. So I says to Smedley that I didn't believe the cat was sick at all.

" 'Then what's the matter with him?' says the old man. 'You saw yourself that he wouldn't fight, and when he's got to that point I consider that he is about done with this world and its joys and sorrows.'

" 'His nose is all right,' said I. 'When I felt it just now it was as cool as a teetotaller's.'

" 'That does look as if he hadn't any fever to speak of,' says Smedley, 'and the book says that if you've got spinal menagerie you're bound to have a fever.'

" 'The trouble with Tom,' says I, 'is mental: that's what it is. He's got something on his mind that is wearing him out.'

" 'What can he have on his mind?' says the captain. 'He's got everything to suit him aboard this ship. If he was a millionaire he couldn't be better fixed. He won all his fights while we were in Boston, and hasn't had a fight since, which shows that he can't be low-spirited on account of a licking. No, sir! You'll find that Tom's mind is all right.'

" 'Then what gives him such a mournful look out of his eyes?' says I. 'When you spoke to him this morning he looked at you as if he was on the point of crying over your misfortunes – that is to say, if you've got any. Come to think of it, Tom began to go into this here decline just after you were married. Perhaps that's what's the matter with him.'

"But there was no convincing Smedley that Tom's trouble was mental, and he was so sure that the cat was going to die, that he got to be about as low-spirited as Tom himself. 'I begin to wish,' says Smedley to me one morning, 'that I was a Methodist again, and believed in a hereafter. It does seem kind of hard that a first-class cat-fighter like Tom shouldn't have a chance when he dies. He was a good religious cat if ever there was one, and I'd like to think that he was going to a better world.'

"Just then an idea struck me. 'Captain Smedley,' says I, 'you remember how Tom enjoyed the meetings that we used to have aboard here on Sunday mornings!'

" 'He did so,' said Smedley. 'I never saw a person who took more pleasure in his Sunday privileges than Tom did.'

" 'Captain Smedley,' says I, putting my hand on the old man's sleeve. 'All that's the matter with Tom is seeing you deserting the religion that you was brought up in, and turning agonyostical, or whatever you call it. I call it turning plain infidel. Tom's mourning about your soul, and he's miserable because you don't have any more Sunday morning meetings. I told you the trouble was mental, and now you know it is.'

" 'Mebbe you're right,' says Smedley, taking what I'd said in a peaceable way, instead of flying into a rage, as I expected he would. 'To tell you the truth, I ain't so well satisfied in my own mind as I used to be, and I was thinking last night, when I started in to say "Now I lay me" – just from habit you know – that if I'd stuck to the Methodist persuasion I should be a blamed sight happier than I am now.'

" 'Tomorrow's Sunday,' says I, 'and if I was you, Captain, I should have the bell rung for service, same as you used to do, and bring Tom up on deck, and let him have the comfort of hearing the rippingest hymns you can lay your hand to. It can't hurt you, and it may do him a heap of good. Anyway, it's worth trying, if you really want the Yellow Terror to get well.'

" 'I don't mind saying,' says Smedley, 'that I'd do almost anything to save his life. He's been with me now going on for seven years, and we've never had a hard word. If a Sunday morning meeting will be any comfort to him, he shall have it. Mebbe if it doesn't cure him, it may sort of smooth his hatchway to the tomb.'

"Now the very next day was Sunday, and at six the Captain had the bell rung for service, and the men were told to lay aft. The bell hadn't fairly stopped ringing, when Tom comes up the companionway, one step at a time, looking as if he was on his way to his own funeral. He came up to his usual place alongside of the capstan, and lay down on his side at the old man's feet, and sort of looked up at him with what anybody would have said was a grateful look. I could see that Smedley was feeling pretty serious. He understood what the cat wanted to say, and when he started in to give out a hymn, his voice sort of choked. It was a ripping good hymn, with a regular hurricane chorus, and the men sang it for all they were worth, hoping that it would meet Tom's views. He was too weak to join in with any of his old-time yells, but he sort of flopped the deck with his tail, and you could see he was enjoying it down to the ground.

"Well, the service went on just as it used to do in old times, and Smedley sort of warmed up as it went along, and by and by he'd got the regular old Methodist glow on his face. When it was all through, and the men had gone forrard again, Smedley stooped down, and picked up Tom, and kissed him, and the cat nestled up in the old man's neck and licked his chin. Smedley carried Tom down into the saloon, and sang out to the steward to bring some fresh meat. The cat turned to and ate as good a dinner as he'd ever eaten in his best days, and after he was through, he went into Smedley's own cabin, and curled up in the old man's bunk, and went to sleep purring fit to take the deck off. From that day Tom improved steadily, and by the time we got to Cape Town he was well enough to go ashore, though he was still considerable weak. I went ashore at the same time, and kept an eye on Tom, to see what he would do. I saw him pick out a small measly-looking cat, that couldn't have stood up to a full-grown mouse, and lick him in less than a minute. Then I knew that Tom was all right again, and I admired his judgment in picking out a small cat that was suited to his weak condition. By the time that we got to Canton, Tom was as well in body and mind as he had ever been; and when we sailed, he came aboard with two inches of his tail missing, and his starboard ear carried away, but he had the air of having licked all creation, which I don't doubt he had done, that is to say, so far as all creation could be found in Canton.

"I never heard any more of Smedley's agonyostical nonsense. He went back to the Methodists again, and he always said that Tom had been the blessed means of showing him the error of his ways. I heard that when he got back to Boston, he gave Mrs Smedley notice that he expected her to go to the Methodist meeting with him every Sunday, and that if she didn't, he should consider that it was a breach of wedding articles, and equivalent to mutiny. I don't know how she took it, or what the consequences were, for I left the *Medford* just then, and took command of a barque that traded between Boston and the West Indies. And I never heard of the Yellow Terror after that voyage, though I often thought of him, and always held that for a cat he was the ablest cat, afloat or ashore, that any man ever met."

Kitty: What She Thinks of Herself

WILLIAM BRIGHTY RANDS (1823–82)

I am the Cat of Cats. I am
The everlasting cat!
Cunning and old and sleek as jam,
The everlasting cat!
I hunt the vermin in the night –
The everlasting cat!
For I see best without the light –
The everlasting cat!

The Poor Girl and Her Cat

W.H. HUDSON (1841–1922)

I must, however, relate one more instance of a cat who hunted
for others, told to me by a very aged friend of mine, a native of
Foothill Bishop. [...]

When she was a young motherless girl and they were very
poor indeed, her father being incapacitated, they had a cat that
was a great help to them; a large black and white animal who
spent a greater part of his time hunting in Fonthill Abbey
woods, and who was always bringing in something for the pot.
The cat was attached to her, and whatever was brought in was
for her exclusively, and I imagine it is so in all cases in which a
cat has the custom of bringing anything it catches into the
house. The cat mind cannot understand a division of food. It
does not and cannot share a mouse or bird with another cat, and
when it gives it gives the whole animal, and to one person
alone. When the cat brought a rabbit home he would not come
into the kitchen with it if he saw her little brother or any other
person there, lest they should take it into their hands; he would
steal off and conceal it among the weeds at the back of the
cottage, then come back to make little mewing sounds under-

stood by his young mistress, and she would thereupon follow him out to where the rabbit was hidden and take it up, and the cat would then be satisfied.

The cat brought her rabbits and di-dappers, as she called the moorhen, caught in the sedges by the lake in the park. This was the first occasion of my meeting with this name for a bird, but it comes no doubt from dive-dapper, an old English vernacular name (found in Shakespeare) of the dabchick, or little grebe. Moorhens were not the only birds it captured: on two or three occasions it brought in a partridge and on one occasion a fish. Whether it was a trout or not she could not say; she only knew that she cooked and ate it and that it was very good.

One day, looking out, she spied her cat coming home with something very big, something it had caught larger than itself; and it was holding its head very high, dragging its burden along with great labour. It was a hare, and she ran out to receive it, and when she got to the cat and stooped down to take it from him he released it too soon, for it was uninjured, and away it bounded and vanished into the woods, leaving them both very much astonished and disgusted.

For a long time her cat managed to escape the poaching animal's usual fate in the woods, which were strictly preserved then, in the famous Squire Beckford's day, as they are now; but a day arrived when it came hobbling in with a broken leg. It had been caught in a steel trap, and some person who was not a keeper had found and released it. She washed the blood off, and taking it on her lap put the bones together and bound up the broken limb as well as she was able, and the bones joined, and before very long the cat was well again. And no sooner was it well than it resumed its hunting in the woods and bringing in rabbits and di-dappers.

But alas, it had but nine lives, and having generously spent them all in the service of its young mistress it came to its end; at all events it finally disappeared, and it was conjectured that a keeper had succeeded in killing it.

from *A Shepherd's Life* (1910)

When the Cat's Away the Mice May Play

MATTHEW PRIOR (1664–1721)

A *Lady* once (so Stories say)
   By *Rats* and *Mice* infested,
With Gins and Traps long sought to slay
The *Thieves*; but still they scap'd away,
   And daily her molested.

Great Havock 'mongst her Cheese was made,
   And much the loss did grieve her:
At length *Grimalkin* to her Aid
She call'd (no more of *Cats* afraid)
   And begg'd him to relieve her.

Soon as *Grimalkin* came in view,
   The *Vermin* back retreated;
Grimalkin swift as Lightning flew,
Thousands of *Mice* he daily slew,
   Thousands of *Rats* defeated.

Ne'er *Cat* before such Glory won,
   All People did adore him:
Grimalkin far all *Cats* out-shone,
And in his *Lady*'s Favour none
   Was then preferr'd before him.

Pert Mrs *Abigail* alone
   Envy'd *Grimalkin*'s Glory:
Her favourite *Lap Dog* now was grown
Neglected, him she did bemoan,
   And rav'd like any Tory.

She cannot bear, she swears she won't,
   To see the *Cat* regarded,
But firmly is resolv'd upon 't,
And vows, that, whatsoe'er comes on 't,
   She'll have the *Cat* discarded.

She Begs, she Storms, she Fawns, she Frets,
 (Her Arts are all employ'd)
And tells her *Lady* in a Pett,
Grimalkin cost her more in Meat
 Than all the *Rats* destroy'd.

At length this Spiteful *Waiting-maid*
 Produc'd a Thing amazing;
The Favourite *Cat*'s a Victim made,
To satisfy this prating Jade,
 And fairly turn'd a-grazing.

Now *Lap Dog* is again restor'd
 Into his *Lady*'s Favour;
Sumptuously kept at Bed and Board,
And He (so *Nab* has given her word)
 Shall from all *Vermin* save Her.

Nab much exults at this Success,
 And, overwhelm'd with Joy,
Her *Lady* fondly does caress,
And tells her *Fubb* can do no less,
 Than all Her Foes destroy.

But vain such Hopes; The *Mice* that fled
 Return, now *Grim*'s discarded;
Whilst *Fubb* till Ten, on Silken Bed,
Securely lolls his drowsy Head,
 And leaves Cheese unregarded.

Nor *Rats*, nor *Mice* the *Lap Dog* fear,
 Now uncontrol'd their Theft is:
And whatsoe'er the Vermin spare,
Nab and her *Dog* betwixt them share,
 Nor Pie, nor Pippin left is.

Mean while, to cover their Deceit,
 At once, and slander *Grim*;

Nab says, the *Cat* comes out of spight
To rob her *Lady* every Night,
   So lays it all on him.

Nor Corn secure in Garret high,
   Nor Cheesecake safe in Closet;
The *Cellars* now unguarded lie,
On ev'ry Shelf the *Vermin* Prey,
   And still *Grimalkin* does it.

The Gains from Corn apace decay'd,
   No Bags to Market go:
Complaints came from the Dairy-maid,
The *Mice* had spoil'd her Butter Trade,
   And eke her Cheese also.

With this same *Lady* once there liv'd
   A trusty *Servant Maid*,
Who, hearing this, full much was griev'd,
Fearing her *Lady* was deceiv'd,
   And hasten'd to her Aid.

Much Art she us'd for to disclose
   And find out the Deceit;
At length she to the *Lady* goes,
Discovers her Domestic Foes,
   And opens all the Cheat.

Struck with the Sense of Her Mistake,
   The *Lady* discontented,
Resolves again Her *Cat* to take,
And ne'er again Her *Cat* forsake
   Least she again repent it.

Childebrand

THÉOPHILE GAUTIER (1811–72)

Childebrand was a splendid gutter-cat, short-haired, striped
black and tan . . . His great green eyes, with the almond-
shaped pupils, and his regular velvet stripes, gave him a distant,
tigerish look that I liked. "Cats are the tigers of poor devils," I
once wrote . . .

from *La Ménagerie Intime* translated by Lady Chance

To a Cat Which Had Killed a Favourite Bird

RICHARD GARNETT (1835–1906)

O Cat in semblance, but in heart akin
To canine raveners, whose ways are sin;
Still at my hearth a guest thou dar'st to be?
Unwhipt of Justice, hast no dread of me?
Or deem'st the sly allurements shall avail
Of purring throat and undulating tail?
No! as to pacify Patroclus dead
Twelve Trojans by Pelides' sentence bled,
So shall thy blood appease the feathery shade,
And for one guiltless life shall nine be paid.

after the sixth-century poet Agathias

The Fastidious Cat

ANONYMOUS

Catus amat pisces, sed non vult tingere plantas.

Fain would the cat fish eat,
But she's loath to wet her feet.

A Downy Cove

ANONYMOUS

A downy cove is our old tom-cat,
Just turned thirty years old;
He eateth the lean, and leaveth the fat,
And won't touch his meals when too cold.
His food must be crumbled, and not decayed,
To pleasure his dainty whim,
But a turkey bone from the kitchen-maid
Is a very good meal for him.

Chorus:
Creeping over the tiles pit-pat,
A downy cove is the old tom-cat.

Whole joints have fled, and their bones decayed,
And dishes have broken been,
But old tom still follows the kitchen-maid,
And slyly licks up the cream.
Now, old tom-cat, in his lonely days,
Shall joyously think of the past,
And a big leg of mutton, that never was touched,
Shall be food for our Tommy at last.

Fast creepeth he, though he hath no wings,
And a sly old dodger is he,
As under the garret window he sings –
Ain't you coming out tonight, love, to me?
Then slyly he creepeth the gutters all round,
And his old tail he joyously waves,
As his lady love from a garret he spies,
And he sings his amorous staves.

A Dictionary Definition

SAMUEL JOHNSON (1709–84)

Cat: A domestic animal that catches mice, commonly reckoned by naturalists the lowest order of the leonine species.

To My Child Carlino

WALTER SAVAGE LANDOR (1775–1864)

Carlino! What art thou about, my boy? . . .
Does Cincirillo follow thee about?
Inverting one swart foot suspensively,
And wagging his dread jaw, at every chirp
Of bird above him in the olive-branch?
Frighten him then away! 'twas he who slew
Our pigeons, our white pigeons, peacock-tailed,
That fear'd not you and me . . . alas, nor him!
I flattened his striped sides along my knee,
And reasoned with him on his bloody mind,
Till he looked blandly, and half-closed his eyes
To ponder on my lecture in the shade.
I doubt his memory much, his heart a little
And in some minor matters (may I say it?)
Could wish him rather sager. But from thee
God hold back wisdom yet for many years!

from *The Pentameron* (1837)

Cat and King

AMBROSE BIERCE (1842–1914)

A cat was looking at a king, as permitted by the proverb.

"Well," said the monarch, observing her inspection of the royal person, "how do you like me?"

"I can imagine a king," said the Cat, "whom I should like better."

"For example?"

"The King of Mice."

The sovereign was so pleased with the wit of the reply that he gave her permission to scratch his Prime Minister's eyes out.

Belling the Cat

WILLIAM LANGLAND (*c.* 1330–*c.*1386)

[...] Then forth ran a rout of great rats, all at once,
Where met them small mice, yea, more than a thousand;
All came to a council for their common profit.
For a cat of the court would come, when he liked,
And chase them and clutch them, and catch them at will,

Play with them perilously, and push them about:
"For dread of the danger, look round us we dare not;
If we grudge him his game, he will grieve us the more,
Tease us or toss us, or take in his claws,
That we loathe our own lives, ere he lets us go free.
If by wit or by wile we his will might withstand,
We might lord it aloft, and might live at our ease."

Then a rat of renown, very ready of tongue,
Said, for a sovereign help to themselves,
"Some cits have I seen, in the city of London,
Wear chains on their necks of the choicest gold,
Or collars of crafty work; uncoupled they go
Both in warren and waste, as their will inclines,
And elsewhere at odd times, as I hear tell.
If they bore each a bell, by its ringing, me thinketh,
One might wit where they were, and away soon run!
Right so," quoth the rat, "doth reason suggest
To buy a bell of brass or of bright silver,
To be bound on a collar, for our common profit,

On the cat's neck to hang; then each hearer can tell
If he rambles or rests him, or runs out to play!
When mild is his mood, we can move as we list
And appear in his presence, when playful and pleased,
Or, when angry, beware; and away will we run!"

All the rout of great rats to his reasons assented,
But when bought was the bell, and well bound on the
    collar,
Not a rat in the rout, for the realm of all France,
Durst bind the said bell about the cat's neck,
Nor hang it beside him, all England to win!
They owned they were cowards, and their counsel weak;
So their labour was lost, and all their long study.

Then a mouse of mind, who had merit, methought,
Strode forth sternly, and stood before them all,
And to the rout of rats rehearsèd these words:
"Though we killed the old cat, yet another would come
To catch all our kin, though we crept under benches.
I counsel the commons to let the cat be;
Be we never so bold as to show him the bell.
For I heard my sire say, some seven years since,
'Where the cat is a kitten, the court is a sad one';
So witnesseth scripture, who willeth may read it,

Woe to thee, land, when thy king is a child! (Eccl. x. 16).
For no one could rest him, for rats in the night!
While the cat catches rabbits, he covets us less,
But is fed as with venison; defame we him never!
Better a little loss than a livelong sorrow,
By loss of a loathed one to live in disorder!
For many men's malt we mice would destroy,
And ye, rout of rats, would rend men's clothes,
If the cat of the court could not catch you at will!
Ye rats, if unruled, could not rule o'er yourselves.
I see," quoth the mouse, "such a mischief might follow,
Neither kitten nor cat, by my counsel, shall suffer;

Nor care I for collars that have cost me nothing;
Had they cost me a crown, I would keep it unknown,
And suffer our rulers to rove where they like,
Uncoupled, or coupled, to catch what they can.
I warn well each wise man to ward well his own."
What this vision may mean, ye men that are merry,
Discern ye! I dare not discern it myself!

from *Piers Plowman* (*c.* 1367–70)
translated by W.W. Skeat

The Kitten and the Cat

ANONYMOUS

Domestic and fond, see
    The kitten and the cat;
Clear houses of vermin,
    The mouse and the rat;
They live in contentment,
    And keep you in peace,
Or these foes in number,
    Would greatly increase.

On Lutestrings Catt-Eaten

THOMAS MASTER

Are these the strings that poets feigne
Have clear'd the Ayre, and calm'd the mayne?
Charm'd wolves, and from the mountaine creasts
Made forests dance with all their beasts?
Could these neglected shreads you see
Inspire a Lute of Ivorie
And make it speake? Oh! think then what
Hath beene committed by my catt,
Who, in the silence of this night

Hath gnawne these cords, and marr'd them quite;
Leaving such reliques as may be
For fretts, not for my lute, but me.
Pusse, I will curse thee; may'st thou dwell
With some dry Hermit in a cell
Where Ratt neere peep'd, where mouse neere fedd,
And flyes go supperlesse to bedd;
Or with some close-par'd Brother, where
Thou'lt fast each Saboath in the yeare;
Or else, prophane, be hang'd on Munday,
For butchering a mouse on Sunday;
Or may'st thou tumble from some tower,
And misse to light upon all fower,
Taking a fall that may untie
Eight of nine lives, and let them flye;
Or may the midnight embers sindge
Thy daintie coate, or Jane beswinge
Thy hide, when she shall take thee biting
Her cheese clouts, or her house beshiting.
What, was there neere a ratt nor mouse,
Nor Buttery ope? nought in the house
But harmelesse Lutestrings could suffice
Thy paunch, and draw thy glaring eyes?
Did not thy conscious stomach finde
Nature prophan'd, that kind with kind
Should stanch his hunger? thinke on that,
Thou caniball, and Cyclops catt.
For know, thou wretch, that every string
Is a catt-gutt, which art doth spinne
Into a thread; and how suppose
Dunstan, that snuff'd the divell's nose,
Should bid these strings revive, as once
He did the calfe, from naked bones;
Or I, to plague thee for thy sinne,
Should draw a circle, and beginne
To conjure, for I am, look to't,
An Oxford scholler, and can doo't.

Then with three setts of mapps and mowes,
Seaven of odd words, and motley showes,
A thousand tricks, that may be taken
From Faustus, Lambe, or Fryar Bacon:
I should beginne to call my strings
My catlings, and my mynikins;
And they recalled, straight should fall
To mew, to purr, to catterwaule
From puss's belly. Sure as death,
Pusse should be an Engastranith;
Pusse should be sent for to the king
For a strange bird, or some rare thing.
Pusse should be sought to farre and neere,
As she some cunning woman were.
Pusse should be carried up and downe,
From shire to shire, from Towne to Towne,
Like to the camell, Leane as Hagg,
The Elephant, or Apish negg,
For a strange sight; pusse should be sung
In Lousy Ballads, midst the Throng
At markets, with as good a grace
As Agincourt, or Chevy-chase.
The Troy-sprung Brittan would forgoe
His pedigree he chaunteth soe,
And singe that Merlin – long deceast –
Returned is in a nyne-liv'd beast.

Thus, pusse, thou seest what might betyde thee;
But I forbeare to hurt or chide thee;
For may be pusse was melancholy
And so to make her blythe and jolly,
Finding these strings, shee'ld have a fitt
Of mirth; nay, pusse, if that were it,
Thus I revenge mee, that as thou
Hast played on them, I've plaid on you;
And as thy touch was nothing fine,
Soe I've but scratched these notes of mine.

The Old Cat and the Young Mouse

JEAN DE LA FONTAINE (1621–95)

A young and inexperienced mouse
Had faith to try a veteran cat –
Raminagrobis, death to rat,
And scourge of vermin through the house –
Appealing to his clemency
With reasons sound and fair.
"Pray let me live; a mouse like me
It were not much to spare.
Am I, in such a family,
A burden? Would my largest wish
Our wealthy host impoverish?
A grain of wheat will make my meal;
A nut will fat me like a seal.
I'm lean at present; please to wait,
And for your heirs reserve my fate."
The captive mouse thus spake.
Replied the captor, "You mistake;
To me shall such a thing be said?
Address the deaf! address the dead!
A cat to pardon! – old one too!
Why, such a thing I never knew.
Thou victim of my paw,
By well-establish'd law,
Die as a mousling should,
And beg the sisterhood
Who ply the thread and shears,
To lend thy speech their ears.
Some other like repast
My heirs may find, or fast."
He ceased. The moral's plain.
Youth always hopes its ends to gain,
Believes all spirits like its own:
Old age is not to mercy prone.

from *The Fables* (1842) translated by Elizur Wright

The Ancient Hero-Cat

J.V. VON SCHEFFEL (1826–86)

When the storm o'er hill and valley
   Howls, at midnight's darkest hour,
Clamb'ring over ridge and chimney,
   Hiddigeigei seeks the tower.

Mounts in triumph, like a spirit,
   Stands in all his beauty there,
Sparks from out his eyes are flashing,
   Flashing from his bristling hair.

And he sings in wildest measure,
   His old feline battle-song,
That like distant peals of thunder,
   Through the night is borne along.

Human creatures cannot hear him,
   Each asleep within his house;
But far down in deepest cellar,
   Hears and straight turns pale the mouse.

Well she knew his awful singing,
   Sore she trembled as she sat:
Fearful in his wrath and grimness
   Is the ancient Hero-Cat.

from "Songs of the Tom-cat Hiddigeigei"
in *The Trumpeter* (1893)

CLEVER
CATS

"Cats have gnosis to a degree that is
granted to few bishops."
Carl van Vechten (1880–1954)

The System of the Seasons

J.V. VON SCHEFFEL (1826–86)

It is May; nor doth he marvel,
  He, the Thinker, who can fathom
The Phenomena of Being.
  In the Centre of Creation
Stand two Cats, snow-white and agèd,
  Turn the Earth's enormous axis;
And the System of the Seasons
  Is the outcome of their turning.

from "Songs of The Tom-cat Hiddigeigei"
in *The Trumpeter* (1893)

Dame Wiggins of Lee and Her Seven Wonderful Cats

ANONYMOUS (1823)

Dame Wiggins of Lee,
Was a worthy old soul,
As e'er threaded a nee-
dle, or wash'd in a bowl:
She held mice and rats
In such antipa–thy;
That seven fine cats
Kept Dame Wiggins of Lee.

The rats and mice scared
By this fierce whisker'd crew,
The poor seven cats
Soon had nothing to do;
So, as anyone idle

She ne'er loved to see,
She sent them to school,
Did Dame Wiggins of Lee.

But soon she grew tired
Of living alone;
So she sent for her cats
From school to come home.
Each rowing a wherry,
Returning you see:
The frolic made merry
Dame Wiggins of Lee.

The Dame was quite pleas'd,
And ran out to market,
When she came back
They were mending the carpet.
The needle each handled
As brisk as a bee:
"Well done, my good cats,"
Said Dame Wiggins of Lee.

To give them a treat,
She ran out for some rice;
When she came back,
They were skating on ice;
"I shall soon see one down,
Aye, perhaps, two or three,
I'll bet half-a-crown,"
Said Dame Wiggins of Lee.

While to make a nice pudding,
She went for a sparrow,
They were wheeling a sick lamb
Home in a barrow.
"You shall all have some sprats
For your humani–ty,

My seven good cats,"
Said Dame Wiggins of Lee.

While she ran to the field,
To look for its dam,
They were warming the bed
For the poor sick lamb:
They turn'd up the clothes
All as neat as could be;
"I shall ne'er want a nurse,"
Said Dame Wiggins of Lee.

She wish'd them good night,
And went up to bed:
When, lo! in the morning,
The cats were all fled.
But soon – what a fuss!
"Where can they all be?
Here, pussy, puss, puss!"
Cried Dame Wiggins of Lee.

The Dame's heart was nigh broke,
So she sat down to weep,
When she saw them come back
Each riding a sheep:
She fondled and patted
Each purring Tom–my:
"Ah! welcome, my dears,"
Said Dame Wiggins of Lee.

The Dame was unable
Her pleasure to smother;
To see the sick Lamb
Jump up to its mother.
In spite of the gout,
And a pain in her knee,
She went dancing about:
Did Dame Wiggins of Lee.

The Farmer soon heard
Where his sheep went astray;
And arrived at Dame's door.
With his faithful dog Tray.
He knock'd with his crook,
And the stranger to see,
Out of window did look
Dame Wiggins of Lee.

For their kindness he had them
All drawn by his team;
And gave them some field-mice,
And raspberry-cream.
Said he, "All my stock
You shall presently see;
For I honour the cats
Of Dame Wiggins of Lee."

To shew them his poultry,
He turn'd them all loose,
When each nimbly leap'd
On the back of a Goose,
Which frighten'd them so
That they ran to the sea,
And half-drown'd the poor cats
Of Dame Wiggins of Lee.

He sent his maid out
For some muffins and crumpets:
And when he turn'd round
They were blowing of trumpets.
Said he, "I suppose,
She's as deaf as can be,
Or this ne'er could be borne
By Dame Wiggins of Lee."

For the care of his lamb,
And their comical pranks,

He gave them a ham,
And abundance of thanks.
"I wish you good day,
My fine fellows," said he,
"My compliments, pray,
To Dame Wiggins of Lee."

You see them arrived
At their Dame's welcome door,
They shew her their presents,
And all their good store,
"Now come in to supper,
And sit down with me;
All welcome once more,"
Cried Dame Wiggins of Lee.

Tobermory

SAKI (1870–1916)

It was a chill, rain-washed afternoon of a late August day, that
indefinite season when partridges are still in security or cold
storage, and there is nothing to hunt – unless one is bounded on
the north by the Bristol Channel, in which case one may lawfully
gallop after fat red stags. Lady Blemley's house-party was not
bounded on the north by the Bristol Channel, hence there was a
full gathering of her guests round the tea-table on this particular
afternoon. And, in spite of the blankness of the season and the
triteness of the occasion, there was no trace in the company of that
fatigued restlessness which means a dread of the pianola and a
subdued hankering for auction bridge. The undisguised open-
mouthed attention of the entire party was fixed on the homely
negative personality of Mr Cornelius Appin. Of all her guests, he
was the one who had come to Lady Blemley with the vaguest
reputation. Someone had said he was "clever", and he had got his
invitation in the moderate expectation, on the part of his hostess,

that some portion at least of his cleverness would be contributed to the general entertainment. Until tea-time that day she had been unable to discover in what direction, if any, his cleverness lay. He was neither a wit nor a croquet champion, a hypnotic force nor a begetter of amateur theatricals. Neither did his exterior suggest the sort of man in whom women are willing to pardon a generous measure of mental deficiency. He had subsided into mere Mr Appin, and the Cornelius seemed a piece of transparent baptismal bluff. And now he was claiming to have launched on the world a discovery beside which the invention of gunpowder, of the printing-press, and of steam locomotion were inconsiderable trifles. Science had made bewildering strides in many directions during recent decades, but this thing seemed to belong to the domain of miracle rather than to scientific achievement.

"And do you really ask us to believe," Sir Wilfrid was saying, "that you have discovered a means for instructing animals in the art of human speech, and that dear old Tobermory has proved your first successful pupil?"

"It is a problem at which I have worked for the last seventeen years," said Mr Appin, "but only during the last eight or nine months have I been rewarded with glimmerings of success. Of course I have experimented with thousands of animals, but latterly only with cats, those wonderful creatures which have assimilated themselves so marvellously with our civilization while retaining all their highly developed feral instincts. Here and there among cats one comes across an outstanding superior intellect, just as one does among the ruck of human beings, and when I made the acquaintance of Tobermory a week ago I saw at once that I was in contact with a 'Beyond-cat' of extraordinary intelligence. I had gone far along the road to success in recent experiments; with Tobermory, as you call him, I have reached the goal."

Mr Appin concluded his remarkable statement in a voice which he strove to divest of a triumphant inflection. No one said "Rats", though Clovis's lips moved in a monosyllabic contortion which probably invoked those rodents of disbelief.

"And do you mean to say," asked Miss Resker, after a slight

pause, "that you have taught Tobermory to say and understand easy sentences of one syllable?"

"My dear Miss Resker," said the wonder-worker patiently, "one teaches little children and savages and backward adults in that piecemeal fashion; when one has once solved the problem of making a beginning with an animal of highly developed intelligence one has no need for those halting methods. Tobermory can speak our language with perfect correctness."

This time Clovis very distinctly said, "Beyond-rats!" Sir Wilfrid was more polite, but equally sceptical.

"Hadn't we better have the cat in and judge for ourselves?" suggested Lady Blemley.

Sir Wilfrid went in search of the animal, and the company settled themselves down to the languid expectation of witnessing some more or less adroit drawing-room ventriloquism.

In a minute Sir Wilfrid was back in the room, his face white beneath its tan and his eyes dilated with excitement.

"By Gad, it's true!"

His agitation was unmistakably genuine, and his hearers started forward in a thrill of awakened interest.

Collapsing into an armchair he continued breathlessly: "I found him dozing in the smoking-room, and called out to him to come for his tea. He blinked at me in his usual way, and I said, 'Come on, Toby; don't keep us waiting'; and, by Gad! he drawled out in a most horribly natural voice that he'd come when he dashed well pleased! I nearly jumped out of my skin!"

Appin had preached to absolutely incredulous hearers; Sir Wilfrid's statement carried instant conviction. A Babel-like chorus of startled exclamation arose, amid which the scientist sat mutely enjoying the first fruit of his stupendous discovery.

In the midst of the clamour Tobermory entered the room and made his way with velvet tread and studied unconcern across to the group seated round the tea-table.

A sudden hush of awkwardness and constraint fell on the company. Somehow there seemed an element of embarrassment in addressing on equal terms a domestic cat of acknowledged dental ability.

"Will you have some milk, Tobermory?" asked Lady Blemley in a rather strained voice.

"I don't mind if I do," was the response, couched in a tone of even indifference. A shiver of suppressed excitement went through the listeners, and Lady Blemley might be excused for pouring out the saucerful of milk rather unsteadily.

"I'm afraid I've spilt a good deal of it," she said apologetically.

"After all, it's not my Axminster," was Tobermory's rejoinder.

Another silence fell on the group, and then Miss Resker, in her best district-visitor manner, asked if the human language had been difficult to learn. Tobermory looked squarely at her for a moment and then fixed his gaze serenely on the middle distance. It was obvious that boring questions lay outside his scheme of life.

"What do you think of human intelligence?" asked Mavis Pellington lamely.

"Of whose intelligence in particular?" asked Tobermory coldly.

"Oh, well, mine for instance," said Mavis, with a feeble laugh.

"You put me in an embarrassing position," said Tobermory, whose tone and attitude certainly did not suggest a shred of embarrassment. "When your inclusion in this house-party was suggested Sir Wilfrid protested that you were the most brainless woman of his acquaintance, and that there was a wide distinction between hospitality and the care of the feeble-minded. Lady Blemley replied that your lack of brain-power was the precise quality which had earned you your invitation, as you were the only person she could think of who might be idiotic enough to buy their old car. You know, the one they call 'The Envy of Sisyphus', because it goes quite nicely uphill if you push it."

Lady Blemley's protestations would have had greater effect if she had not casually suggested to Mavis only that morning that the car in question would be just the thing for her down at her Devonshire home.

Major Barfield plunged in heavily to effect a diversion.

"How about your carryings-on with the tortoiseshell puss up at the stables, eh?"

The moment he had said it everyone realized the blunder.

"One does not usually discuss these matters in public," said Tobermory frigidly. "From a slight observation of your ways since you've been in this house I should imagine you'd find it inconvenient if I were to shift the conversation on to your own little affairs."

The panic which ensued was not confined to the Major.

"Would you like to go and see if cook has got your dinner ready?" suggested Lady Blemley hurriedly, affecting to ignore the fact that it wanted at least two hours to Tobermory's dinner-time.

"Thanks," said Tobermory, "not quite so soon after my tea. I don't want to die of indigestion."

"Cats have nine lives, you know," said Sir Wilfrid heartily.

"Possibly," answered Tobermory; "but only one liver."

"Adelaide!" said Mrs Cornett, "do you mean to encourage that cat to go out and gossip about us in the servants' hall?"

The panic had indeed become general. A narrow ornamental balustrade ran in front of most of the bedroom windows at the Towers, and it was recalled with dismay that this had formed a favourite promenade for Tobermory at all hours, whence he could watch the pigeons – and heaven knew what else besides. If he intended to become reminiscent in his present outspoken strain the effect would be something more than disconcerting. Mrs Cornett, who spent much time at her toilet table, and whose complexion was reputed to be of a nomadic though punctual disposition, looked as ill at ease as the Major. Miss Scrawen, who wrote fiercely sensuous poetry and led a blameless life, merely displayed irritation; if you are methodical and virtuous in private you don't necessarily want everyone to know it. Bertie van Tahn, who was so depraved at seventeen that he had long ago given up trying to be any worse, turned a dull shade of gardenia white, but he did not commit the error of dashing out of the room like Odo Finsberry, a young gentleman who was understood to be reading for the Church and who was possibly disturbed at the thought of scandals he might hear concerning other people. Clovis had the presence of mind to maintain a composed exterior; privately he was calculating how long it would take to procure a box of fancy mice through the agency of the *Exchange and Mart* as a species of hush-money.

Even in a delicate situation like the present, Agnes Resker could not endure to remain too long in the background.

"Why did I ever come down here?" she asked dramatically. Tobermory immediately accepted the opening.

"Judging by what you said to Mrs Cornett on the croquet-lawn yesterday, you were out for food. You described the Blemleys as the dullest people to stay with that you knew, but said they were clever enough to employ a first-rate cook; otherwise they'd find it difficult to get anyone to come down a second time."

"There's not a word of truth in it! I appeal to Mrs Cornett –" exclaimed the discomfited Agnes.

"Mrs Cornett repeated your remark afterwards to Bertie van Tahn," continued Tobermory, "and said, 'That woman is a regular Hunger Marcher; she'd go anywhere for four square meals a day,' and Bertie van Tahn said –"

At this point the chronicle mercifully ceased. Tobermory had caught a glimpse of the big yellow tom from the Rectory working his way through the shrubbery towards the stable wing. In a flash he had vanished through the open French window.

With the disappearance of his too brilliant pupil Cornelius Appin found himself beset by a hurricane of bitter upbraiding, anxious inquiry, and frightened entreaty. The responsibility for the situation lay with him, and he must prevent matters from becoming worse. Could Tobermory impart his dangerous gift to other cats? was the first question he had to answer. It was possible, he replied, that he might have initiated his intimate friend the stable puss into his new accomplishment, but it was unlikely that his teaching could have taken a wider range as yet.

"Then," said Mrs Cornett, "Tobermory may be a valuable cat and a great pet; but I'm sure you'll agree, Adelaide, that both he and the stable cat must be done away with without delay."

"You don't suppose I've enjoyed the last quarter of an hour, do you?" said Lady Blemley bitterly. "My husband and I are very fond of Tobermory – at least, we were before this horrible accomplishment was infused into him; but now, of course, the only thing is to have him destroyed as soon as possible."

"We can put some strychnine in the scraps he always gets at dinner-time," said Sir Wilfrid, "and I will go and drown the stable cat myself. The coachman will be very sore at losing his pet, but I'll say a very catching form of mange has broken out in both cats and we're afraid of it spreading to the kennels."

"But my great discovery!" expostulated Mr Appin; "after all my years of research and experiment –"

"You can go and experiment on the short-horns at the farm, who are under proper control," said Mrs Cornett, "or the elephants at the Zoological Gardens. They're said to be highly intelligent, and they have this recommendation, that they don't come creeping about our bedrooms and under chairs, and so forth."

An archangel ecstatically proclaiming the Millennium, and then finding that it clashed unpardonably with Henley and would have to be indefinitely postponed, could hardly have felt more crestfallen than Cornelius Appin at the reception of his wonderful achievement. Public opinion, however, was against him – in fact, had the general voice been consulted on the subject it is probable that a strong minority vote would have been in favour of including him in the strychnine diet.

Defective train arrangements and a nervous desire to see matters brought to a finish prevented an immediate dispersal of the party, but dinner that evening was not a social success. Sir Wilfrid had had rather a trying time with the stable cat and subsequently with the coachman. Agnes Resker ostentatiously limited her repast to a morsel of dry toast, which she bit as though it were a personal enemy; while Mavis Pellington maintained a vindictive silence throughout the meal. Lady

Blemley kept up a flow of what she hoped was conversation, but her attention was fixed on the doorway. A plateful of carefully dosed fish scraps was in readiness on the sideboard, but sweets and savoury and dessert went their way, and no Tobermory appeared either in the dining-room or kitchen.

The sepulchral dinner was cheerful compared with the subsequent vigil in the smoking-room. Eating and drinking had at least supplied a distraction and cloak to the prevailing embarrassment. Bridge was out of the question in the general tension of nerves and tempers, and after Odo Finsberry had given a lugubrious rendering of "Melisande in the Wood" to a frigid audience, music was tacitly avoided. At eleven the servants went to bed, announcing that the small window in the pantry had been left open as usual for Tobermory's private use. The guests read steadily through the current batch of magazines, and fell back gradually on the "Badminton Library" and bound volumes of *Punch*. Lady Blemley made periodic visits to the pantry, returning each time with an expression of listless depression which forestalled questioning.

At two o'clock Clovis broke the dominating silence.

"He won't turn up tonight. He's probably in the local newspaper office at the present moment, dictating the first instalment of his reminiscences. Lady What's-her-name's book won't be in it. It will be the event of the day."

Having made this contribution to the general cheerfulness, Clovis went to bed. At long intervals the various members of the house-party followed his example.

The servants taking round the early tea made a uniform announcement in reply to a uniform question. Tobermory had not returned.

Breakfast was, if anything, a more unpleasant function than dinner had been, but before its conclusion the situation was relieved. Tobermory's corpse was brought in from the shrubbery, where a gardener had just discovered it. From the bites on his throat and the yellow fur which coated his claws it was evident that he had fallen in unequal combat with the big tom from the Rectory.

By midday most of the guests had quitted the Towers, and after lunch Lady Blemley had sufficiently recovered her spirits to write an extremely nasty letter to the Rectory about the loss of her valuable pet.

Tobermory had been Appin's one successful pupil, and he was destined to have no successor. A few weeks later an elephant in the Dresden Zoological Garden, which had shown no previous signs of irritability, broke loose and killed an Englishman who had apparently been teasing it. The victim's name was variously reported in the papers as Oppin and Eppelin, but his front name was faithfully rendered Cornelius.

"If he was trying German irregular verbs on the poor beast," said Clovis, "he deserved all he got."

from *The Chronicles of Clovis* (1911)

The Cat and the Rat

JEAN DE LA FONTAINE (1621–95)

Four creatures, wont to prowl –
Sly Grab-and-Snatch, the cat,
Grave Evil-bode, the owl,
Thief Nibble-stitch, the rat,
And Madam Weasel, prim and fine –
Inhabited a rotten pine.
A man their home discover'd there,
And set, one night, a cunning snare.
The cat, a noted early-riser,
Went forth, at break of day.
To hunt her usual prey.
Not much the wiser
For morning's feeble ray,
The noose did suddenly surprise her.
Waked by her strangling cry,
Grey Nibble-stitch drew nigh:
As full of joy was he

As of despair was she,
For in the noose he saw
His foe of mortal paw.
"Dear friend," said Mrs Grab-and-Snatch,
"Do, pray, this cursed cord detach.
I've always known your skill,
And often your good-will;
Now help me from this worst of snares,
In which I fell at unawares.
'Tis by a sacred right,
You, sole of all your race,
By special love and grace,
Have been my favourite –
The darling of my eyes.
'Twas order'd by celestial cares,
No doubt: I thank the blessed skies,
That, going out to say my prayers,
As cats devout each morning do,
This net has made me pray to you.
Come, fall to work upon the cord."

Replied the rat, "And what reward
Shall pay me, if I dare?"
"Why," said the cat. "I swear
To be your firm ally:
Henceforth, eternally.
These powerful claws are yours.
Which safe your life insures.
I'll guard from quadruped and fowl;
I'll eat the weasel and the owl."
"Ah," cried the rat, "you fool!
I'm quite too wise to be your tool."
He said, and sought his snug retreat,
Close at the rotten pine-tree's feet.
Where plump he did the weasel meet;
Whom shunning by a happy dodge,
He climb'd the hollow trunk to lodge;

And there the savage owl he saw.
Necessity became his law,
And down he went, the rope to gnaw.
Strand after strand in two he bit,
And freed, at last, the hypocrite.
That moment came the man in sight;
The new allies took hasty flight.

A good while after that,
Our liberated cat
Espied her favourite rat,
Quite out of reach, and on his guard.
"My friend," said she, "I take your shyness hard;
Your caution wrongs my gratitude;
Approach, and greet your staunch ally.
Do you suppose, dear rat, that I
Forget the solemn oath I mew'd?"
"Do I forget," the rat replied,
"To what your nature is allied?
To thankfulness, or even pity,
Can cats be ever bound by treaty?"

Alliance from necessity
Is safe just while it has to be.

from *The Fables* (1842) translated by Elizur Wright

Cat and Mouse in Partnership

J.L.C. GRIMM (1785–1863) AND W.C. GRIMM (1786–1859)

A certain cat had made the acquaintance of a mouse, and had said so much to her about the great love and friendship she felt for her, that at length the mouse agreed that they should live and keep house together. "But we must make a provision for winter, or else we shall suffer from hunger," said the cat; "and you, little mouse, cannot venture everywhere, or you will be caught in a trap some day." The good advice was followed, and a pot of fat was bought, but they did not know where to put it. At length, after much consideration, the cat said: "I know no place where it will be better stored up than in the church, for no one dares take anything away from there. We will set it beneath the altar, and not touch it until we are really in need of it." So the pot was placed in safety, but it was not long before the cat had a great yearning for it, and said to the mouse: "I want to tell you something, little mouse; my cousin has brought a little son into the world, and has asked me to be godmother; he is white with brown spots, and I am to hold him over the font at the christening. Let me go out today, and you look after the house by yourself."

"Yes, yes," answered the mouse, "by all means go, and if you get anything very good to eat, think of me, I should like a drop of sweet red christening wine myself."

All this, however, was untrue; the cat had no cousin, and had not been asked to be godmother. She went straight to the church, stole to the pot of fat, began to lick at it, and licked the top of the fat off. Then she took a walk upon the roofs of the town, looked out for opportunities, and then stretched herself in the sun, and licked her lips whenever she thought of the pot of fat, and not until it was evening did she return home.

"Well, here you are again," said the mouse, "no doubt you have had a merry day."

"All went off well," answered the cat.

"What name did they give the child?"

"Top-off!" said the cat quite coolly.

"Top-off!" cried the mouse, "that is a very odd and uncommon name, is it a usual one in your family?"

"What does that matter," said the cat, "it is no worse than Crumb-stealer, as your godchildren are called."

Before long the cat was seized by another fit of yearning. She said to the mouse: "You must do me a favour, and once more manage the house for a day alone. I am again asked to be godmother, and, as the child has a white ring round its neck, I cannot refuse." The good mouse consented, but the cat crept behind the town walls to the church, and devoured half the pot of fat. "Nothing ever seems so good as what one keeps to oneself," said she, and was quite satisfied with her day's work.

When she went home the mouse inquired: "And what was this child christened?"

"Half-done," answered the cat.

"Half-done! What are you saying? I never heard the name in my life, I'll wager anything it is not in the calendar!"

The cat's mouth soon began to water for some more licking. "All good things go in threes," said she, "I am asked to stand godmother again. The child is quite black, only it has white paws, but with that exception, it has not a single white hair on its whole body; this only happens once every few years, you will let me go, won't you?"

"Top-off! Half-done!" answered the mouse, "they are such odd names, they make me very thoughtful."

"You sit at home," said the cat, "in your dark-grey fur coat and long tail, and are filled with fancies, that's because you do not go out in the daytime." During the cat's absence the mouse cleaned the house, and put it in order, but the greedy cat entirely emptied the pot of fat. "When everything is eaten up one has some peace," said she to herself, and well filled and fat she did not return home till night. The mouse at once asked what name had been given to the third child. "It will not please you more than the others," said the cat. "He is called All-gone."

"All-gone," cried the mouse, "that is the most suspicious name of all! I have never seen it in print. All-gone; what can that mean?" and she shook her head, curled herself up, and lay down to sleep.

From this time forth no one invited the cat to be godmother, but when the winter had come and there was no longer anything to be found outside, the mouse thought of their provision, and said: "Come, cat, we will go to our pot of fat which we have stored up for ourselves – we shall enjoy that."

"Yes," answered the cat, "you will enjoy it as much as you would enjoy sticking that dainty tongue of yours out of the window."

They set out on their way, but when they arrived, the pot of fat certainly was still in its place, but it was empty. "Alas!" said the mouse, "now I see what has happened, now it comes to light! You a true friend! You have devoured all when you were standing godmother. First top off, then half done, then –"

"Will you hold your tongue," cried the cat, "one word more, and I will eat you too."

"All gone" was already on the poor mouse's lips; scarcely had she spoken it before the cat sprang on her, seized her, and swallowed her down. Verily, that is the way of the world.

from *German Popular Stories* (1823)

The Cat and the Rain

JONATHAN SWIFT (1667–1745)

Careful observers may foretell the hour
(By sure prognostics) when to dread a shower;
While rain depends, the pensive cat gives o'er
Her frolics, and pursues her tail no more.

Sir Henry Wyatt's Cat

W.H. HUDSON (1841–1922)

And here I recall an old story of a cat (an immortal puss) who only hunted pigeons. This tells that Sir Henry Wyatt was imprisoned in the Tower of London by Richard III, and was cruelly treated, having no bed to sleep on in his cell and scarcely food enough to keep him alive. One winter night, when he was half dead with cold, a cat appeared in his cell, having come down the chimney, and was very friendly, and slept curled up on his chest, thus keeping him warm all night. In the morning it vanished up the chimney, but appeared later with a pigeon, which it gave to Sir Henry, and then again departed. When the jailer appeared and repeated that he durst not bring more than the few morsels of food provided, Sir Henry then asked: "Wilt thou dress any I provide?" This the jailer promised to do, for he pitied his prisoner, and taking the pigeon had it dressed and cooked for him. The cat continued bringing pigeons every day, and the jailer, thinking they were sent miraculously, continued to cook them, so that Sir Henry fared well, despite the order which Richard gave later, that no food at all was to be provided. He was getting impatient of his prisoner's power to keep alive on very little food, and he didn't want to behead him – he wanted him to die naturally. Thus in the end Sir Henry outlived the tyrant and was set free, and the family preserve the story to this day. It is classed as folklore, but there is no reason to prevent one from accepting it as literal truth.

from *A Shepherd's Life* (1910)

The Story of the Faithful Cat

LORD REDESDALE (1837–1916)

About sixty years ago, in the summer-time, a man went to pay a visit at a certain house at Osaka, and, in the course of conversation, said, "I have eaten some very extraordinary cakes today," and on being asked what he meant, he told the following story.

"I received the cakes from the relatives of a family who were celebrating the hundredth anniversary of the death of a cat that had belonged to their ancestors. When I asked the history of the affair, I was told that, in former days, a young girl of the family, when she was about sixteen years old, used always to be followed about by a tom-cat, who was reared in the house, so much so that the two were never separated for an instant. When her father perceived this, he was very angry, thinking that the tom-cat, forgetting the kindness with which he had been treated for years in the house, had fallen in love with his daughter, and intended to cast a spell upon her; so he determined that he must kill the beast. As he was planning this in secret, the cat overheard him, and that night went to his pillow, and, assuming a human voice, said to him, 'You suspect me of being in love with your daughter; and although you might well be justified in so thinking, your suspicions are groundless. The fact is this: there is a very large old rat who has been living for many years in your granary. Now it is this old rat who is in love with my young mistress, and this is why I dare not leave her side for a moment, for fear the old rat should carry her off. Therefore I pray you to dispel your suspicions. But as I, by myself, am no match for the rat, there is a famous cat, named Buchi, at the house of Mr So-and-so, at Ajikawa: if you will borrow that cat, we will soon make an end of the old rat.'

"When the father awoke from his dream, he thought it so wonderful, that he told the household of it; and the following day he got up very early and went off to Ajikawa, to inquire for the house which the cat had indicated, and had no difficulty in finding it; so he called upon the master of the house, and told him what his own cat had said, and how he wished to borrow the cat Buchi for a little while.

" 'That's a very easy matter to settle,' said the other: 'pray take him with you at once'; and accordingly the father went home with the cat Buchi in charge. That night he put the two cats into the granary; and after a little while, a frightful clatter was heard, and then all was still again; so the people of the house opened the door, and crowded out to see what had happened; and there they beheld the two cats and the rat all locked together, and panting for breath; so they cut the throat of the rat, which was as big as either of the cats: then they attended to the two cats; but, although they gave them ginseng and other restoratives, they both got weaker and weaker, until at last they died. So the rat was thrown into the river; but the two cats were buried with all honours in a neighbouring temple."

from *Tales of Old Japan* (1871)

Red Slippers

HEINRICH HEINE (1797–1856)

A wicked cat, grown old and grey,
That she was a shoemaker chose to say,
And put before her window a board
Where slippers for young maidens were stored;
While some were of morocco made,
Others of satin were there display'd;
Of velvet some, with edges of gold,
And figured strings, all gay to behold.
But fairest of all exposed to view
Was a pair of slippers of scarlet hue;
They gave full many a lass delight
With their gorgeous colours and splendour bright.

A young and snow-white noble mouse
Who chanced to pass the shoemaker's house
First turn'd to look, and then stood still,
And then peep'd over the window sill.
At length she said: "Good day, mother cat;
You've pretty red slippers, I grant you that.
If they're not dear, I'm ready to buy,
So tell me the price, if it's not too high."

"My good young lady," the cat replied,
"Pray do me the favour to step inside,
And honour my house, I venture to pray,
With your gracious presence. Allow me to say
That the fairest maidens come shopping to me,
And duchesses too, of high degree.
The slippers I'm willing full cheap to sell,
Yet let us see if they'll fit you well.
Pray step inside, and take a seat" –
Thus the wily cat did falsely entreat,
And the poor white thing in her ignorance then

Fell plump in the snare in that murderous den.
The little mouse sat down on a chair,
And lifted her small leg up in the air,
In order to try how the red shoes fitted,
A picture of innocent calm to be pitied.
When sudden the wicked cat seized her fast,
Her murderous talons around her cast,
And bit right off her poor little head.
"My dear white creature," the cat then said,
"My sweet little mouse, you're as dead as a rat.
The scarlet red slippers that served me so pat
I'll kindly place on the top of your tomb,
And when is heard, on the last day of doom,
The sound of the trump, O mouse so white,
From out of your grave you'll come to light,
Like all the rest, and then you'll be able
To wear your red slippers." Here ends my fable.

MORAL

Ye little white mice, take care where you go,
And don't be seduced by worldly show;
I counsel you sooner barefooted to walk,
Than buy slippers of cats, however they talk.

from *The Poems of Heine* (1861) translated by E.A. Bowring

The Cheshire Cat

LEWIS CARROLL (1832–98)

The Cat only grinned when it saw Alice. It looked good-natured, she thought: still it had *very* long claws and a great many teeth, so she felt that it ought to be treated with respect.

"Cheshire Puss," she began, rather timidly, as she did not at all know whether it would like the name: however, it only grinned a little wider. "Come, it's pleased so far," thought

Alice, and she went on. "Would you tell me, please, which way I ought to go from here?"

"That depends a good deal on where you want to get to," said the Cat.

"I don't much care where —" said Alice.

"Then it doesn't matter which way you go," said the Cat.

"— so long as I get *somewhere*," Alice added as an explanation.

"Oh, you're sure to do that," said the Cat, "if you only walk long enough."

Alice felt that this could not be denied, so she tried another question. "What sort of people live about here?"

"In *that* direction," the Cat said, waving its right paw round, "lives a Hatter: and in *that* direction," waving the other paw, "lives a March Hare. Visit either you like: they're both mad."

"But I don't want to go among mad people," Alice remarked.

"Oh, you can't help that," said the Cat: "we're all mad here. I'm mad. You're mad."

"How do you know I'm mad?" said Alice.

"You must be," said the Cat, "or you wouldn't have come here."

Alice didn't think that proved it at all; however, she went on. "And how do you know that you're mad?"

"To begin with," said the Cat, "a dog's not mad. You grant that?"

"I suppose so," said Alice.

"Well, then," the Cat went on, "you see, a dog growls when it's angry, and wags its tail when it's pleased. Now *I growl* when I'm pleased and wag my tail when I'm angry. Therefore I'm mad."

"*I* call it purring, not growling," said Alice.

"Call it what you like," said the Cat. "Do you play croquet with the Queen today?"

"I should like it very much," said Alice, "but I haven't been invited yet."

"You'll see me there," said the Cat, and vanished.

Alice was not much surprised at this, she was getting so well used to queer things happening. While she was still looking at the place where it had been, it suddenly appeared again.

"By the bye, what became of the baby?" said the Cat. "I'd nearly forgotten to ask."

"It turned into a pig," Alice answered very quietly, just as if the Cat had come back in a natural way.

"I thought it would," said the Cat, and vanished again.

Alice waited a little, half expecting to see it again, but it did not appear, and after a minute or two she walked on in the direction in which the March Hare was said to live. "I've seen hatters before," she said to herself; "the March Hare will be much the most interesting, and perhaps, as this is May, it won't be raving mad – at least not so mad as it was in March." As she said this, she looked up, and there was the Cat again, sitting on a branch of a tree.

"Did you say pig, or fig?" said the Cat.

"I said pig," replied Alice; "and I wish you wouldn't keep appearing and vanishing so suddenly: you make one quite giddy."

"All right," said the Cat; and this time it vanished quite slowly, beginning with the end of the tail, and ending with the grin, which remained some time after the rest of it had gone.

"Well! I've often seen a cat without a grin," thought Alice; "but a grin without a cat! It's the most curious thing I ever saw in all my life!"

from *Through the Looking Glass and What Alice Found There* (1871)

The Mind of the Cat

SAMUEL BUTLER (1835–1902)

If you say "Hallelujah" to a cat, it will excite no fixed set of fibres in connection with any other set and the cat will exhibit none of the phenomena of consciousness. But if you say "Me-e-at", the cat will be there in a moment . . .

from *Notebooks of Samuel Butler*

The Poor Miller's Boy and the Cat

J.L.C. GRIMM (1785–1863)
AND W.C. GRIMM (1786–1859)

In a certain mill lived an old miller who had neither wife nor child, and three apprentices served under him. As they had been with him several years, he one day said to them, "I am old, and want to sit in the chimney-corner, go out, and whichsoever of you brings me the best horse home, to him will I give the mill, and in return for it he shall take care of me till my death." The third of the boys was, however, the drudge, who was looked on as foolish by the others; they begrudged the mill to him, and afterwards he would not have it.

Then all three went out together, and when they came to the village, the two said to stupid Hans, "Thou mayst just as well stay here, as long as thou livest thou wilt never get a horse." Hans, however, went with them, and when it was night they came to a cave in which they lay down to sleep. The two sharp ones waited until Hans had fallen asleep, then they got up, and went away leaving him where he was. And they thought they had done a very clever thing, but it was certain to turn out ill for them.

When the sun arose, and Hans woke up, he was lying in a deep cavern. He looked around on every side and exclaimed, "Oh, heavens, where am I?" Then he got up and clambered out of the cave, went into the forest, and thought, "Here I am quite alone and deserted, how shall I obtain a horse now?"

Whilst he was thus walking full of thought, he met a small tabby-cat which said quite kindly, "Hans, where are you going?"

"Alas, thou canst not help me."

"I well know your desire," said the cat. "You wish to have a beautiful horse. Come with me, and be my faithful servant for seven years long, and then I will give you one more beautiful than any you have ever seen in your whole life."

"Well, this is a wonderful cat!" thought Hans, "but I am determined to see if she is telling the truth."

So she took him with her into her enchanted castle, where there were nothing but cats who were her servants. They leapt nimbly upstairs and downstairs, and were merry and happy. In the evening when they sat down to dinner, three of them had to make music. One played the bassoon, the other the fiddle, and the third put the trumpet to his lips, and blew out his cheeks as much as he possibly could. When they had dined, the table was carried away, and the cat said, "Now, Hans, come and dance with me."

"No," said he, "I won't dance with a pussy cat. I have never done that yet."

"Then take him to bed," said she to the cats.

So one of them lighted him to his bedroom, one pulled his shoes off, one his stockings, and at last one of them blew out the candle. Next morning they returned and helped him out of bed, one put his stockings on for him, one tied his garters, one brought his shoes, one washed him, and one dried his face with her tail. "That feels very soft!" said Hans. He, however, had to serve the cat, and chop some wood every day, and to do that he had an axe of silver, and the wedge and saw were of silver and the mallet of copper. So he chopped the wood small; stayed there in the house and had good meat and drink, but never saw anyone but the tabby-cat and her servants.

Once she said to him, "Go and mow my meadow, and dry the grass," and gave him a scythe of silver, and a whetstone of gold, but bade him deliver them up again carefully. So Hans went thither, and did what he was bidden, and when he had finished the work, he carried the scythe, whetstone, and hay to the house, and asked if it was not yet time for her to give him his reward. "No," said the cat, "you must first do something more for me of the same kind, there is timber of silver, carpenter's axe, square, and everything that is needful, all of silver, with these build me a small house."

Then Hans built the small house, and said that he had now done everything, and still he had no horse. Nevertheless, the seven years had gone by with him as if they were six months. The cat asked him if he would like to see her horses? "Yes," said Hans. Then she opened the door of the small house, and when she had opened it, there stood twelve horses – such horses, so bright and shining, that his heart rejoiced at the sight of them.

And now she gave him to eat and to drink, and said, "Go home, I will not give thee thy horse away with thee; but in three days' time I will follow thee and bring it." So Hans set out, and she showed him the way to the mill. She had, however, never once given him a new coat, and he had been obliged to keep on his dirty old smock-frock, which he had brought with him, and which during the seven years had everywhere become too small for him. When he reached home, the two other apprentices were there again as well, and each of them certainly had brought a horse with him, but one of them was a blind one, and the other lame. They asked Hans where his horse was.

"It will follow me in three days' time."

Then they laughed and said, "Indeed, stupid Hans, where wilt thou get a horse? It will be a fine one!"

Hans went into the parlour, but the miller said he should not sit down to table, for he was so ragged and torn, that they would all be ashamed of him if anyone came in. So they gave him a mouthful of food outside, and at night, when they went to rest, the two others would not let him have a bed, and at last he was forced to creep into the goose-house, and lie down on a little hard straw. In the morning when he awoke, the three days had passed, and a coach came with six horses and they shone so bright that it was delightful to see them – and a servant brought a seventh as well, which was for the poor miller's boy. And a magnificent princess alighted from the coach and went into the mill, and this princess was the little tabby-cat whom poor Hans had served for seven years. She asked the miller where the miller's boy and drudge was? Then the miller said, "We cannot have him here in the mill, for he is so ragged; he is lying in the goose-house." Then the king's daughter said that they were to bring him immediately. So they brought him out, and he had to hold his little smock-frock together to cover himself. The servants unpacked splendid garments, and washed him and dressed him, and when that was done, no king could have looked more handsome. Then the maiden desired to see the horses which the other apprentices had brought home with them, and one of them was blind and the other lame. So she ordered the servant to bring the seventh horse, and when the miller saw it, he said that such a horse as that had never yet entered his yard.

"And that is for the third miller's boy," said she.

"Then he must have the mill," said the miller, but the king's daughter said that the horse was there, and that he was to keep his mill as well, and took her faithful Hans and set him in the coach, and drove away with him. They first drove to the little house which he had built with the silver tools, and behold it was a great castle, and everything inside it was of silver and gold; and then she married him, and he was rich, so rich that he had enough for all the rest of his life. After this, let no one ever say that anyone who is silly can never become a person of importance.

The King of the Cats

WASHINGTON IRVING (1783–1859)

The evening passed away delightfully in this quaint-looking apartment, half study half drawing-room. Scott read several passages from the old romance of Arthur, with a fine deep sonorous voice and a gravity of tone that seemed to suit the antiquated, black-letter volume. It was a rich treat to hear such a work, read by such a person and in such a place; and his appearance as he sat reading, in a large armed chair, with his favourite hound Maida at his feet, and surrounded by books, and relics and border trophies, would have formed an admirable and most characteristic picture.

While Scott was reading, the sage grimalkin already mentioned had taken his seat in a chair beside the fire, and remained with fixed eye and grave demeanour, as if listening to the reader. I observed to Scott that his cat seemed to have a black-letter taste in literature.

"Ah," said he, "these cats are a very mysterious kind of folk. There is always more passing in their minds than we are aware of. It comes no doubt from their being so familiar with witches and warlocks." He went on to tell a little story about a good man who was returning to his cottage one night, when in a lonely out of the way place he met with a funeral procession of cats all in mourning, bearing one of their race to the grave in a coffin covered with a black velvet pall. The worthy man, astonished and half frightened, at so strange a pageant, hastened home and told what he had seen to his wife and children. Scarce had he finished when a great black cat that sat beside the fire raised himself up, exclaimed, "Then am I king of the cats," and vanished up the chimney. The funeral seen by the good man was of one of the cat dynasty.

"Our grimalkin, here," added Scott, "sometimes reminds me of the story by the airs of sovereignty which he assumes; and I am apt to treat him with respect from the idea that he may be a great prince incog: and may sometime or other come to the throne."

In this way Scott would make the habits and peculiarities of even the dumb animals about him subjects for humorous remark or whimsical story.

from "Abbotsford" in *The Crayon Miscellany* (1849)

The Cat, The Weasel, and the Young Rabbit

JEAN DE LA FONTAINE (1621–95)

John Rabbit's palace under ground
Was once by Goody Weasel found.
She, sly of heart, resolved to seize
The place, and did so at her ease.
She took possession while its lord

Was absent on the dewy sward,
Intent upon his usual sport,
A courtier at Aurora's court.
When he had browsed his fill of clover
And cut his pranks all nicely over.
Home Johnny came to take his drowse,
All snug within his cellar-house.
The weasel's nose he came to see.
Outsticking through the open door.
"Ye gods of hospitality!"
Exclaim'd the creature, vexed sore,
"Must I give up my father's lodge?
Ho! Madam Weasel, please to budge,
Or, quicker than a weasel's dodge,
I'll call the rats to pay their grudge!"
The sharp-nosed lady made reply,
That she was first to occupy.
The cause of war was surely small —
A house where one could only crawl!
And though it were a vast domain,
Said she, "I'd like to know what will
Could grant to John perpetual reign —
The son of Peter or of Bill —
More than to Paul, or even me."
John Rabbit spoke — great lawyer he —
Of custom, usage, as the law,
Whereby the house, from sire to son,
As well as all its store of straw,
From Peter came at length to John.
Who could present a claim so good
As he, the first possessor, could?
"Now," said the dame, "let's drop dispute,
And go before Raminagrobis,
Who'll judge, not only in this suit,
But tell us truly whose the globe is."
This person was a hermit cat,
A cat that play'd the hypocrite,

A saintly mouser, sleek and fat,
   An arbiter of keenest wit.
John Rabbit in the judge concurr'd,
   And off went both their case to broach
Before his majesty, the furr'd.
   Said Clapperclaw, "My kits, approach,
And put your noses to my ears:
I'm deaf, almost, by weight of years."
And so they did, not fearing aught.
   The good apostle, Clapperclaw,
   Then laid on each a well-arm'd paw,
And both to an agreement brought,
   By virtue of his tusked jaw.

This brings to mind the fate
Of little kings before the great.

from *The Fables* (1842) translated by Elizur Wright

The Achievement of the Cat

SAKI (1870–1916)

In the political history of nations it is no uncommon experience to find States and peoples which but a short time since were in bitter conflict and animosity with each other, settled down comfortably on terms of mutual goodwill and even alliance. The natural history of the social developments of species affords a similar instance in the coming-together of two once warring elements, now represented by civilized man and the domestic cat. The fiercely waged struggle which went on between humans and felines in those far-off days when sabre-toothed tiger and cave lion contended with primeval man, has long ago been decided in favour of the most fitly equipped combatant – the Thing with a Thumb – and the descendants of the dispossessed family are relegated today, for the most part, to the waste lands of jungle and veld, where an existence of self-effacement is the only alternative to extermination. But the *Felis catus*, or whatever species was the ancestor of the modern domestic cat (a vexed question at present), by a master-stroke of adaptation avoided the ruin of its race, and "captured" a place in the very keystone of the conqueror's organization. For not as a bond-servant or dependent has this proudest of mammals entered the human fraternity; not as a slave like the beasts of burden, or a humble camp-follower like the dog. The cat is domestic only as far as suits its own ends; it will not be kennelled or harnessed nor suffer any dictation as to its goings out or comings in. Long contact with the human race has developed in it the art of diplomacy, and no Roman Cardinal of medieval days knew better how to ingratiate himself with his surroundings than a cat with a saucer of cream on its mental horizon. But the social smoothness, the purring innocence, the softness of the velvet paw may be laid aside at a moment's notice, and the sinuous feline may disappear, in deliberate aloofness, to a world of roofs and chimney-stacks where the human element is distanced and disregarded. Or the innate savage spirit that helped its survival in the bygone days of tooth and claw may be summoned forth from beneath the sleek exterior, and the torture-instinct (common alone to human and feline) may find free play in the death-throes of some luckless bird or rodent. It is, indeed, no small triumph to have combined the untrammelled liberty of primeval savagery with the luxury which only a highly developed civilization can command; to be lapped in the soft stuffs that commerce has gathered from the far ends of the world, to bask in the warmth that labour and industry have dragged from the bowels of the earth; to banquet on the dainties that wealth has bespoken for its table, and withal to be a free son of nature, a mighty hunter, a spiller of life-blood. This is the victory of the cat. But besides the credit of success the cat has other qualities which compel recognition. The animal which the Egyptians worshipped as divine, which the Romans venerated as a symbol of liberty, which Europeans in the ignorant Middle Ages anathematized as an agent of demonology, has displayed to all ages two closely blended characteristics − courage and self-respect. No matter how unfavourable the circumstances, both qualities are always to the fore. Confront a child, a puppy, and a kitten with a sudden danger, the child will turn instinctively for assistance, the puppy will grovel in abject submission to the impending visitation, the kitten will brace its tiny body for a frantic resistance. And disassociate the luxury-loving cat from the atmosphere of social comfort in which it usually contrives to move, and observe it critically under the adverse conditions of civilization − that civilization which can impel a man to the degradation of clothing himself in tawdry ribald garments and capering mountebank dances in the streets for the earning of the few coins that keep him on the respectable, or non-criminal, side of society. The cat of the slums and alleys, starved, outcast, harried, still keeps amid the prowlings of its adversity the bold, free, panther-tread with which it paced of yore the temple courts of Thebes, still displays the self-reliant watchfulness which man has never taught it to lay aside. And when its shifts and clever managings have not sufficed to stave off inexorable fate, when its enemies have proved too strong or too many for its defensive powers, it dies fighting to the last, quivering with the choking rage of mastered resistance, and voicing in its death-yell that agony of bitter remonstrance which human animals, too, have flung at the powers that may be the last protest against a destiny that might have made them happy − and has not.

from *The Square Egg* (1924)

The Fox and the Cat

J.L.C. GRIMM (1785−1863)
AND W.C. GRIMM (1786−1859)

It happened that the cat met the fox in a forest, and as she thought to herself, "He is clever and full of experience, and much esteemed in the world," she spoke to him in a friendly way. "Good-day, dear Mr Fox, how are you? How is all with you? How are you getting through this dear season?"

The fox, full of all kinds of arrogance, looked at the cat from head to foot, and for a long time did not know whether he would give any answer or not. At last he said, "Oh, thou wretched beard-cleaner, thou piebald fool, thou hungry mouse-hunter, what canst thou be thinking of? Dost thou venture to ask how I am getting on? What hast thou learnt? How many arts dost thou understand?"

"I understand but one," replied the cat, modestly.

"What art is that?" asked the fox.

"When the hounds are following me, I can spring into a tree and save myself."

"Is that all?" said the fox. "I am master of a hundred arts, and have into the bargain a sackful of cunning. Thou makest me sorry for thee; come with me, I will teach thee how people get away from the hounds."

Just then came a hunter with four dogs. The cat sprang nimbly up a tree, and sat down at the top of it, where the branches and foliage quite concealed her. "Open your sack, Mr Fox, open your sack," cried the cat to him, but the dogs had already seized him, and were holding him fast. "Ah, Mr Fox," cried the cat. "You with your hundred arts are left in the lurch! Had you been able to climb like me, you would not have lost your life."

The Comic Adventures of
Old Dame Trot, and Her Cat
ANONYMOUS (1803)

Here you behold Dame Trot, and here
    Her comic Cat you see;
Each seated in an elbow chair
    As snug as they can be.

Dame Trot came home one wintry night,
  A shivering, starving soul,
But Puss had made a blazing fire,
  And nicely truss'd a Fowl.

The Dame was pleased, the Fowl was dress'd,
  The table set in place;
The wondrous Cat began to carve,
  And Goody said her grace.

The cloth withdrawn, old Goody cries,
  "I wish we'd liquor too":
Up jump'd Grimalkin for some wine,
  And soon a cork she drew.

The wine got up in Pussy's head:
  She would not go to bed;
But purr'd and tumbled, leap'd and danced,
  And stood upon her head.

Old Goody laugh'd to see the sport,
  As though her sides would crack;
When Puss, without a single word,
  Leap'd on the Spaniel's back.

"Ha, ha! well done!" old Trot exclaims,
  "My Cat, you gallop well";
But Spot grew surly, growl'd and bit,
  And down the rider fell.

Now Goody sorely was fatigued,
  Nor eyes could open keep,
So Spot, and she, and Pussy too,
  Agreed to go to sleep.

Next morning Puss got up betimes,
  The breakfast-cloth she laid:

And ere the village clock struck eight,
    The tea and toast she made.

Goody awoke and rubb'd her eyes,
    And drank her cup of tea;
Amazed to see her Cat behave
    With such propriety.

The breakfast ended, Trot went out
    To see old neighbour Hards;
And coming home, she found her Cat
    Engaged with Spot at cards.

Soon after this, as she came in
    (It happen'd quite by chance),
Pussy was playing on the flute,
    And teaching Spot to dance.

Another time the Dame came in,
    When Spot demurely sat
Half lather'd to the ears and eyes,
    Half shaven by the Cat.

Grimalkin, having shaved her friend,
    Sat down before the glass,
And wash'd her face, and dress'd her hair,
    Like any modern lass.

A hat and feather then she took,
    And stuck it on aside;
And o'er a gown of crimson silk,
    A handsome tippet tied.

Just as her dress was all complete,
    In came the good old Dame;
She look'd, admired, and curtsied low,
    And Pussy did the same.

Puss in Boots

CHARLES PERRAULT (1628–1703)

There was a miller, who had left no more estate to the three sons he had, than his mill, his ass and his cat. The partition was soon made. Neither the scrivener nor attorney were sent for. They would soon have eaten up all the patrimony. The eldest had the mill, the second the ass and the youngest nothing but the cat.

The poor young fellow was quite comfortless at having so poor a lot. "My brothers," said he, "may get their living handsomely enough, by joining their stocks together; but for my part, when I have eaten up my cat, and made me a muff of his skin, I must die with hunger."

The Cat, who heard all this, but made as if he did not, said to him with a grave and serious air, "Do not thus afflict yourself, my good master; you have nothing else to do, but to give me a bag, and get a pair of boots made for me, that I may scamper through the dirt and brambles, and you shall see that you have not so bad a portion of me as you imagine."

Though the Cat's master did not build very much upon what he said, he had, however, often seen him play a great many cunning tricks to catch rats and mice; as when he used to hang by the heels, or hide himself in the meal, and make as if he were dead; so that he did not altogether despair of his affording him some help in his miserable condition. When the Cat had what he asked for, he booted himself very gallantly; and putting his bag about his neck, he held the strings of it in his forepaws, and went into a warren where was great abundance of rabbits. He put bran and sow thistle into his bag, and stretching himself out at length, as if he had been dead, he waited for some young rabbits, not yet acquainted with the deceits of the world, to come and rummage his bag for what he had put into it.

Scarce was he laid down, but he had what he wanted; a rash and foolish young rabbit jumped into his bag, and Monsieur Puss, immediately drawing close the strings, took and killed him without pity. Proud of his prey, he went with it to the palace, and asked to speak with his Majesty. He was shown upstairs into the King's apartments and, making a low reverence, said to him, "I have brought you, Sir, a rabbit of the warren, which my noble Lord, the Marquis of Carabas" – for that was the title which Puss was pleased to give his master – "has commanded me to present to your Majesty from him."

"Tell thy master," said the King, "that I thank him, and that he does me a great deal of pleasure."

Another time he went and hid himself among some standing corn, holding still his bag open; and when a brace of partridges ran into it, he drew the strings, and so caught them both. He went and made a present of them to the King, as he had done before of the rabbits which he took in the warren. The King, in like manner, received the partridges with great pleasure, and ordered him some money to drink.

The Cat continued for two or three months thus to carry his Majesty, from time to time, game of his master's taking. One day in particular, when he knew for certain that he was to take the air, along the riverside, with his daughter, the most beautiful princess in the world, he said to his master, "If you will follow my advice, your fortune is made; you have nothing else to do, but go and wash yourself in the river, in that part I shall show you, and leave the rest to me." The Marquis of Carabas did what the Cat advised him to, without knowing why or wherefore.

While he was washing, the King passed by, and the Cat began to cry out as loud as he could, "Help, help, my Lord Marquis of Carabas is going to be drowned." At this noise the King put his head out of the coach window and, finding it was the Cat who had often brought him such good game, he commanded his guards to run immediately to the assistance of his Lordship the Marquis of Carabas.

While they were drawing the poor Marquis out of the river, the Cat came up to the coach, and told the King that while his master was washing there came by some rogues, who went off with his clothes, though he had cried out, "Thieves! Thieves!" several times, as loud as he could. This cunning Cat had hidden them under a great stone. The King immediately commanded the officers of his wardrobe to run and fetch one of his best suits for the Lord Marquis of Carabas.

The King caressed him after a very extraordinary manner; and as the fine clothes he had given him extremely set off his good mien (for he was well made and very handsome in his person), the King's daughter took a secret inclination to him, and the Marquis of Carabas had no sooner cast two or three respectful and somewhat tender glances, but she fell in love with him to distraction. The King would needs have him come into the coach, and partake of the airing. The Cat, quite overjoyed to see his project begin to succeed, marched on before and, meeting some countrymen who were mowing a meadow, he said to them, "Good people, you who are mowing, if you do not tell the King that the meadow you mow belongs to my Lord Marquis of Carabas, you shall be chopped as small as herbs for the pot."

The King did not fail of asking of the mowers, to whom the meadow they were mowing belonged; "To my Lord Marquis of Carabas," answered they all together; for the Cat's threats had made them terribly afraid.

"You see, Sir," said the Marquis, "this is a meadow which never fails to yield a plentiful harvest every year."

The Master Cat, who went still on before, met with some reapers, and said to them, "Good people, you who are reaping, if you do not tell the King that all this corn belongs to the Marquis of Carabas, you shall be chopped as small as herbs for the pot."

The King, who passed by a moment after, would needs know to whom all that corn, which he then saw, did belong; "To my Lord Marquis of Carabas," replied the reapers; and the King was very well pleased with it, as well as the Marquis, whom he congratulated thereupon. The Master Cat, who went always before, said the same words to all he met; and the King was astonished at the vast estates of my Lord Marquis of Carabas.

Monsieur Puss came at last to a stately castle, the master of which was an Ogre, the richest that had ever been known; for all the lands which the King had then gone over belonged, with this castle, to him. The Cat, who had taken care to inform himself who this Ogre was, and what he could do, asked to speak to him, saying he could not pass so near the castle without having the honour of paying his respects to him.

The Ogre received him as civilly as an Ogre could do, and made him sit down. "I have been assured," said the Cat, "that you have the gift of being able to change yourself into all sorts of creatures you have a mind to; you can, for example, transform yourself into a lion, or elephant, and the like."

"This is true," answered the Ogre very briskly, "and to convince you, you shall see me now become a lion." Puss was so sadly terrified at the sight of a lion so near him, that he immediately got into the gutter, not without abundance of trouble and danger, because of his boots, which were of no use at all to him in walking upon the tiles. A little while after, when Puss saw that the Ogre had resumed his natural form, he came down, and owned he had been very much frightened.

"I have been moreover informed," said the Cat, "but I know not how to believe it, that you have also the power to take upon you the shape of the smallest animals; for example, to change yourself into a rat or a mouse; but I must own to you, I take this to be impossible."

"Impossible!" cried the Ogre. "You shall see that presently," and at the same time changed himself into a mouse, and began to run about the floor. Puss no sooner perceived this, but he fell upon him and ate him up.

Meanwhile the King, who saw, as he passed, this fine castle of the Ogre, had a mind to go into it. Puss, who heard the noise of his Majesty's coach running over the drawbridge, ran out, and said to the King, "Your Majesty is welcome to the castle of my Lord Marquis of Carabas."

"What! my Lord Marquis," cried the King, "and does this castle also belong to you? There can be nothing finer than this court, and all the stately buildings which surround it; let us go into it, if you please." The Marquis gave his hand to the Princess, and followed the King, who went up first. They passed into a spacious hall, where they found a magnificent collation, which the Ogre had prepared for his friends, who were that very day to visit him, but dared not to enter, knowing the King was there.

His Majesty was perfectly charmed with the good qualities of my Lord Marquis of Carabas, as was his daughter, who was fallen violently in love with him; and seeing the vast estate he possessed, said to him; after having drunk five or six glasses, "It will be owing to yourself only, my Lord Marquis, if you are not my Son-in-Law." The Marquis, making several low bows, accepted the honour which his Majesty conferred upon him, and forthwith, that very same day, married the Princess.

Puss became a great Lord and never ran after mice any more, only for his diversion.

translated by G.M. Gent (1802)

The Cat and the Cow

ST GEORGE MIVART (1827–1900)

My friend Captain Noble, of Maresfield, informs me that he has himself known a cat which was in the habit of catching starlings by getting on a cow's back and waiting till the cow happened to approach the birds, which little suspected what the approaching inoffensive beast bore crouching upon it. He assures me he has himself witnessed this elaborate trick, by means of which the cat managed to catch starlings which otherwise it could never have got near.

from The Cat (1881)

Spiegel the Cat

GOTTFRIED KELLER (1819–90)

When a Seldwyler has made a bad bargain, or been outwitted, the Seldwylers say of him, "He's bought the fat off the cat."

This saying is certainly to be heard elsewhere, but nowhere as often as here: the reason may be that there exists in the town an old legend on its origin and meaning.

Some hundreds of years ago, they say, an elderly lady lived alone in Seldwyla with a fine tabby cat, the very picture of sagacity and content, who shared her life and never did any harm to anyone who left him alone. His one passion was hunting, but he indulged it within the bounds of reason and temperance, taking no credit to himself for the fact that his passion also served a useful purpose and pleased his mistress, and never giving way to undue cruelty. He accordingly caught and killed only the most intrusive and shameless mice who were found trespassing on a certain part of the house, but, having decided to kill, he did so with reliable skill. It was but rarely that he pursued some particularly cunning mouse, which had provoked his wrath, beyond this pale. When such a case arose, he most politely asked permission from the neighbours to do a little mousing in their homes, and the permission was willingly given, for he never touched the milk-jugs, nor jumped up at the hams which hung on the walls, but went about his business quietly and attentively, and having dispatched it, withdrew discreetly with the mouse in his mouth. Nor was the cat shy and cross: he was friendly to everybody, and never ran away from sensible people: on the contrary, he would put up with a joke from them, and even let them pull his ears a bit without scratching. But a certain type of silly folk he could not bear, declaring that their silliness was the sign of a puerile and worthless nature, and he would get out of their way or give them a good scratch on the hand if they molested him with their clumsy pleasantries.

Thus Spiegel [Looking-glass] – for so the cat was called from his smooth and glossy coat – lived, cheerful, comely and contemplative, in decent ease and without arrogance. He would not sit too often on his kind mistress's shoulder, snatching the bits from her fork, but would wait until she was in the mood for fun, and during the day he seldom lay and slept on his warm cushion behind the stove, but preferred to take his rest on the narrow banisters on the stairs, or in the roof gutter, there to give himself up to meditation and the contemplation of the world. This quiet life, however, was interrupted for a week each spring and autumn, when the violets were blooming or when, in the mild warmth of St Martin's summer, a mimic violet-time returned. Then Spiegel went his own way, roamed in love-born rapture over the most distant roofs, and sang the loveliest songs. In true Don Juan fashion, he carried on the gravest adventures by day and night, and when by chance he showed himself at home, he looked so bold, so jovial, so debauched and so unkempt that his gentle mistress would exclaim almost angrily, "Spiegel, Spiegel, aren't you ashamed to lead such a life?" But it never occurred to Spiegel to be ashamed. Like the man of principle he was, knowing how far he could go in the way of healthy change, he quite quietly set about restoring the sheen of his coat and the innocent gaiety of his expression, and passed his damp paw over his nose with as little embarrassment as if nothing had happened.

But a sad event suddenly broke the even tenor of his days. Just as Spiegel was in the prime of life, his mistress unexpectedly died of old age, leaving the handsome puss orphaned and alone. It was the first sorrow he had known, and with the piercing wails which anxiously question whether a great grief has a real and just cause, he followed the body to the door, and wandered helplessly in and about the house for the rest of the day. But the natural soundness of his nature, his common sense and philosophic habit made him pull himself together, face the inevitable, and prove his grateful affection to his dead mistress by offering his services to her rejoicing heirs, and he prepared to support them in word and deed, to keep the mice down and to give them many a sound piece of advice which the silly people would not have scorned if they had not been silly. But they never gave Spiegel a chance. They threw the slippers and the pretty footstool of the deceased at his head whenever he appeared, quarrelled with each other for a week, began a law-suit and shut up the house until further notice, so that it now stood quite empty.

So there poor Spiegel sat on the doorstep, sad and forlorn, and there was nobody to let him in. At night he certainly crept in by devious ways under the house roof, and at the beginning, he spent the best part of the day there, trying to sleep away his grief. But hunger soon drove him into the light of day and forced him to reappear in the warm sunlight, among the people, to be on the spot and ready if any poor mouthful of food should show itself. The more rarely this happened, the more watchful Spiegel grew, and soon all his moral qualities were so absorbed in this watchfulness that his own mistress would not have known him. He made many a sally from his doorstep, and slunk hastily across the street, only to return, now with some poor unwholesome scraps such as he would never have looked at formerly, now with nothing at all. He grew thinner and more unkempt from day to day, and greedy too, and cringing and cowardly: all his courage, his dainty feline dignity, his good sense and philosophy disappeared. When the boys came home from school, he would creep into a dark corner as soon as he heard them coming, only peeping out to see if one of them might throw away a crust of bread and to note the place where it fell. At the approach of the most miserable cur he would scuttle off, while before, he had looked danger in the face, and often chastised vicious dogs with a firm hand. Yet when some uncouth yokel came along, whom at one time he would have cautiously avoided, he would stay where he was, although, poor cat, he could well size up the wretch with the remainder of his intelligence; necessity forced Spiegel to deceive himself and hope that the man would, as an exception, stroke him kindly and give him something to eat. Even when no such thing happened, and he was only beaten or had his tail pulled, he would not scratch, but would turn aside without a word and look longingly at the hand which had struck him or pulled his tail, and which smelt of sausage or herring.

One day, when the noble and intelligent Spiegel had come so far down in the world, he was sitting, thin and dejected, on his doorstep, blinking at the sun. Then the Town Wizard,

Master Pineiss, came along and stopped in front of him. Hoping for something good, although he knew the uncanny creature well enough, Spiegel sat meekly on his doorstep and waited for what Master Pineiss might say or do. But when he addressed him with the words, "Well, Cat, shall I buy your fat off you?" Spiegel's heart sank, for he thought the Town Wizard was making fun of his leanness. Still, not wishing to fall out with anybody, he replied with a modest smile, "You do like your little joke, Master Pineiss!"

"Not at all!" cried Pineiss. "I really mean it. Above all things I need cat's fat for my sorcery, but it must be voluntarily ceded to me by legal agreement with the gentlemen in question, otherwise it is powerless. I do think that if ever a stout puss was by way of making a good bargain you are the one. Come into my service. I will make you round and fat with sausage and roast quail. On the sunniest heights of the enormously high roof of my house, which, by the way, is the most alluring roof in the world for cats, being full of interesting nooks and crannies, fine grass, emerald green, waves delicately in the breeze, inviting you to nibble off its most tender tips if all my tit-bits should prove too much for your digestion. In this way you will remain in the best of health, and, when the time comes, yield rich and valuable fat."

Spiegel had long since pricked up his ears and was listening with watering mouth. Yet to his weakened intelligence, the thing was not yet clear, so he replied, "So far, so good, Master Pineiss. But what I can't make out is this. How can I, since my life goes with my fat, get possession of the price agreed upon, and enjoy it when I am no more?"

"Get your price?" said the wizard in astonishment. "Why, you will be getting your price all the time in the rich, copious food with which I shall fatten you, of course! Still, I won't force you!" and he began to move off.

But Spiegel said, hastily and anxiously, "You must at least grant me a moderate respite beyond the period of my greatest fatness and rotundity, so that I shall not suddenly be called upon to lay down my life when that agreeable and alas! so mournful moment has arrived and been recognized."

"So be it!" said Master Pineiss, with apparent good-nature. "You shall be allowed to enjoy your pleasant condition until the following full moon, but not a day longer, for the matter must not drag on into the waning moon, since that would tend to reduce my legitimate profit."

The cat hastened to agree, and signed a spare contract which the wizard had on him with the pointed handwriting which was his last possession and sign of better days.

"You can come to dinner, Cat!" said the wizard. "I dine at twelve sharp."

"I will make so free, if I may," said Spiegel, and presented himself punctually at twelve at the wizard's house.

Then there began a few highly agreeable months for the cat, for he had nothing whatever to do save to consume the good things which were set before him, to watch his master making magic whenever he got the chance, and to go walking on the roof. This roof was like an enormous chimney-pot hat, or one of those tricorns which the Swabian peasants wear, and just as such a hat covers a head full of tricks and shifts, so this roof covered a great, gloomy, cornery house full of all manner of hocus-pocus. Master Pineiss was a jack of all trades and did a thousand odd jobs. He cured various ailments, exterminated bugs, pulled out teeth, and lent money on interest: he was the guardian of all widows and children, cut quill pens in his spare time at a penny the dozen, and made fine black ink: he dealt in ginger and pepper, in waggon-grease and maraschino, in little note-books and hobnails: he mended the town clock, and drew up the almanack for the year with the phases of the moon, the laws of husbandry and the blood-letting manikins [in the old popular calendars, a sign marking the days on which bleeding was considered advisable]. He did a thousand perfectly lawful things by day for small pay, and just a few unlawful ones by night for his personal satisfaction, or clipped on to the lawful ones, before he despatched them, a tiny unlawful tail, as tiny as a young frog's, just out of natural waggishness. Moreover, he made the weather in difficult times, kept a knowing eye on the witches, and when they were ripe, he had them burned. So far as he was concerned, he carried on witchcraft as a scientific experiment and for domestic use: and he privately tested and twisted the town laws, which he drafted and copied out with his own hand, to make sure of their durability. As the Seldwylers always needed someone to do their disagreeable jobs for them, big or little, he had been appointed Town Wizard, and had already filled this office for many years, early and late, with indefatigable devotion and efficiency, so that his house was full, from garret to cellar, with all manner of things, and Spiegel found it most entertaining to examine and sniff at everything. But at first all his attention was concentrated on food. He gobbled up everything which Pineiss set before him, and could scarcely wait from one meal to the next. In this way he overloaded his stomach and was really obliged to go on to the roof to eat some of the fine green grass to cure himself of all manner of sickness.

When the wizard saw this ravening, he was glad, and thought to himself that Spiegel would soon grow fat in this way, and that the more he spent now, the craftier he really was and the more he would save in the long run. So he made quite a little landscape for Spiegel in his room, setting up a forest of miniature pine-trees with diminutive hills of stones and moss and a tiny lake. On the trees he hung roasted larks, chaffinches, tits and sparrows, so that Spiegel always found something there to pull down and pick at. He made artificial mouse-holes in the mountains and in them he hid fine mice, which he carefully fattened on corn-flour, then drew, larded with tender strips of bacon, and fried. Spiegel could reach out a few of these with his hands; the others were put further in to increase the fun, but these were tied to a string and Spiegel had to draw them out cautiously when he wished to enjoy the pleasures of a mimic hunt. The basin of the lake, however, Pineiss filled daily with fresh milk so that Spiegel might quench his thirst in the sweet liquid, and sometimes he put fried gudgeon to float in it, for he knew that cats like to fish from time to time. But since Spiegel was leading such a fine life, and could do or leave undone, eat or drink, whatever he liked and when he liked, he visibly flourished as to the outer man, his coat once more became sleek and glossy and his eye bright; at the same time, his mental powers being restored in a like degree, his manners improved, his wild craving subsided, and, as he had a bitter experience behind him, his wits grew keener than ever. He moderated his desires and ate no more than was good for him, while he resumed his habit of sage and profound reflection and began to see things more clearly. Thus one day he took down a pretty little fieldfare from the branches and as he pensively tore it to pieces he found its little stomach quite round and full with fresh, undigested food. Little green herbs, prettily rolled up, seeds, black and white, and a shining red berry were packed in as daintily and as close as if a mother had packed her son's knapsack for a journey. When Spiegel had slowly devoured the bird, he took the pleasantly filled little stomach on his claws and contemplated it philosophically. He was moved by the fate of the poor fieldfare, who, having peacefully done his work, had to quit life so suddenly that he could not even digest the things he had swallowed. "What did he have of it, poor fellow?" meditated Spiegel, "feeding so eagerly and so busily that this little paunch looks like a well-spent day? It was that red berry which decoyed him out of the free life of the woods into the snare of the fowler. But he thought, at least, that he was doing well for himself and prolonging his life with such berries, while I, who have just eaten the unhappy bird, have simply eaten myself a step nearer death. Can a man conclude a more miserable and cowardly contract than to save his life for a little while, only to lose it for the price of saving it? Would not a quick and voluntary death have been better for a resolute cat? But my wits were all confused, and now that I can think again, I can see nothing before me but the fate of this wild bird. When I am fat enough, I must go hence, simply because I am fat! Is that a reason for a lusty and nimble-witted he-cat? If only I could get out of the trap!"

He brooded this way and that as to how it could be done, but as the time of danger was not yet at hand, he could not see things clearly enough to find a way out. Like the wise man he was, however, he devoted himself to virtue and self-control, which is always the best way of passing the time while preparing a decision. He spurned the soft cushion which Pineiss had laid down for him to lie and grow fat on, and again preferred to lie on narrow ledges and high, dangerous places when he wanted to rest. He scorned the roasted birds and larded mice, and, having now a regular hunting ground, he chose rather to exercise his own cunning and agility by catching a simple, living sparrow on the roof, or a nimble mouse in the attics. Such prey tasted far better than the roasted game in Pineiss's artificial preserves, while it did not make him too fat: and the exercise, with his return to virtue and philosophy, prevented him from putting on flesh too rapidly, so that Spiegel looked healthy and sleek, but, to Pineiss's astonishment, remained at a fixed point of embonpoint which was far from that which the wizard proposed to reach with his benevolent fattening, for he had in mind a great obese animal, as round as a ball, which would not move from its cushion and literally consisted of fat. But here his witchcraft had gone wrong, and for all his cunning he did not know that, if you feed an ass, it remains an ass, but if you feed a fox, it will never be anything but a fox, for each animal grows according to its own nature. When it was borne in upon Master Pineiss that Spiegel remained at the same point of well-nourished but lithe and vigorous slimness, he suddenly attacked him one evening and said rudely, "Well, Spiegel, what about it? Why don't you eat the good food which I cook so well and set down for you? Why don't you catch the roasted birds on the trees? Why don't you hunt the tasty mice in the caves? Why don't you fish in the lake? Why do you rush about the whole time, so that you don't get fat?"

"Why, Master Pineiss, because I feel better so! Shall I not pass the short remainder of my life in the way I like best?"

"What's that?" cried Pineiss. "You shall live so as to get round and fat and not wear yourself out hunting! But I know what you're after. You think you're going to play your monkey tricks on me, and that I'm going to let you run about for ever in that condition, neither fat nor lean? But you may just make up your mind to it. You shan't get the better of me! It's your duty to eat and drink and look after yourself so as to put on flesh and acquire fat. Have the goodness to give up this deceitful and fraudulent temperance on the spot, or I shall have something to say to you!"

Spiegel interrupted the comfortable purring he had set going to keep himself in hand and said, "This is the first I have heard of anything in the contract about giving up temperance and a healthy life. If you, Master Pineiss, counted on my being a lazy glutton, that's not my fault. You do a thousand lawful things by day, so add this to them and let us both stick to our rights, for you know that my fat is only of use to you if it has grown legitimately."

"Chattering beast!" said Pineiss. "Do you think you can teach me? Let's see how far you've got, you idle devil. Perhaps we could deal with you soon." He caught hold of the cat by the stomach, but Spiegel, feeling an unpleasant irritation, gave the wizard a good scratch across the hand. Pineiss looked at it reflectively, then said, "Is that the way of it, you beast? Good! I solemnly declare you, in virtue of the contract, fat enough. I am satisfied with the result and will see that I get it! Full moon is in five days. Till then you can enjoy life, as stipulated in the contract, but not a day longer." And thereupon he turned his back and left Spiegel to his thoughts.

These were heavy and sombre. The hour was then near when the good Spiegel must lay down his life. With all his wits, was there no way out? Sighing, he climbed on to the high roof, the ridge of which loomed dark in the autumn evening sky. Then the moon rose over the town and cast its beams on the dark mossy tiles of the old roof; a lovely song fell on Spiegel's ears, and a snow-white she-cat passed shining over a neighbouring roof-top. Spiegel at once forgot his approaching death, and raised his noblest caterwaul in answer to the beauty's hymn of praise. He hurled himself towards her, and was straightway engaged in hot combat by three strange tom-cats, whom he put to flight with a wild courage. Then he paid fiery and humble court to the lady, and passed his days and nights by her side without thinking of Pineiss or showing himself at home. He sang like a nightingale through the long moonlight nights, dashed headlong after his lady-love over the roofs and through the gardens, and more than once, in the jousts of love, or in fights with his rivals, he rolled off high roofs and tumbled into the street, but only to pick himself up, shake himself and dash off again in hot pursuit of his love. Hours of turmoil and hours of ease, the sweetness of passion and the heat of battle, graceful conversation and witty discussions, the machinations of love and jealousy, caresses and scuffles, the elation of success and the misery of mischance – all this filled up the love-sick Spiegel's time so completely that, by the time the moon's disc gleamed full, he was so reduced by all these excitements and passions that he looked more miserable, emaciated and unkempt than ever. At that moment Pineiss put his head out of an attic window and called to him, "Spiegel, Spiegel, where are you? Aren't you coming home for a bit?"

Then Spiegel took his leave of his white mistress, who went her way mewing in cool content, and turned proudly to meet his torturer. The latter went down into the kitchen, rustled the contract, and said, "Come along, Spiegel, my dear!" and Spiegel followed him, and, thin and dishevelled as he was, stood defiantly before him in the wizard's kitchen. When Pineiss saw how scurvily he had been tricked of his profit, he sprang up like one possessed and yelled savagely, "What's that? You rascal, you unscrupulous rogue! What have you been at?" Beside himself with rage, he snatched up a broom and made as if to beat Spiegel, but Spiegel arched his black back, ruffled up his fur until the sparks flew, laid his ears back, and hissed and spat at the old man with such rage that he, aghast, leapt back three paces. He began to suspect that he was up against some wizard who was fooling him and was more advanced in the art than himself. Dismayed and subdued, he said, "Can it be that the honourable Master Spiegel is one of us? Has some learned sorcerer deigned to assume his outward form, seeing that he can command his physique at his pleasure and attain precisely the corpulence he desires, not a shade too much or too little, or even waste away to a skeleton to avoid death?"

Spiegel calmed down and said candidly, "No, I am no sorcerer. The sweet power of passion alone has reduced me to this state and used your fat for my pleasure; but if you like to begin the whole business again, I will do my share stoutly and feed well. Try me with a fine fat sausage, for I am quite weak with hunger."

Then Pineiss took Spiegel wrathfully by the scruff of the neck, shut him up in the goose-house, which was always empty, and shouted, "Now see if your sweet power of passion will help you out and if it is more potent than the power of sorcery and my lawful contract."

Then he fried a long sausage which smelt so good that he could not refrain from nibbling a bit off both ends before he stuck it through the netting. Spiegel ate it up from end to end, and as he comfortably stroked his moustache and licked his coat, he said to himself, "Upon my word, love is a fine thing. It has got me out of the trap again. Now I will rest a bit and see that I come to reasonable thoughts again by meditation and good food. There is a time for everything – today a little passion, tomorrow a little rest and reflection – each is good in its way. This prison is by no means so bad, and I can surely think out something useful here." But Pineiss pulled himself together, and daily cooked toothsome tit-bits, so wholesome and so varied, that Spiegel in his cage could not resist them, for the wizard's stock of voluntary and legitimate cat's fat was dwindling from day to day, and without this, the chief matter of his trade, the sorcerer was a beaten man. But the good wizard, in feeding Spiegel's body, fed his mind too, and could by no means get rid of this annoying detail, at which point his witchcraft proved itself defective.

When he judged that Spiegel in his cage was fat enough, he hesitated no longer, but before the eyes of the watching cat, arranged all the dishes and made a bright fire on the hearth to boil out the yield he had so ardently longed for. Then he sharpened a great knife, pulled Spiegel out, after having first carefully closed the kitchen door, and said cheerily, "Come on, you rascal! We'll cut off your head first, then skin you. That will make a nice warm cap for me. Simpleton that I was not to think of that before. Shall I flay you first, then cut off your head?"

"No, if you would be so good," said Spiegel humbly. "Please, the head first!"

"Quite right, poor fellow!" said Pineiss. "We won't torture you for nothing. Anything that's right!"

"That's well said," replied Spiegel, with a piteous sigh, bending his head in resignation. "Oh! if I had always done what's right and not frivolously neglected such an important matter, I could die now with a clearer conscience, for I am glad to die; but an evil deed embitters the death which in all else is so welcome. For what does life offer to me? Nothing but care, fear and poverty, with, for a change, a storm of devastating passion, which is worse than quiet, trembling fear!"

"What evil deed -- what important matter?" asked Pineiss inquisitively.

"What's the use of talking now?" sighed Spiegel. "What has happened has happened, and remorse comes too late!"

"Now you see, you rogue, what a sinner you are," said Pineiss, "and how you have deserved your death! But what in the world have you been at? Have you purloined, removed, destroyed, something belonging to me? Have you done me some crying wrong of which I know, fear, suspect nothing, you Satan? A pretty business! I'm glad I've got on the track of it. Out with it on the spot or I shall skin and boil you alive!"

"Ah! no," said Spiegel. "I have nothing on my conscience so far as you are concerned. It's about the ten thousand guilders of my late mistress – but talking won't mend matters. Yet when I think the matter over and look at you, there may yet be time. When I look at you, I see that you are still a hale and handsome man in the prime of life. Tell me, Master Pineiss, have you never felt you might like to marry, honourably and well? But there, how I do chatter! How could a wise and ingenious man indulge such idle thoughts? How could an adept so usefully employed fill his head with those silly women? Of course, even the worst of them has something about her which might be useful to a man – that one can't deny. And if she is only half a woman, then a good housewife may even be white of body, careful of mind, obliging of manners, faithful of heart, economical in the house but lavish in the care of her husband, entertaining in word and pleasing in deed, and fond in all her doings. She kisses a man with her mouth and strokes his beard and embraces him with her arms and scratches him gently behind the ears – just as he likes it done – in short, she does a thousand things which are not to be despised. She stays near him or withdraws to a modest distance, just as he feels inclined, and when he goes about his business, she does not disturb him but sings meanwhile his praises at home and abroad, for she won't hear a word against him and extols everything about him. But the sweetest thing about her is the wonderful nature of her delicate bodily being, which, for all the apparent human likeness, has been made so different from ours that it works perpetual prodigies in a happy marriage and, in fact, contains the most subtle magic. Yet listen to me, chattering like a fool on the threshold of death! Forgive me, Master Pineiss, and cut off my head!"

But Pineiss cried hotly, "Have done, you chatterer! and tell me, where is such a woman, and has she ten thousand guilders?"

"Ten thousand guilders?" asked Spiegel.

"Of course," cried Pineiss, impatiently, "didn't you begin with that?"

"No," replied the other. "That's another story. They are buried somewhere."

"What are they doing there? Whose are they?" shouted Pineiss.

"They're nobody's. That's just why I am so conscience-stricken about them, for I ought to have disposed of them somehow. They really belong to the man who marries such a woman as I have described. But who could bring three such things together in this godless town – ten thousand guilders, a clever, comely and virtuous housewife, and a wise and upright man? So my sin is not too great, for the task was too heavy for a poor he-cat."

"If," yelled Pineiss, "you don't stick to your subject and explain the thing clearly and in order, I will cut off your tail and both ears at once. Now begin!"

"Well, since you will have it, I must tell the story," said Spiegel, coolly sitting down on his hind legs, "although this delay only increases my sufferings!"

Pineiss stuck his knife into the floor between them and, all agog, sat down on a little cask to listen, while Spiegel continued: "You must know, Master Pineiss, that that good woman, my late mistress, died an old maid, having quietly done a great deal of good, and never hurt anyone. But things had not always been so still and calm about her, and although she was never an ill-natured person, she had done a good deal of harm in her day, for in her youth she was the loveliest young woman far and near, and every gallant gentleman and bold youth living in the neighbour-hood or passing by on his travels fell in love with her and wanted to marry her. Now she really wanted to marry, and take a handsome, honest and clever husband, and she had her choice, for men far and wide fought for her and there were duels to the death for the first chance with her. Suitors, bold and faint-hearted, crafty and sincere, rich and poor, flocked to pay court to her, some with good and honest businesses, some who lived delicately on their means like gentlemen. One had this advan-tage, another that: one was glib, the next silent, a third merry and kind, while yet another seemed to have more in him although he looked a bit simple. In short, she had as perfect a choice as a marriageable spinster could wish.

"However, she possessed, in addition to her beauty, a handsome fortune of many thousand guilders, and that was the reason why she never got so far as making a choice and settling on a husband, for she was remarkably far-sighted and prudent in the care of her property, and thought very much of it, and as we always judge others from the standpoint of our own inclinations, it came about that, as soon as a decent man came near her and she felt half attracted to him, she at once imagined that he only wanted her fortune. If he were rich, she thought he would not want her if she were not rich too, and as for the poor ones, she took it for granted that they were only after her money, and were thinking what a good thing they would make out of it, and the poor young lady, who herself attached so much importance to worldly goods, was quite incapable of distinguishing the love of money in her suitors from their love to herself, or, if they did care for money, of making allowances for it and forgiving them. More than once she was as good as betrothed and her heart at last began to beat faster, but she would suddenly take it into her head from some word or look that she was betrayed and that her lover was thinking only of her fortune, and she would immediately break off the whole matter and withdraw, sorrowful but resolute. All she liked she tested in a thousand ways, and they had to be very adroit not to fall into the trap, and in the end, nobody could have the least hope of her unless he were a thorough-paced rogue and hypocrite, so, for that reason alone, the choice became really difficult, because in the long run such men create a strangely uneasy atmosphere and awake the most painful anxiety in the heart of a lady, the more insidious and clever they are. Her chief way of putting her admirers to the test was to inveigle them into great expenses, rich gifts and charitable actions. But try as they would, they were never right, for if they were generous and devoted, made her fine presents, gave brilliant parties or confided large sums for the poor to her, she would suddenly say they were throwing a sprat to catch a salmon, as the saying goes. And she gave the money and the presents to convents and fed the poor, but she mercilessly dismissed the discomfited suitors. But if they proved a bit economical, or even a little stingy, they had no chance at all, for she thought that much worse, and declared that they were openly base, callous and selfish. So it came about that she, who sought a pure heart, devoted to herself alone, was in the end surrounded by hypocritical, perfidious and self-seeking men, whom she could never make out and who embittered her life.

"One day she felt herself out of humour and depressed, so she turned the whole lot out of the house, locked it up and set out for Milan, where she had a cousin. As she rode over the Gotthard on an ass, her mood was as gloomy and terrifying as the wild rocks which towered from the abyss, and she felt the strongest temptation to throw herself over the Devil's Bridge into the raging waters of the Reuss. It was only with difficulty that she could be pacified and dissuaded from her dark impulse by the guide and the two maids she had with her, whom I knew, though they are long since dead. And she was pale and low-spirited when she arrived in the lovely land of Italy, and however blue the sky, her gloomy thoughts would not brighten. Yet but few days were to pass before another song was to be heard, and a springtime dawn in her heart of which she had known little till then, and for which she had ceased to hope. For a young compatriot came to her cousin's house to whom she took such a liking at first sight that one may say she fell in love for the first time of her own free will. He was a handsome youth, well-bred and of noble manners, and at the time neither rich nor poor, for all he had was ten thousand guilders which he had inherited from his parents, and with which, having learned the trade, he was to set up a silk business in Milan, for he was enterprising and shrewd, and lucky, as simple-minded and honest people often are, and that the young man was. With all his experience, he looked as frank and innocent as a child. And though he was a merchant, yet of so ingenuous a disposition, a combination in itself delightfully rare, he was firm and knightly in his bearing and wore his sword by his side as boldly as only an experienced soldier can do. All this, with his fresh, handsome face, so won the young lady's heart that she could hardly contain her pleasure, and received him with the utmost graciousness. Her spirits rose, and if from time to time she felt sad, her sadness came only from the alternating hopes and fears of love, and that, after all, is a nobler feeling than all the miserable perplexity she had felt among her suitors. Now only one anxious problem faced her – how to find favour in the sight of the handsome and good young man, and the more beautiful she knew herself to be, the more humble and uncertain she felt now that real love had entered her heart.

"But the young merchant himself had never seen so lovely a woman, or been so warmly received by one. Now she, as I have already said, was not only beautiful, but kind of heart and courteous of manners, so it is not to be wondered at that the young man, whose heart was still free and inexperienced, fell in love with her too, as deeply as he knew how. Still, perhaps nobody would ever have known anything about it if he, in his innocence, had not been encouraged by the lady's complaisance, which, with much secret trembling and hesitation, he dared to take for a return of his affection, for he himself knew no pretence. Yet he contained himself for a few weeks and imagined he was keeping it all very dark, although everybody could see from far off that he was in love, and if he happened to be near the lady, or to hear her name mentioned, it was as clear as day with whom. And indeed, he was not long in love, but began really to love with all the passion of his youth so that the young lady became for him the highest and best in the world, and he set upon her once for all the salvation of his soul and the whole worth of his life. This was very delightful to her, for there was in everything he said and did something different from all she had known hitherto, and it exhilarated her and touched her so deeply that she now fell passionately in love herself and there was no further question of choice for her. Everybody saw the little drama being played out, and it was quite openly spoken of and many a joke was made. The young lady was highly pleased with it all, and though her heart was nearly bursting with timid expectation, she did all she could to complicate and spin out the romance from her side, so as to enjoy it to the full. For in his confusion, the young man did the most charming, childish things, the like of which she had never seen, and they were more flattering and sweet to her than anything else could be. But he, in his candour and frankness, could not bear it long, for everyone hinted and joked, and the whole thing seemed to be turning into a farce, and his beloved was too good and too sacred to him for that; what enchanted

her, grieved him, and made him sad, perplexed and embarrassed about her. Moreover, he thought that it was insulting
and deceitful towards her to be full of passion for her and
constantly thinking of her, while she had not the least suspicion
of it, and that it was not at all right and proper and not fair to
himself! So, one morning, it was quite clear that he had some
project on hand, and he confessed his love to her in a few
words, never to repeat them if he should not find favour in her
sight. For he could not but think that such a beautiful young
lady would say what she meant the first time, and pronounce
her irrevocable yes or no. He was as sensitive as he was loving,
as pure as he was child-like, and as proud as he was candid, and
for him it was a matter of life and death. But the very moment
the lady heard the declaration she had so longed for, her old
suspicion came over her again, and, to her misfortune, it
occurred to her that her lover was a merchant who probably
only wanted her money to extend his business. After all, if he
were a little in love with her at the same time, that was scarcely
to his credit, considering her beauty, and really it was all the
more revolting that she should represent nothing but a desirable
addition to her own money. So, instead of confessing her love
to him and receiving him well, she put on a grave, half-sad
expression, and confided to him that she was already betrothed
to a young man from her native town whom she most dearly
loved. She had often wished to tell him – the merchant – that
she was very fond of him as a friend, as he had probably seen
from her behaviour, and that she trusted him like a brother. But
the silly jokes which had been made in their presence had made
a confidential conversation impossible; still, as he himself had
taken her by surprise, and opened his good and noble heart to
her, she could thank him in no better way than by confiding in
him just as frankly. Yes, she went on, she could only belong to
the man she had once chosen, and she could never turn her
heart to another – that was written in flaming golden letters in
her soul, and the dear man himself did not know how dear he
was to her, however well he might know her. But a sad
misfortune had befallen her. Her betrothed was a merchant,

but desperately poor, so they had planned to set up business with the bride's money. A start had been made, and everything was going on well, when, as ill-luck would have it, unexpected claims had been made involving her whole property, and perhaps it would be lost for ever, while the poor man had shortly to make his first payments to merchants from Milan and Venice, on which depended his credit, his prosperity and his honour, not to speak of their reunion and happy marriage. She had in all haste to set out for Milan, where she had wealthy relatives, to find ways and means, but she had come at a bad time, for nothing could be arranged: the fateful day was fast approaching and if she could not help her beloved, she must die of sorrow, for he was the dearest and best man in the world and would become a great merchant if he could be helped, and she could imagine no happiness on earth save that of being his wife. When she had finished her story, the poor handsome youth, who had long since turned pale, was as white as a sheet. Yet he uttered no sound of complaint, and spoke no more of his unhappy love, but merely asked sadly what were the liabilities of the happy unhappy betrothed. 'Ten thousand guilders,' she replied, still more sadly. The sad young merchant rose, bade the lady be of good courage as a way out would surely be found, and went away without daring to look at her, so confused and ashamed he felt at having set his heart upon a lady who loved another so faithfully and so passionately. For he took every word of her story for gospel. Then he went straight to his business friends, and by begging, and by forfeiting a certain sum, got them to cancel the orders and purchases which he himself just then wished to pay for with his ten thousand guilders and on which he was founding his whole career, and before six hours had passed, he reappeared before the lady and begged her for God's sake to accept this help from him. Her eyes sparkled with glad surprise and her heart beat furiously. She asked him where he had raised the capital, and he replied that he had borrowed it on the security of his good name and that he would be able to return it without inconvenience, as his own business was going very well. She saw clearly that he was lying and that he was sacrificing his whole fortune and hopes to her happiness, but she pretended to believe him. She gave way to her glee and cruelly gave him to think that it arose from her joy at being able to help her lover and marry the man of her choice, and she could find no words to express her gratitude. Yet suddenly she bethought herself and declared that she could only accept the generous deed on one condition, and that otherwise, all prayers were in vain. When asked what this condition was, she demanded a sacred promise that he would come to her on a certain day to be present at her wedding and to become the best friend and patron of her future husband and her own most loyal friend, protector and adviser. Blushing, he begged her to give up the idea, but it was in vain that he put forward all possible reasons for making her give it up; in vain he pointed out to her that his own affairs did not permit him to return to Switzerland, and that his business would suffer considerably from such an absence. She stuck to her demand, and when he refused to give in, she even pushed his gold back to him. In the end, he promised, but he had to give her his hand on it and swear it on his honour and salvation. Only then did she accept his sacrifice and have the treasure carried into her bedroom, where she locked it into her travelling-chest with her own hands and put the key in her bosom. Then she delayed no longer in Milan, but travelled as joyously back over the Gotthard as she had come sadly. On the Devil's Bridge, where she had wanted to throw herself down, she laughed like mad, and raising her pleasing voice in a cry of exultation, she cast into the Reuss a bunch of pomegranate flowers she wore in her bosom. In short, her joy knew no bounds, and it was the happiest journey that had ever been made. But once at home, she opened and aired her house from top to bottom as if she were expecting a prince, and at the head of her bed she laid the sack with the ten thousand guilders, and at night she lay and slept on the hard lump as if it had been the softest down pillow.

"As the day approached, she could hardly contain her impatience, for she knew he would not break the simplest promise, let alone an oath, though it should cost him his life.

But the day dawned and the beloved did not come, and many days and weeks passed without any news of him. Then she began to tremble in every limb, and fell a prey to the deepest dread and despondency. She sent letter after letter to Milan, but nobody knew where he was. Finally it came out by chance that the young man had had a suit made of a piece of blood-red damask he had had in the house ever since he set up business, and had already paid for, and had gone with the Swiss mercenaries, who were fighting the Milanese wars in the pay of King Francis. After the battle of Pavia, in which so many Swiss lost their lives, he was found lying on a heap of dead Spaniards, mortally wounded, with his fine red suit slashed and torn from top to bottom. But before he died, he dictated to a Seldwyler, who was lying beside him in less desperate case, the following message, made him learn it by heart and begged him to deliver it if he should escape with his life. 'Dearest lady, although I swore by my faith, by my honour and by my salvation to come to your wedding, I could not bring myself to see you again, and to see another possess what is for me the greatest happiness in the world. I first felt this when I had left you, and did not know before what a grievous and mysterious thing is such a love as I bear to you, else I had kept it from my heart. But since it is so, I had rather lose my honour in this world and my salvation in the next, and go to eternal damnation for a broken oath, than appear before you with a fire in my breast which is stronger and more unquenchable than hell fire, which it will scarcely let me feel. Do not pray for me, loveliest of women, for I cannot and never shall be happy without you, here or there, and now farewell and my greeting to you.' So in that battle, after which King Francis said, 'All is lost save honour,' the luckless lover had lost everything, hope, honour, life and eternal salvation, but not the love which consumed him. The Seldwyler escaped, and as soon as he had recovered and was out of danger, he wrote the dead man's words on his tablets so as not to forget them, journeyed home, presented himself before the unhappy lady, and read her the message, as stiff and soldierly as he was wont to be when reading the roll of his regiment, for he was a field lieutenant. But the lady tore her hair and rent her clothes, and began to scream and weep so loud that all the people came running. She dragged out the ten thousand guilders like a madwoman, scattered them on the floor, flung herself at full length upon them, and kissed the glittering gold. Completely beside herself, she tried to collect the rolling coins, and to embrace them as if the lost beloved were bodily in them. She lay day and night on the treasure, refused to eat or drink and continually kissed and caressed the cold metal until once, in the dead of night, she suddenly got up, carried the treasure into the garden and there, with bitter tears, threw it into a deep well and laid a curse upon it, that it should not belong to anyone else."

When Spiegel had got so far, Pineiss said, "And is all that money still lying in the well?"

"Where else could it lie?" asked Spiegel, "for only I can get it out, and so far I have not done so."

"Oh! yes, quite so!" said Pineiss. "I quite forgot that in your tale. You can tell a story, you vagabond, and really, I quite begin to hanker after a little woman who would be so taken with me. But she would have to be very beautiful! However, go on and tell me how the whole thing hangs together."

"Many years passed," continued Spiegel, "before the lady recovered sufficiently from her bitter anguish to become the quiet old maid that I knew. I may pride myself on being her one consolation and her most trusted friend in her lonely life until her peaceful end. But when she saw death approach, she recalled once more the distant time of her youth and beauty, and suffered again, with milder and more resigned thoughts, the sweet passion and bitter sorrow of that time, and she wept quietly seven days and nights for the love of the youth she had lost through her own suspicions, so that, just before her death, her poor old eyes were blinded. Then she repented of the curse she had laid upon the treasure, and entrusted its disposal to me in these words: 'I direct otherwise now, dear Spiegel, and give you full power to execute my will. Look about until you find a lovely but poor woman who can find no suitor on account of her poverty. Then if you can find a sensible, honest and handsome man with a good income, who will ask the woman to be his wife in spite of her poverty, and moved only by her beauty, make him swear by the most sacred oaths to be as loyal, self-sacrificing and unchangingly devoted to her as my unhappy lover to me. Then give the girl the ten thousand guilders as a dowry, so that she can surprise her bridegroom with them on her wedding morning.' Thus spoke the deceased, and as, owing to untoward events, I have neglected to carry out her directions, I must fear that the poor woman cannot rest quiet in her grave, and that would not have very pleasant consequences for me."

Pineiss eyed Spiegel dubiously and said, "Could you, my good fellow, show me the way to the treasure and let me see it with my own eyes?"

"At any time," replied Spiegel. "But you must know, Master Town Wizard, that you cannot simply fish up the treasure like that. You would certainly have your neck wrung, for there is something weird about that well. I have had certain signs of it which I cannot discuss further for reasons of my own."

"But who said anything about fishing it up?" said Pineiss, with some apprehension. "Take me there once and show me the treasure – or rather I will take you there at the end of a nice stout string, so that you don't run away."

"As you like," rejoined Spiegel. "But take another long string and a dark lantern with you which you can let down into the well, for it is very deep and dark."

Pineiss followed his directions, and led the cheery puss to the dead lady's garden. They climbed the wall together, and Spiegel showed the sorcerer the way to the well, which was hidden under wild-growing bushes. There Pineiss let down his lantern, looking greedily after it and keeping a firm hold on Spiegel. But there it was – in the depths, he saw gold glittering under the green water and cried, "It's perfectly true – I see it! Spiegel, you really are a fine fellow." Then he peered eagerly down again and said, "Are there really ten thousand there?"

"Well, I won't swear," said Spiegel, "I never was down

there, and I haven't counted. It may be that the lady lost a few pieces on the way, for she was very agitated."

"A dozen more or less," said Master Pineiss, "that doesn't matter." He sat down on the edge of the well. Spiegel did likewise and licked his paw. "So there's the treasure," said Pineiss, scratching himself behind the ear. "And here's the man. We only need the lovely woman."

"What?" said Spiegel.

"I only mean that we still need the woman who will get the ten thousand guilders as a dowry, to surprise me with on our wedding morning, and who has all the attractive qualities you spoke of."

"H'm!" said Spiegel. "That's not quite the point: to speak candidly, I have already unearthed the lovely woman, but the real hitch is the man who would marry her in these difficult circumstances, for nowadays, beauty must be gilded, like nuts at Christmas, and the emptier men's heads get, the harder they try to fill the void with a bit of dowry, so that they may pass their time more pleasantly. For then, they can strut about inspecting a horse or buying a length of velvet, run all over the town to order a fine cross-bow, and the smith is never out of the house. Then 'I must get in wine and clean my casks, have my trees pruned or my house roofed; I must send my wife to a watering-place – she isn't very strong and costs a good deal of money; I must cut my wood and call in outstanding debts; I have bought some greyhounds and given away my watchdog; I have bought a fine oak table and given my great walnut chest in part exchange; I have cut my beans and dismissed my gardener, sold my hay and sown my salad' – it's 'mine, mine, mine' from morning till night. There are even men who say – 'I have my washing next week; I must get a new maid and see about a butcher, for I shall have to get rid of the old one; I have got hold of a fine wafer-iron and sold my spice-box – it wasn't any good to me anyhow.' Now all this is the wife's business, and a fellow of that kind passes his time and steals a day from the Lord counting up all these little matters and never doing a hand's turn. At the very outside, if a fellow like that has to knuckle under a bit, he may go so far as to say – 'our cows and our pigs', but –"

Pineiss pulled Spiegel by the string until he miaowed again and bawled, "Enough, out with it! Where is she?" For the tale of all the splendid doings which a wife's property brings with it had made the withered old wizard's mouth water more than ever.

But Spiegel said in surprise, "Will you really undertake it, Master Pineiss?"

"Of course I will. Who else? So now, out with it! Where is she?"

"So that you can go and court her?"

"Of course!"

"Well, you must realize that you can only act through me! You will have to talk matters over with me if you want the money and the bride," said Spiegel coolly and indifferently, assiduously passing each paw over his ears in turn, having carefully damped it first.

Pineiss reflected carefully, groaned slightly and said, "I can see that you want to suppress our contract and save your skin."

"Do you think that so unfair and unnatural?"

"You'll cheat me in the end, like the rogue you are!"

"That's possible too!"

"I tell you you shan't cheat me!" cried Pineiss, peremptorily.

"Very good, I shan't cheat you."

"If you do –"

"Then I do."

"Don't torture me, Pussy," said Pineiss, almost in tears; and Spiegel now replied gravely: "You're a funny man, Master Pineiss. Look – you've got me on the end of a string and you're nearly strangling me with it. You've had the sword of death hanging over me for more than two hours – two hours I say ! – for six months, and now you say, 'Don't torture me, Pussy.' Now, to put the matter shortly, I should be glad enough to fulfil my loving duty to the dead by finding a good husband for the lady in question, and you seem to me in every way suitable. It's no laughing matter to get a woman settled these days, whatever it may seem, and I tell you once more, I am glad you are ready to undertake it. But it's no use killing me. Before I say another word or take another step, before I even open my mouth again, I must have my freedom and security for my life. So take off this string and lay the contract down here by the well, or cut off my head – one or the other."

"But why, you bedlamite, you scatter-pate," said Pineiss, "you hot-head, you don't really mean it! Come, we must discuss the thing properly, and in any case draw up a new contract."

Spiegel answered never a word and sat there motionless one, two, three minutes. Then the wizard began to get frightened: he pulled out his letter-case, clawed out the contract, read it through again, then laid it hesitatingly before Spiegel. Scarcely had it left his hand when Spiegel snapped it up and ate it, and although he had to gulp pretty hard to get it down, it seemed to him the most wholesome meal he had ever enjoyed, and he hoped it would agree with him for a long time to come and make him fat and merry. When he had finished this pleasant repast, he bowed politely to the wizard and said, "You shall certainly hear from me, Master Pineiss, and wife and money you shall have, but you must prepare to fall in love properly, so that you can swear to and fulfil the condition of unchanging devotion to the wife who is as good as yours. And so, for the present, I thank you kindly for board and service, and take my leave."

Therewith Spiegel went his way, chuckling inwardly over the stupidity of the wizard, who imagined he could take himself and everybody else in by setting out to marry the hoped-for bride, not from disinterested motives and pure love to her beauty, but in full knowledge of the little detail of the ten thousand guilders. Meanwhile, he had someone in mind whom he hoped to foist off on the foolish wizard in return for his roast birds, mice and sausages.

Opposite to Master Pineiss's house there stood another: the front of it was cleanly whitewashed and its windows always glittered with fresh scouring. The modest window-curtains were always snow-white and newly ironed, and equally white were the dress, cap and neckerchief of an old beguine who lived in the house, while the nun-like wimple which covered her bosom always looked as if folded in white writing-paper, so that you couldn't help wanting to write on it, which would have been perfectly easy as far as the bosom was concerned, for it was as flat and hard as a board. As sharp as the white edges and corners of the beguine's clothes were her nose and chin, her tongue and the evil look in her eye, though she spoke little with her tongue and looked little with her eye, for she hated waste and only spent at the right time and after much consideration. She went to church three times a day, and when she went down the street in her fresh white crackling dress, and with her sharp white nose, the children ran frightened away from her and even grown people slipped behind the door if there were time. But she had a great reputation for piety and was much respected by the clergy, though even the priests preferred to deal with her in writing, and when she went to confession, the parson rushed out of the confessional sweating as if he came out of an oven. Thus the pious beguine, who never understood a joke, lived on in profound peace and remained unwed. She would have nothing to do with other people and let them go their own way, provided they kept out of hers. Her neighbour Pineiss, however, she had singled out for a particular hate, for every time he appeared at his window she gave him an evil look and immediately drew the white curtains, and Pineiss dreaded her like fire, and only dared to crack a joke about her right at the back of the house when everything was locked up. But, white and fresh though the beguine's house looked from the street, from behind it was black and smoky, sinister and strange, for there it could hardly be seen at all save by the cats on the roof and the birds in the sky, because it was built into an angle of high blind walls, where never a human face was to be seen. Under the roof there hung old torn petticoats, baskets and bags of herbs, on it there grew regular little oaks and thornbushes, and a great sooty chimney rose eerily into the air. But from this chimney, a witch often rode out on her broom, young and beautiful and stark naked, as God made women and as the devil likes to see them. When she rode out of the chimney, she sniffed the night air with delicate nostrils and smiling red lips, and rode off by the gleam of her white body, while her long black hair streamed behind her like a dusky flag. In a hole in the chimney there sat an old owl, and the liberated Spiegel now paid her a visit with a fat mouse in his mouth which he had caught on the way.

"Good evening to you, Mistress Owl! On the watch, as usual!" he said; and the owl replied, "Needs must when the devil drives. Good evening to yourself. I haven't seen you this long while, Master Spiegel."

"And for a good reason. I'll tell you about it. Here's a mouse for you, just what the season offers, if you care for it. Has the mistress gone out riding?"

"Not yet. She will only ride out for an hour or two towards morning. Many thanks for the fine mouse. Always the gentleman, Master Spiegel! Here is a little sparrow which flew too near me today. May I offer it to you? And what has been happening to you?"

"Strange things," replied Spiegel. "They were after my life. I should like to tell you all about it."

While they ate their cosy supper, Spiegel told the attentive owl all that had happened to him, and how he had got out of the clutches of Master Pineiss.

"Well, I congratulate you heartily," said the owl. "Now you are a man again and can do what you like, after all your varied experiences."

"Yes, but that isn't the end of the matter," said Spiegel. "The man must have his wife and his money."

"Are you crazy, wanting to do the wretch a good turn when he wanted to flay you?"

"Well, he could have done it legally, according to the contract, and since I can pay him back in the same coin, why shouldn't I? Who said I wanted to do him a good turn? The story was a pure invention of mine. My late mistress, now with God, was a simple person who had never been in love or had admirers in her life, and the treasure is unlawful property which she inherited and threw into the well so that she should come to no harm by it."

"H'm! That's another story. But where will you find the woman?"

"Here in this chimney! That's why I came – to talk the matter over with you. Wouldn't you like to be free of the witch? Think how we can catch her and marry her to the old scoundrel."

"Spiegel, the mere sight of you stimulates me!"

"There, I knew I hadn't come to the wrong place. You just bring some new spice into it, and we can't go wrong."

"Since everything works together so well, I needn't think long. My plans are already laid."

"How shall we catch her?"

"With a new woodcock snare made of good strong hemp strands. It must have been twisted by a twenty-year-old hunter who has never looked at a woman, and the night dew must have fallen on it three times without a woodcock having been caught in it. The reason for this, however, must be a threefold good action. Such a net is strong enough to catch the witch."

"Now I wonder where you will get that," said Spiegel, "for I trust you not to talk nonsense."

"It's found already – the very thing. In a wood not far from here there lives a hunter's son who is twenty years old and has never looked at a woman, for he is blind. Therefore he is no use for anything save to twist cord, and a few days ago he made a new and very fine woodcock springe. But when the old hunter wanted to set it for the first time, a woman came along and tried to tempt him to sin, but she was so ugly that he fled appalled, leaving the net on the ground, so that the dew fell on it without a woodcock having been caught, and the cause of that was a good action. The next day, when he went to set it again, a horseman rode by with a heavy sack of gold behind him, out of which a gold coin fell every now and then. And the hunter again left the net lying and ran after the rider, collecting the coins until the horseman turned round, saw what was going on and turned his lance on him in anger. Then the hunter bowed in terror and said, 'Allow me, sir. You have dropped a great deal of money which I have picked up for you.' That was another good action, honest finding being one of the most difficult and best; but he was so far from his net that he left it lying and took a short cut home. The third day, however, which was yesterday, as he was on the way, he met a pretty woman who used to cajole the old man a good deal and to whom he had given many a little hare. So then he quite forgot the woodcock and said in the morning, 'I have spared their poor little lives. One must be merciful, even to animals.' And in view of these good deeds, he came to the conclusion that he was too good for this world and went into a monastery early this morning. So the net is still lying unused in the wood. I have only to fetch it."

"Fetch it quickly, then," said Spiegel. "It's the very thing we need."

"All right," said the owl. "Just keep watch for me in this hole and if the mistress calls up the chimney to ask whether the air is clear, you must answer, imitating my voice, 'No; there's no stink yet in the fencing school!' " Spiegel took his place in the chimney and the owl flew quietly away over the town and into the wood. She soon returned with the net and asked, "Has she called up yet?"

"Not yet," said Spiegel.

Then they stretched the net over the chimney, and sat down warily beside it: the air was dark and in the light morning breeze a few stars were twinkling. "You should see," said the owl, "how cleverly she can ride up the chimney without making her white shoulders black."

"I have never seen her so close," whispered Spiegel. "If only she doesn't catch us."

Then the witch called up the chimney from below, "Is the air clear?"

The owl cried, "Quite clear. There's a fine stink in the fencing school," and forthwith the witch came riding up the chimney and was caught in the net, which the owl and the cat pulled tight and tied.

"Hold firm," said Spiegel.

"Bind her fast," said the owl.

The witch struggled and writhed speechless like a fish in a net, but the cord held. Only her broom-handle stuck out through the meshes, and Spiegel tried to draw it out quite gently, but got such a crack on his nose that he nearly fainted and realized that it is unwise to come too near a lioness, even in a net. Finally the witch calmed down and said, "What do you want, you crazy beasts?"

"You are to release me from your service and give me my freedom," said the owl.

"A lot of trouble for nothing," said the witch. "You are free. Untie this cord."

"Not so fast," said Spiegel, who was still rubbing his nose. "You must promise to marry the Town Wizard, Master Pineiss, your neighbour, exactly in the way we tell you and never to leave him."

Then the witch began to struggle again and to spit like the devil, and the owl said, "She won't."

But Spiegel said, "Unless you are quiet and do just what we want, we shall hang the net with you in it in front of the house on the dragon's head on the eaves, so that tomorrow the people will see you and know who is the witch. Now say – would you rather roast under the supervision of Master Pineiss, or roast him by marrying him?"

Then the witch said with a sigh, "How did you think of doing it?" and Spiegel expounded the whole matter to her delicately, explaining what was to be done and what her part was. "Well, we can manage that, if there's no other way out," she said, and pledged herself with the strongest oaths that can bind a witch. Then the animals undid the net and let her out. She at once mounted her broom, the owl got up behind her and Spiegel at the back, and so they set off for the well, into which she rode to fetch up the treasure.

In the morning, Spiegel presented himself at Pineiss's and announced to him that he could visit the lady and pay his respects to her: she was already so poor that she was completely abandoned and forlorn, and was sitting in front of the town gate under a tree and weeping bitterly. Forthwith, Master Pineiss dressed himself in his shabby old yellow velvet doublet, which he only wore on ceremonial occasions, donned his second-best poodle cap and girt on his dagger; in his hand he bore an old green glove, a little balsam-bottle, which had once had balsam in it and still smelt slightly, and a paper carnation; then he set off for the town gate to court the lady. There he saw a woman sitting, more lovely than any he had ever seen before, but her dress was so poor and torn that, however modestly she might bear herself, her white body gleamed through here and there. Pineiss could hardly begin his courting for delight. Then the beauty dried her tears, gave him her hand, thanked him in a voice like heavenly bells for his generosity and swore to be true to him. But at that very moment he conceived such jealousy, such passionate envy of his wife, that he made up his mind never to let her be seen by mortal eyes. He got an old hermit to marry them and celebrated the marriage feast with her in his house with no other guests than Spiegel and the owl, whom Spiegel had asked permission to bring. The ten thousand guilders stood in a dish on the table, and from time to time Pineiss dipped his hand in them and stirred the gold about; then he looked at the lovely woman sitting there in a sea-blue velvet dress, her hair woven through a gold net and adorned with flowers, and with pearls round her lovely neck. He tried to kiss her the whole time, but she modestly held him off and swore that she would never do so in front of strangers and before the fall of night. This made him all the more love-sick and blissful, and Spiegel spiced the feast with charming speeches, which the lady followed up with such pleasant, witty and flattering remarks that the old wizard did not know where he was for joy.

But when darkness fell, the owl and the cat paid their respects and modestly withdrew. Pineiss accompanied them to the front door and thanked Spiegel again, calling him an excellent, polite fellow, and when he returned to the room, there sat the old beguine, his neighbour, leering at him with her evil eye. Pineiss dropped the light and leaned trembling against

237

the wall. His tongue lolled out and his face was as livid as hers. But she rose, and drove him before her to the nuptial chamber, where she tortured him with tortures more fiendish than ever mortal yet experienced.

So now he was irrevocably married to the old woman, and in the town, when the thing got about, they said, "Still waters run deep. Who would have thought that the Town Wizard and the old beguine would have made a match of it? Well, they are an honest couple, if not particularly attractive."

But from that time on, Master Pineiss led a wretched life. His wife had got hold of all his secrets and ruled him with a rod of iron. He never had the slightest rest or freedom and had to make magic from morning till night, and when Spiegel went by and saw him, he would call politely, "Busy as usual, Master Pineiss!"

So from that time on they have said in Seldwyla, "He has bought the fat off the cat," especially if anyone has married a shrewish and ugly wife.

from *The People of Seldwyla*

LADY
GRIMALKIN

"Her elegance and distinction gave one an idea of
aristocratic birth, and among her own kind she must have
been at least a duchess."
Théophile Gautier (1811–72)

Marigold

RICHARD GARNETT (1835–1906)

She moved through the garden in glory because
She had very long claws at the end of her paws.
Her neck was arched, her tail was high.
A green fire glared in her vivid eye;
And all the toms, though never so bold,
Quailed at the martial Marigold.

Seraphita

THÉOPHILE GAUTIER (1811–72)

Don Pierrot had a companion of the same race as himself, and
no less white. All the imaginable snowy comparisons it were
possible to pile up would not suffice to give an idea of that
immaculate fur, which would have made ermine look yellow.

I called her Seraphita, in memory of Balzac's Swedenborgian
romance. The heroine of that wonderful story, when she
climbed the snow peaks of the Falberg with Minna, never
shone with a more pure white radiance. Seraphita had a dreamy
and pensive character. She would lie motionless on a cushion
for hours, not asleep, but with eyes fixed in rapt attention on
scenes invisible to ordinary mortals.

Caresses were agreeable to her, but she responded to them
with great reserve, and only to those of people whom she
favoured with her esteem, which it was not easy to gain. She
liked luxury, and it was always in the newest armchair or on the
piece of furniture best calculated to show off her swan-like
beauty, that she was to be found. Her toilette took an immense
time. She would carefully smooth her entire coat every morning, and wash her face with her paw, and every hair on her

body shone like new silver when brushed by her pink tongue. If anyone touched her she would immediately efface all traces of the contact, for she could not endure being ruffled. Her elegance and distinction gave one an idea of aristocratic birth, and among her own kind she must have been at least a duchess. She had a passion for scents. She would plunge her nose into bouquets, and nibble a perfumed handkerchief with little paroxysms of delight. She would walk about on the dressing-table sniffing the stoppers of the scent-bottles, and she would have loved to use the violet powder if she had been allowed.

Such was Seraphita, and never was a cat more worthy of a poetic name.

from "The White and Black Dynasties"
in *La Ménagerie Intime* translated by Lady Chance

Lady Grimalkin's Concert and Supper

ANONYMOUS (1809)

Miss TABITHA GOSSIP, a mischievous Vandal,
Professor of Spite in the College of Scandal,
Among other passengers, happen'd to stop,
To look at the pictures in Harris's shop.
When she found there was scarcely a bird or a beast,
But had given a ball, or provided a feast;
Always ready to hear, or to tell, something new,
She determin'd her friends should know of it too;
So to Lady GRIMALKIN's milk-party she went,
To spit out her venom, and mew discontent:
And thus, while the ladies were drinking their tea,
The whisper went round through the whole coterie.
When TABITHA spoke of the Butterfly's Ball,
In horrible chorus they set up a squall.
GRIMALKIN, of Cats the experienc'd Nestor,
Stood up, and gave vent to the cares which oppress'd her,

"Shall others stick up their impertinent phizzes,
Whilst *we* are proscribed as a set of old quizzes?
Shall Grubs of the earth, and contemptible Sprats,
Presume to compare with the Duchess of Cats?"
When their tables they spread, and their fine clothes
    they tie on,
I cou'd scratch out their eyes – for a month I cou'd
    cry on,
These whiskers – this beard, are the emblems of
    knowledge,
For my rank, I refer to the Heraldry College,
Great heroes I reckon among my relations,
Who back to the flood stretch in long generations;
By my ancestors brave has been glorious fun done,
I allude to the Cat and the Lord Mayor of London.
They say we're allied to the Tiger's grim race,
That the family likeness appears in our face;
But let us set insults like these at defiance,
We've cause to be proud of so great an alliance.
Yes! GRIZZLE GRIMALKIN so handsome and tall,
Shall hold up her head with the best of them all;
To the Bookseller's window we'll put in our claim,
And find a snug niche in the Temple of Fame."
She finish'd – the Cats gave a mew of applause,
And the party broke up with much shaking of paws.
Now Lady GRIMALKIN made great preparation,
To accommodate all the Feline generation;
So busy was she in arranging her house,
'Twas a holiday then for poor Master Mouse;
The chairs were uncover'd, the tables set out,
The drawing-room swept for her Ladyship's route;
When the cook was well scolded, the lustres well
    lighted,
She sent out her cards, and her neighbours invited:
"Lady GRIZZLE GRIMALKIN her friends hopes to see
To a Concert and Supper, sans ceremonie."

Now arming for conquest, the pretty Miss Cats
Curl'd up their sweet whiskers, and put on their hats,
To Bond-street they sent for the *Poke* and the *Gypsy*
Which stuck all aside made the wearers look tipsy;
They brush'd their fur-tippets, and tied on their
    pinners,
As city dames do at the Mansion House dinners.
To display their fine shape they sported no pockets,
But plenty of necklaces, bracelets, and lockets;
The belle who wears pockets is voted a fool,
For John stands behind with the smart *ridicule*.
The single Miss TABBIES call out for a fan,
To screen their coy charms from the vile monster
    Man.
Due regard to the time of the year must be had,
So in Russian pelisses of fur they were clad;
But some Cats of taste thinking red most becoming,
In scarlet cloaks wrap themselves up like old women;
While those who a Patriot's ardour maintain
Put on velvet mantles in honour of Spain.
The elderly Ladies stay'd long at their glass,
Like Ninon of old, that sweet evergreen lass;
Cruel Time had the province of beauty invaded,
Some teeth had dropp'd out, and some roses had
    faded,
So an ivory row must be planted instead,
And Kitty give two or three touches of *red*.
Then, arm'd at all points with pins and with brooches,
The Ladies step into their chariots and coaches.
Meanwhile let us see what's become of the Beaux,
'Tis said each appear'd in a new suit of clothes,
They had wigs à la Titus, and Opera hats,
Such vanity swells in the bosoms of Cats!
As a finishing stroke of polite education,
To see more of the world they had left their own
    nation,
'Til their heads were in danger they travell'd in France,

And learn'd to eat frogs, and like Parisot dance;
When the troubles broke out, they had fled for their
    lives,
And came back to England to look sharp for wives.

Now! ye Tabbies advanc'd in your grand climacteric
Try a blush if ye can – if not, try an hysteric!
Ah! those killing eyes will convince each Adonis,
How hapless the case of a damsel alone is.
Genteelly unpunctual they reach'd the Saloon,
For Cats of the Ton must not get there too soon;
Let us stand in the ante-room counting each comer,
And so set them down like the Ships of old Homer.
SQUALLINI was there, a great amateur,
Who sang in the Concerts of fashion sans peur,
Mr CATGUT perform'd on the violoncello,
Like Orpheus, a very harmonious fellow,
A solo was sung by Signor SOPRANO,
And Miss CROTCHET play'd on the Forte Piano.
But why should we mention each musical name,
In the circles of science, of fashion and fame?
Suffice it to say, that each Mademoiselle SCRATCHI
Was equal – superior indeed, to STORACE.
Each Signor had talents, and well cou'd display 'em,
Hide your heads, Messrs INCLEDON, DIGNUM, and
    BRAHAM!
At each exquisite strain they all cried encore,
We can give CATALANI, GRASSINI no more;
And oft as a signal of Feline applause,
They mew'd approbation, kept time with their paws.
What they sang, what they play'd, 'tis not easy to say
    well,
A ballad of DIBDIN, or quartet of PLEYEL.
After many a rondo, and sweet pastorale,
'Twas time the Orchestra shou'd play their finale;
So clos'd with a chorus this grand Concertante;
What is HANDEL compared with such dilettanti?

Now wearied at length with melodious notes,
They adjourn'd to the supper to moisten their throats;
The fare might have answer'd an Alderman's wishes,
Nor could *Birch* have provided more elegant dishes.
Her Ladyship's chaplain, a reverend divine,
Who wond'rous to tell, was no lover of wine,
Before they sat down, being call'd to say grace,
Full half an inch longer extended his face;
Each damsel he pledg'd in a saucer of milk,
And ogl'd and smirk'd in his cassock of silk.
Men are fond of roast beef, but a barbicued mouse,
Is the great standing dish in every Cat's house.
'Twas an animal worthy the pencil of Snyders,
And near it was plac'd a side-dish of spiders.
In the midst was a china tureen of Gold-fish,
Beware, oh ye Cats, of so fatal a dish!
Tho' smiling the Lake of Inchantment appear,
Remember, poor SELIMA ventur'd too near,
Come, drink to her shade! o'er her fate drop a tear!
This libation pour'd out, at the bottom was put on,
A roast leg of rat, for a roast leg of mutton;
Bastill'd in a pie, came some sweet little wrens,
Teal, and widgeon, were sent by a friend from the
    fens.

Then came in the cheese, which most likely was
    toasted,
With chesnuts, by Æsop's receipt, so well roasted;
Odoriferous civet was brought in an urn,
And Valerian roots in a silver Epergne.
After Supper, went round the most popular toasts,
"May Monsieur Le Chat never land on our coasts!
By these beards, by these Patriot Mustachios we
    swear,
That if in a freak the invader should dare,
To disturb our firesides, we'll each turn volunteer,
And send him away with a flea in his ear.

French monkeys shall ne'er put a ring in our noses,
For we sharpen our claws *pro aris et focis.*"
Between every sentiment, every toast,
They sang catches and glees, that no time might be
    lost;
The ladies were shy, and reluctant of course,
Protesting they'd sung 'til they'd made themselves
    hoarse;
Mrs BLAND had a cold, Mrs DICKONS was husky,
And 'twas time to depart, for the evening grew dusky.
In chariots, and chairs, went the velvets and satins;
For ladies of rank must not hobble in pattens.
Some chose in barouches, to drive themselves home;
But all made a solemn engagement to come
On a mouse-hunting party, at some future day,
Ah! tremble ye mice, when they sound "Hark away!"

Venus and the Cat

AESOP (6th century BC)

In ancient times there lived a beautiful cat who fell in love with a young man. Naturally, the young man did not return the cat's affections, so she besought Venus, the goddess of love and beauty, for help. The goddess, taking compassion on her plight, changed her into a fair damsel.

No sooner had the young man set eyes on the maiden than he became enamoured of her beauty and in due time led her home as his bride. One evening a short time later, as the young couple were sitting in their chamber, the notion came to Venus to discover whether in changing the cat's form she had also changed her nature. So she set down a mouse before the beautiful damsel. The girl, reverting completely to her former character, started from her seat and pounced upon the mouse as if she would eat it on the spot, while her husband watched her in dismay.

The goddess, provoked by such clear evidence that the girl had revealed her true nature, turned her into a cat again.

MORAL:

What is bred in the bone will never be absent in the flesh.

from *Fables*

The Owl and the Pussy-Cat

EDWARD LEAR (1812–88)

The Owl and the Pussy-cat went to sea
   In a beautiful pea-green boat,
They took some honey, and plenty of money,
   Wrapped up in a five-pound note.
The Owl looked up to the stars above,
   And sang to a small guitar,
"O lovely Pussy! O Pussy, my love,
    What a beautiful Pussy you are,
      You are,
      You are!
   What a beautiful Pussy you are!"

Pussy said to the Owl, "You elegant fowl!
   How charmingly sweet you sing!
Oh let us be married! too long we have tarried:
   But what shall we do for a ring?"
They sailed away, for a year and a day,
   To the land where the Bong-tree grows
And there in a wood a Piggy-wig stood
   With a ring at the end of his nose,

     His nose,
     His nose,
   With a ring at the end of his nose.

"Dear Pig, are you willing to sell for one shilling
   Your ring?" Said the Piggy, "I will."
So they took it away, and were married next day
   By the Turkey who lives on the hill.
They dined on mince, and slices of quince,
   Which they ate with a runcible spoon;
And hand in hand, on the edge of the sand,
   They danced by the light of the moon,
      The moon,
      The moon,
They danced by the light of the moon.

from *Nonsense Songs* (1871)

Ginger

SYDNEY, LADY MORGAN (1776–1859)

Though my mother could never teach me to read, she taught
me hymns and poetry by rote, which incited me to write
rhymes on my own account. I had many favourites among cats,
dogs and birds, my mother's reprobation and the servants'
nuisance; but I turned them all to account and wove them into
stories, to which I tried to give as much personal interest as old
Mother Hubbard bestowed on her dog.

The head favourite of my menagerie was a magnificent and
very intelligent cat, "Ginger" by name, from the colour of her
coat, which though almost orange was very much admired. She
was the last of a race of cats sacred in the traditions of the Music
Hall. Pat Brennan, "The sad historian of the ruined towers",
held them in the greatest reverence mingled with superstitious
awe. Brennan was a good Catholic, but rather given to
exaggeration, which rendered his testimony to matters of fact
proverbially questionable; and it became a byword among
unbelieving neighbours when anyone told a wonderful story,
to ask, "Do you know Brennan? Well, then, enough said!"
After this, there was nothing left for the disconcerted narrator

but to walk away. One of his stories was – that the monastic cats had *stings* in their tails, which after their death were preserved by the monks for purposes of flagellation, or by the nuns – Brennan was not sure which!

Ginger was as much the object of my idolatry as if she had had a temple and I had been a worshipper in ancient Egypt; but, like other deities, she was reprobated by those who were not of my faith.

I made her up a nice little cell, under the beaufet, as sideboards were then called in Ireland – a sort of alcove cut out of the wall of our parlour where the best glass and the family "bit of plate" – a silver tankard – with the crest of the Hills upon it (a dove with an olive branch in its mouth), which commanded great respect in our family.

Ginger's sly attempts to hide herself from my mother, to whom she had that antipathy which animals so often betray to particular individuals, were a source of great amusement to my little sister and myself; but when she chose the retreat of the beaufet as the scene of her *accouchement*, our fear lest it should come to my mother's knowledge was as great as if we had been concealing a moral turpitude.

It was a good and pious custom of my mother's to hear our prayers every night; when Molly tapped at the parlour door at nine o'clock, we knelt at my mother's feet, our four little hands clasped in hers, and our eyes turned to her with looks of love, as they repeated that simple and beautiful invocation, the Lord's Prayer; to this was always added the supplication, "Lighten our darkness we beseech Thee"; after which we were accustomed to recite a prayer of our affectionate suggestion, calling a blessing on the heads of all we knew and loved, which ran thus, "God bless papa, mamma, my dear sister, and Molly, and Betty, and Joe, and James, and all our good friends." One night, however, before my mother could pronounce her solemn "amen", a soft muttered "purr" issued from the cupboard, my heart echoed the appeal, and I added, "God bless Ginger the cat!" Wasn't my mother shocked! She shook both my shoulders and said, "What do you mean by that, you stupid child?"

"May I not say, 'Bless Ginger?' " I asked humbly.

"Certainly *not*," said my mother emphatically.

"Why, mamma?"

"Because Ginger is not a Christian."

"*Why* is not Ginger a Christian?"

"Why? because Ginger is only an animal."

"Am I a Christian, mamma, or an animal?"

"I will not answer any more foolish questions tonight. Molly, take these children to bed, and do teach Sydney not to ask those silly questions."

So we were sent off in disgrace, but not before I had given Ginger a wink, whose bright eyes acknowledged the salute through the half-open door.

The result of this was that I tried my hand at a poem.

The jingle of rhyme was familiar to my ear through my mother's constant recitation of verses, from the sublime Universal Prayer of Pope to the nursery rhyme of Little Jack Horner, whilst my father's dramatic citations, which had descended even to the servants, had furnished me with the tags of plays from Shakespeare to O'Keefe; so that "I lisped in numbers" though the numbers never came.

Here is my first attempt:

> My dear pussy cat,
> Were I a mouse or rat,
>   Sure I never would run off from you,
> You're so funny and gay,
> With your tail when you play,
>   And no song is so sweet as your "mew";
> But pray keep in your press,
> And don't make a mess,
>   When you share with your kittens our posset;
> For mamma can't abide you,
> And I cannot hide you,
>   Except you keep close in your closet!

I tagged these doggrels together while lying awake half the night, and as soon as I could get a hearing in the morning I recited them to the kitchen, and no elocution ever pronounced in *that* kitchen (although it was dedicated to Melpomene, whose image shone on an orchestra that had been converted into a dresser, the whole apartment being the remains of the fantastic Ridotto, though now being converted to culinary purposes in the same floor as our dining-room), no elocution had ever excited more applause. James undertook to write it down, and Molly corrected the press. It was served up at breakfast to my father, and it not only procured me his rapturous praise but my mother's forgiveness.

My father took me to Moira House; made me recite my poem, to which he had taught me to add appropriate emphasis and action, to which my own tendency to grimace added considerable comicality. The Countess of Moira laughed heartily at the "infant Muse" as my father called me, and ordered the housekeeper to send up a large plate of bread and jam, the earliest recompense of my literary labours.

from Lady Morgan's Memoirs (1862)

She Sights a Bird

EMILY DICKINSON (1830–86)

She sights a Bird – she chuckles –
She flattens – then she crawls –
She runs without the look of feet –
Her eyes increase to Balls –

Her Jaws stir – twitching – hungry –
Her Teeth can hardly stand –
She leaps, but Robin leaped the first –
Ah, Pussy, of the Sand,

The Hopes so juicy ripening –
You almost bathed your Tongue –
When Bliss disclosed a hundred Toes –
And fled with every one –

Ye Marvellous Legend of Tom Connor's Cat

SAMUEL LOVER (1797–1868)

"There was a man in these parts, sir, you must know, called
Tom Connor, and he had a cat that was equal to any dozen of
rat traps, and he was proud of the baste, and with rayson; for she
was worth her weight in goold to him in saving his sacks of
meal from the thievery of the rats and mice; for Tom was an
extensive dealer in corn, and influenced the rise and fall of that
article in the market, to the extent of a full dozen of sacks at a
time, which he either kept or sold, as the spirit of free trade or
monopoly came over him. Indeed, at one time, Tom had
serious thoughts of applying to the government for a military
force to protect his granary when there was a threatened famine
in the country."

"Pooh pooh, sir!" said the matter-of-fact little man. "As if a
dozen sacks could be of the smallest consequence in a whole
country – pooh pooh!"

"Well, sir," said Murtough, "I can't help you if you don't
believe; but it's truth what I'm telling you, and pray don't
interrupt me, though you may not believe; by the time the
story's done you'll have heard more wonderful things than *that*
– and besides, remember you're a stranger in these parts, and
have no notion of the extraordinary things, physical, meta-
physical, and magical, which constitute the idiosyncrasy of rural
destiny."

The little man did not know the meaning of Murtough's last
sentence – nor Murtough either; but, having stopped the little
man's throat with big words, he proceeded: "This cat, sir, you
must know, was a great pet, and was so up to everything, that

Tom swore she was a most like a Christian, only she couldn't speak, and had so sensible a' look in her eyes, that he was sartin sure the cat knew every word that was said to her. Well, she used to set by him at breakfast every morning, and the eloquent cock of her tail, as she used to rub against his leg, said: 'Give me some milk, Tom Connor,' as plain as print, and the plentitude of her purr afterwards spoke a gratitude beyond language. Well, one morning, Tom was going to the neighbouring town to market, and he had promised the wife to bring home shoes to the childre' out o' the price of the corn; and sure enough before he sat down to breakfast, there was Tom taking the measure of the children's feet, by cutting notches on a bit of stick; and the wife gave him so many cautions about getting a 'nate fit' for 'Billy's purty feet' that Tom, in his anxiety to nick the closest possible measure, cut off the child's toe. This disturbed the harmony of the party, and Tom was obliged to breakfast alone, while the mother was endeavouring to cure Billy; in short, trying to make a *heal* of his *toe*. Well, sir, all the time Tom was taking measure for the shoes, the cat was observing him with that luminous peculiarity of eye for which her tribe is remarkable and when Tom sat down to breakfast the cat rubbed up against him more vigorously than usual; but Tom being bewildered, between his expected gain in corn and the positive loss of his child's toe, kept never minding her, until the cat, with a sort of caterwauling growl, gave Tom a dab of her claws, that went clean through his leathers, and a little further. 'Wow!' says Tom, with a jump, clapping his hand on the part and rubbing it. 'By this and that, you drew the blood out of me,' says Tom. 'You wicked divil – tish! – go along!' says he, making a kick at her. With that the cat gave a reproachful look at him, and her eyes glared just like a pair of mail-coach lamps in a fog. With that, sir, the cat, with a mysterious 'meow', fixed a most penetrating glance on Tom, and distinctly uttered his name.

"Tom felt every hair on his head as stiff as a pump handle; and scarcely crediting his ears, he returned a searching look at the cat, who very quietly proceeded in a sort of nasal twang:

"Tom Connor,' says she.

" 'The Lord be good to me!' says Tom. 'If it isn't spakin' she is!'

" 'Tom Connor,' says she again.

" 'Yes, ma'am,' says Tom.

" 'Come here,' says she. 'Whisper – I want to talk to you, Tom,' says she, 'the laste taste in private,' says she – rising on her hams and beckoning him with her paw out o' the door, with a wink and a toss o' the head aiqual to a milliner.

"Well, as you may suppose, Tom didn't know whether he was on his head or his heels, but he followed the cat, and off she went and squatted herself under the hedge of a little paddock at the back of Tom's house; and as he came round the corner, she held up her paw again, and laid it on her mouth, as much as to say 'Be cautious, Tom.' Well, divil a word Tom could say at all, with the fright, so up he goes to the cat, and says she:

'Tom,' says she, 'I have a great respect for you, and there's something I must tell you, because you're losing character with your neighbours,' says she, 'by your goin's on,' says she, 'and it's out o' the respect that I have for you, that I must tell you,' says she.

" 'Thank you, ma'am,' says Tom.

" 'You're going off to the town,' says she, 'to buy shoes for the childre',' says she, 'and never thought o' getting me a pair.'

" 'You!' says Tom.

" 'Yis, me, Tom Connor,' says she, 'and the neighbours wondhers that a respectable man like you allows your cat to go about the counthry barefutted,' says she.

" 'Is it a cat to ware shoes?' says Tom.

" 'Why not?' says she. 'Doesn't horses ware shoes? And I have a prettier foot than a horse, I hope,' says she with a toss of her head.

" 'Faix, she spakes like a woman; so proud of her feet,' says Tom to himself, astonished, as you may suppose, but pretending never to think it remarkable all the time; and so he went on discoursin'; and says he: 'It's thrue for you, ma'am,' says he, 'that horses ware shoes – but that stands to rayson, ma'am, you see – seeing the hardship their feet has to go through on the hard roads.'

" 'And how do you know what hardship my feet has to go through?' says the cat, mighty sharp.

" 'But, ma'am,' says Tom, 'I don't well see how you could fasten a shoe on you,' says he.

" 'Lave that to me,' says the cat.

" 'Did anyone ever stick walnut shells on you, pussy?' says Tom, with a grin.

" 'Don't be disrespectful, Tom Connor,' says the cat, with a frown.

" 'I ax your pard'n, ma'am,' said he, 'but as for the horses you wor spakin' about warin' shoes, you know their shoes is fastened on with nails, and how would your shoes be fastened on?'

" 'Ah, you stupid thief!' says she, 'haven't I illigant nails o' my own?' and with that she gave him a dab of her claw, that made him roar.

" 'Ow! murdher!' says he.

" 'Now no more of your palaver, Misther Connor,' says the cat. 'Just be off and get me the shoes.'

" 'Tare and ouns!' says Tom. 'What'll become o' me if I'm to get shoes for my cats?' says he. 'For you increase your family four times a year, and you have six or seven every time,' says he; 'and then you must all have two pair apiece – wirra! wirra! – I'll be ruined in shoeleather,' says Tom.

" 'No more o' your stuff,' says the cat; 'don't be standin' here undher the hedge talkin' or we'll lose our characters – for I've remarked your wife is jealous, Tom.'

" ''Pon my sowl, that's thrue,' says Tom, with a smirk.

" 'More fool she,' says the cat, 'for 'pon my conscience, Tom, you're as ugly as if you wor bespoke.'

"Off ran the cat with these words, leaving Tom in amazement. He said nothing to the family, for fear of fright'ning them, and off he went to the town, as he pretended – for he saw the cat watching him through a hole in the hedge; but when he came to a turn at the end of the road, the dickings a mind he minded the market, good or bad, but went off to Squire Botherum's, the magisthrit, to swear examinations agen the cat."

"Pooh pooh – nonsense!" broke in the little man, who had listened thus far to Murtough with an expression of mingled wonder and contempt, while the rest of the party willingly gave up the reins to nonsense, and enjoyed Murtough's legend and their companion's more absurd common sense.

"Don't interrupt him, Coggins," said Mr Wiggins.

"How can you listen to such nonsense!" returned Coggins. "Swear examinations against a cat, indeed! Pooh pooh!"

"My dear sir," said Murtough, "remember this is a fairy story, and that the country all round here is full of enchantment. As I was telling you, Tom went off to swear examinations."

"Ay, ay!" shouted all but Coggins. "Go on with the story."

"And when Tom was asked to relate the events of the morning, which brought him before Squire Botherum, his brain was so bewildered between his corn, and his cat, and his child's toe, that he made a very confused account of it.

" 'Begin your story from the beginning,' said the magistrate to Tom.

" 'Well, your honour,' says Tom, 'I was goin' to market this mornin', to sell the child's corn – I beg your pard'n – my own toes, I mane, sir.'

" 'Sell your toes!' said the Squire.

" 'No, sir, takin' the cat to market, I mane –'

" 'Take a cat to market!' said the Squire. 'You're drunk, man.'

" 'No, your honour, only confused a little; for when the toes began to spake to me – the cat, I mane – I was bothered clane –'

" 'The cat speak to you!' said the Squire. 'Phew! Worse than before. You're drunk, Tom.'

" 'No, your honour; it's on the strength of the cat I come to spake to you –'

" 'I think it's on the strength of a pint of whiskey, Tom.'

" 'By the vartue o' my oath, your honour, it's nothin' but the cat.' And so Tom then told him all about the affair, and the Squire was regularly astonished. Just then the bishop of the diocese and the priest of the parish happened to call in, and heard the story; and the bishop and the priest had a tough argument for two hours on the subject: the former swearing she must be a witch; but the priest denying *that*, and maintaining she was *only* enchanted, and that part of the argument was afterward referred to the primate, and subsequently to the conclave at Rome; but the Pope declined interfering about cats, saying he had quite enough to do minding his own bulls.

" 'In the meantime, what are we to do with the cat?' says Botherum.

" 'Burn her,' says the bishop. 'She's a witch.'

" '*Only* enchanted,' said the priest, 'and the ecclesiastical court maintains that —'

" 'Bother the ecclesiastical court!' said the magistrate; 'I can only proceed on the statutes'; and with that he pulled down all the lawbooks in his library, and hunted the laws from Queen Elizabeth down, and he found that they made laws against everything in Ireland, *except a cat*. The divil a thing escaped them but a cat, which did *not* come within the meaning of any Act of Parliament — *the cats only had escaped.*

" 'There's the alien act, to be sure,' said the magistrate, 'and perhaps she's a French spy in disguise.'

" 'She spakes like a French spy, sure enough,' says Tom, 'and she was missin', I remember, all last Spy Wednesday.'

" 'That's suspicious,' says the Squire, 'but conviction might be difficult; and I have a fresh idea,' says Botherum.

" 'Faith, it won't keep fresh long, this hot weather,' says Tom, 'so your honour had betther make use of it at wanst.'

" 'Right,' says Botherum. 'We'll make her a subject to the game laws; we'll hunt her,' says he.

" 'Ow! Elegant!' says Tom; 'we'll have a brave run out of her.'

" 'Meet me at the crossroads,' says the Squire, 'in the morning, and I'll have the hounds ready.'

" 'Well, off Tom went home; and he was racking his brain what excuse he could make to the cat for not bringing the shoes; and at last he hit one off, just as he saw her cantering up to him, half a mile before he got home.

" 'Where's the shoes, Tom?' says she.

" 'I have not got them today, ma'am,' says he.

" 'Is that the way you keep your promise, Tom?' says she. 'I'll tell you what it is, Tom – I'll tare the eyes out o' the childre' if you don't get me those shoes.'

" 'Whist, whist!' says Tom, frightened out his life for his children's eyes. 'Don't be in a passion, pussy. The shoemaker said he had not a shoe in his shop, nor a last that would make one to fit you; and he says I must bring you into the town for him to take your measure.'

" 'And when am I to go?' says the cat, looking savage.

" 'Tomorrow,' says Tom.

" 'It's well you said that, Tom,' said the cat, 'or the divil an eye I'd leave in your family this night,' and off she hopped.

"Tom thrimbled at the wicked look she gave.

" 'Remember!' says she, over the hedge, with a bitter caterwaul.

" 'Never fear,' says Tom.

"Well, sure enough, the next mornin' there was the cat at cockcrow, licking herself as nate as a new pin, to go into the town, and out came Tom with a bag undher his arm and the cat after him.

" 'Now git into this, and I'll carry you into the town,' says Tom, opening the bag.

" 'Sure, I can walk with you,' says the cat.

" 'Oh, that wouldn't do,' says Tom. 'The people in the town is curious and slandherous people, and sure it would rise ugly remarks if I was seen with a cat afther me – a dog is a man's companion by nature, but cats does not stand to rayson.'

"Well, the cat, seeing there was no use in argument, got into the bag, and off Tom set to the crossroads with the bag over his shoulder, and he came up, quite innocent-like, to the corner, where the Squire, and his huntsman, and the hounds, and a pack of people were waitin'. Out came the Squire on a sudden, just as if it was all by accident.

" 'God save you, Tom,' says he.

" 'God save you kindly, sir,' says Tom.

" 'What's that bag you have at your back?' says the Squire.

" 'Oh, nothin' at all, sir,' says Tom, makin' a face all the time, as much as to say, I have her safe.

" 'Oh, there's something in that bag, I think,' says the Squire. 'You must let me see it.'

" 'If you bethray me, Tom Connor,' says the cat, in a low voice, 'by this and that I'll never spake to you again!'

" ''Pon my honour, sir,' says Tom, with a wink and a twitch of his thumb towards the bag, 'I haven't anything in it.'

" 'I have been missing my praties of late,' says the Squire; 'and I'd just like to examine that bag,' says he.

" 'Is it doubting my character you'd be, sir?' says Tom, pretending to be in a passion.

" 'Tom, your sowl!' says the voice in the sack. 'If you let the cat out of the bag, I'll murther you.'

" 'An honest man would make no objection to be sarched,' said the Squire, 'and I insist on it,' says he, laying hold o' the bag, and Tom purtending to fight all the time; but, my jewel! before two minutes, they shook the cat out o' the bag, sure enough, and off she went, with her tail as big as a sweeping brush, and the Squire, with a thundering view halloo after her, clapped the dogs at her heels, and away they went for the bare life. Never was there seen such running as that day – the cat made for a shaking bog, the loneliest place in the whole country, and there the riders were all thrown out, barrin' the huntsman, who had a web-footed horse on purpose for soft places, and the priest, whose horse could go anywhere by reason of the priest's blessing; and, sure enough, the huntsman and his riverence stuck to the hunt like wax; and just as the cat got on the border of the bog, they saw her give a twist as the foremost dog closed with her, for he gave her a nip in the flank. Still she went on, however, and headed them well, towards an old mud cabin in the middle of the bog, and there they saw her jump in at the window, and up came the dogs the next minit, and gathered round the house, with the most horrid howling ever was heard. The huntsman alighted, and went into the house to turn the cat out again, when what should he see but an old hag lying in bed in the corner!

" 'Did you see a cat come in here?' says he.

" 'Oh, no-o-o-o!' squealed the old hag in a trembling voice. 'There's no cat here,' says she.

" 'Yelp, yelp, yelp!' went the dogs outside.

" 'Oh, keep the dogs out of this,' says the old hag – 'oh-o-o-o!' and the huntsman saw her eyes glare under the blanket, just like a cat's.

" 'Hillo!' says the huntsman, pulling down the blanket – and what should he see but the old hag's flank all in a gore of blood.

" 'Ow, ow! you old divil – is it you? You old cat!' says he, opening the door.

"In rushed the dogs. Up jumped the old hag and, changing into a cat before their eyes, out she darted through the window again, and made another run for it; but she couldn't escape, and the dogs gobbled her while you could say 'Jack Robinson'. But the most remarkable part of this extraordinary story, gentlemen, is that the pack was ruined from that day out; for after having eaten the enchanted cat, *the divil a thing they would ever hunt afterwards but mice.*"

To a Persian Cat

F.C.W. HILEY (19th century)

So dear, so dainty, so demure,
So charming in whate'er position;
By race the purest of the pure,
A little cat of high condition:
Her coat lies not in trim-kept rows
Of carpet-like and vulgar sleekness:
But like a ruffled sea it grows

Of wavy grey (my special weakness):
She vexes not the night with squalls
That make one seize a boot and throw it:
She joins in no unseemly brawls
(At least she never lets me know it!);
She never bursts in at the door
In manner boisterous and loud:
But silently along the floor
She passes, like a little cloud.
Then, opening wide her amber eyes,
Puts an inquiring nose up –
Sudden upon my knee she flies,
Then purrs and tucks her little toes up.
Yet did she once, as I recall,
By Love's o'ermastering power impelled,
Scale Mr C.'s back-garden wall –
A feat before unparalleled –
Alas! the faithless Tom had flown:
Yet on she glides, with body pliant:
And then, when bidden to come down,
Stood half alarmed and half defiant;
One sudden spring sufficed to land her –
When to return she condescended –
Upon my landlord's glass verandah –
I don't suppose they've had it mended!
This set of verses, Puss, to you
I dedicate – and ask in quittance
One thing alone – 'tis nothing new –
A set of quarter-Persian kittens.

A Snobbish Cat

ANDREW LANG (1844–1912)

Some cats are snobs, though not so many cats as dogs share this
human infirmity. A lady had two cats; one was a drawing-room

cat, the other a common kitchen cat. Both, simultaneously, had families. The drawing-room cat carried her kittens downstairs to be nursed by the common kitchen cat, but every day she visited the nursery several times. She was not quite heartless, but she had never read Jean-Jacques Rousseau, on the nursing of children, and she was very aristocratic . . .

To My Lord Buckhurst, Very Young, Playing with a Cat

MATTHEW PRIOR (1664–1721)

The am'rous Youth, whose tender Breast
Was by his darling Cat possest,
Obtain'd of VENUS his Desire,
Howe'er irregular his Fire:
Nature the Pow'r of Love obey'd:
The Cat became a blushing Maid;
And, on the happy Change, the Boy
Imploy'd his Wonder and his Joy.

Take care, O beauteous Child, take care,
Lest Thou prefer so rash a Pray'r:
Nor vainly hope, the Queen of Love
Will e'er thy Fav'rite's Charms improve.
O quickly from her Shrine retreat;
Or tremble for thy Darling's Fate.

The Queen of Love, who soon will see
Her own ADONIS live in Thee,
Will lightly her first Loss deplore;
Will easily forgive the Boar:
Her Eyes with Tears no more will flow;
With jealous Rage her Breast will glow:
And on her tabby Rival's Face
She deep will mark her new Disgrace.

A Strange Affection

GILBERT WHITE (1720–93)

We have remarked in a former letter how much incongruous animals, in a lonely state, may be attached to each other from a spirit of sociality; in this it may not be amiss to recount a different motive which has been known to create as strange a fondness.

My friend had a little helpless leveret brought to him, which the servants fed with milk in a spoon, and about the same time his cat kittened and the young were dispatched and buried. The hare was soon lost, and supposed to be gone the way of most foundlings, to be killed by some dog or cat. However, in about a fortnight, as the master was sitting in his garden in the dusk of the evening, he observed his cat, with tail erect, trotting towards him, and calling with little short inward notes of complacency, such as they use towards their kittens, and something gambolling after, which proved to be the leveret that the cat had supported with her milk and continued to support with great affection. Thus was a graminivorous animal nurtured by a carnivorous and predaceous one!

Why so cruel and sanguinary a beast as a cat, of the ferocious genus of *Feles*, the *murium leo*, as Linnaeus calls it, should be affected with any tenderness towards an animal which is its natural prey, is not so easy to determine.

This strange affection probably was occasioned by that *desiderium*, those tender maternal feelings, which the loss of her kittens had awakened in her breast; and by the complacency and ease she derived to herself from the procuring her teats to be drawn, which were too much distended with milk, till, from habit, she became as much delighted with this foundling as if it had been her real offspring.

This incident is no bad solution of that strange circumstance which grave historians as well as the poets assert, of exposed children being sometimes nurtured by female wild beasts that probably had lost their young. For it is not one whit more marvellous that Romulus and Remus, in their infant state, should be nursed by a she-wolf, than that a poor little sucking leveret should be fostered and cherished by a bloody grimalkin.

from *The Natural History and Antiquities of Selborne* (1789)

My Wife, the Cat

JEROME K. JEROME (1859–1927)

I had a cat once that used to follow me about everywhere, until it even got quite embarrassing, and I had to beg her, as a personal favour, *not* to accompany me any further down the High Street. She used to sit up for me when I was late home, and meet me in the passage. It made me feel quite like a married man, except that she never asked where I had been, and then didn't believe me when I told her.

Another cat I had used to get drunk regularly every day. She would hang about for hours outside the cellar door for the purpose of sneaking in on the first opportunity, and lapping up the drippings from the beer cask. I do not mention this habit of hers in praise of the species, but merely to show how almost human some of them are. If the transmigration of souls is a fact, this animal was certainly qualifying most rapidly for a Christian, for her vanity was only second to her love of drink. Whenever she caught a particularly big rat, she would bring it up into the room where we were all sitting, lay the corpse down in the midst of us, and wait to be praised. Lord! how the girls used to scream.

from "On Cats and Dogs" in *Idle Thoughts
of an Idle Fellow* (1886)

Eponine

THÉOPHILE GAUTIER (1811–72)

The cat named after the interesting Eponine was more delicate and slender than her brothers. Her nose was rather long, and her eyes slightly oblique, and green as those of Pallas Athene, to whom Homer always applied the epithet of γλαυκῶπις. Her nose was of velvety black, with the grain of a fine Périgord truffle; her whiskers were in a perpetual state of agitation, all of which gave her a peculiarly expressive countenance. Her superb black coat was always in motion, and was watered and shot with shadowy markings. Never was there a more sensitive, nervous, electric animal. If one stroked her two or three times in the dark, blue sparks would fly crackling out of her fur.

Eponine attached herself particularly to me, like the Eponine of the novel to Marius, but I, being less taken up with Cosette than that handsome young man, could accept the affection of this gentle and devoted cat, who still shares the pleasures of my suburban retreat, and is the inseparable companion of my hours of work.

She comes running up when she hears the front-door bell, receives the visitors, conducts them to the drawing-room, talks to them – yes, talks to them – with little chirruping sounds, that do not in the least resemble the language cats use in talking to their own kind, but which simulate the articulate speech of man. What does she say? She says in the clearest way, "Will you be good enough to wait till monsieur comes down? Please look at the pictures, or chat with me in the meantime, if that will amuse you." Then when I come in she discreetly retires to an armchair or a corner of the piano, like a well-bred animal who knows what is correct in good society. Pretty little Eponine gave so many proofs of intelligence, good disposition and sociability, that by common consent she was raised to the dignity of a *person*, for it was quite evident that she was possessed of higher reasoning power than mere instinct. This dignity conferred on her the privilege of eating at table like a person instead of out of a saucer in a corner of the room like an animal.

So Eponine had a chair next to me at breakfast and dinner, but on account of her small size she was allowed to rest her two front paws on the edge of the table. Her place was laid, without spoon or fork, but she had her glass. She went right through dinner dish by dish, from soup to dessert, waiting for her turn to be helped, and behaving with such propriety and nice manners as one would like to see in many children. She made her appearance at the first sound of the bell, and on going into the dining-room one found her already in her place, sitting up in her chair with her paws resting on the edge of the table-cloth, and seeming to offer you her little face to kiss, like a well-brought-up little girl who is affectionately polite towards her parents and elders.

As one finds flaws in diamonds, spots on the sun, and shadows on perfection itself, so Eponine, it must be confessed, had a passion for fish. She shared this in common with all other cats. Contrary to the Latin proverb, "*Catus amat pisces, sed non vult tingere plantas*", she would willingly have dipped her paw into the water if by so doing she could have pulled out a trout or a young carp. She became nearly frantic over fish, and, like a child who is filled with the expectation of dessert, she sometimes rebelled at her soup when she knew (from previous investigations in the kitchen) that fish was coming. When this happened she was not helped, and I would say to her coldly: "Mademoiselle, a person who is not hungry for soup cannot be hungry for fish," and the dish would be pitilessly carried away from under her nose. Convinced that matters were serious, greedy Eponine would swallow her soup in all haste, down to the last drop, polishing off the last crumb of bread or bit of macaroni, and would then turn round and look at me with pride, like someone who has conscientiously done his duty. She was then given her portion, which she consumed with great satisfaction, and after tasting of every dish in turn, she would finish up by drinking a third of a glass of water.

When I am expecting friends to dinner Eponine knows there

is going to be a party before she sees the guests. She looks at her place, and if she sees a knife and fork by her plate she decamps at once and seats herself on a music-stool, which is her refuge on these occasions.

Let those who deny reasoning powers to animals explain if they can this little fact, apparently so simple, but which contains a whole series of inductions. From the presence near her plate of those implements which man alone can use, this observant and reflective cat concludes that she will have to give up her place for that day to a guest, and promptly proceeds to do so. She never makes a mistake; but when she knows the visitor well she climbs on his knee and tries to coax a tit-bit out of him by her pretty caressing ways.

from "The White and Black Dynasties"
in *La Ménagerie Intime* translated by Lady Chance

Mother Cats

HERODOTUS (*c.* 485–425 BC)

There are many household animals; and there would be many more, were it not for what happens to the cats. When the females have kittened they will not consort with the males; and these seek them but cannot get their will of them; so their device is to steal and carry off and kill the kittens (but they do not eat what they have killed). The mothers, deprived of their young and desiring to have more will then consort with the males; for they are creatures that love offspring.

Minouche

EMILE ZOLA (1840–1902)

The priest and the doctor had found Chanteau rolling a paper ball across the table – a ball formed of a prospectus discovered inside a newspaper. Minouche, who was lying near, looked on with her green eyes. She appeared to disdain such an elementary plaything, for she had her paws stowed away beneath her, never deigning to strike out at it with her claws, though it had rolled close to her nose [...]

"Resign yourself, my friend," said Abbé Horteur, who in his turn now tried to carry out his office of consoler. "We each have our own cross to bear, and we are all in the hands of God –"

But he did not fail to notice that these words, so far from consoling Chanteau, only appeared to bore and even disquiet him, so he cut his exhortation short and substituted for it something more efficacious.

"Would you like to have a game at draughts? It will do you good."

He went in person to take the draught-board from the cupboard. Chanteau was delighted, and shook hands with the doctor, who then took his departure. The two others were soon deep in their game, quite forgetful of all else in the world, when all at once Minouche, who had probably got tired of seeing the paper ball under her nose, sprang forward, sent it spinning away, and bounded in wild antics after it all round the room.

"What a capricious creature!" cried Chanteau, put out in his play. "She wouldn't have a game with me on any account a little while ago, and now she prevents one from thinking by playing all by herself."

"Never mind her," said the priest mildly: "cats have their own way of amusing themselves."

from *The Joy of Life* (1901)

Cat and Canary

JANE WELSH CARLYLE (1801–66)

I am sorry for your cat's Influenza (it is a clear case of Influenza!) but it would have been worse if she had given way to passion, as her mother has just done, and done no end of mischief in attempting a great crime! For several days there had been *that* in her eyes when raised to my canary, which filled my heart with alarm. I sent express for a carpenter, and had the cage attached to the drawing-room ceiling, with an elaborate apparatus of chain and pulley and weight. "Most expensive!" (as my Scotch servant exclaimed with clasped hands over a Picture of the *Virgin and Child* in the National Gallery!) and there had it swung for two days; to Mr C.'s intense disgust, who regards thy pet as '*the most inanely chimerical of all*' – the cat meanwhile spending all its spare time in gazing up at the bird with eyes aflame! But it was safe *now* – I thought! and went out for a walk. On my return Charlotte met me with "Oh! whatever *do* you think the cat has gone and done?" – "Eaten my canary?" – "No, *far worse*! – pulled down the cage and the weight, and broke the chain and upset the little table and broken everything on it!" – "And not eaten the canary?" – "Oh, I suppose the dreadful crash she made frightened *herself*; for I met *her* running downstairs as I ran up – tho' the cage was on the floor, and the door open and the canary in *such* a way!" You never saw such a scene of devastation. The carpet was covered with fragments of a pretty terra cotta basket given me by Lady Airlie – and fragments of the glass which covered it, and with the earth and ferns that had been growing in it, and with birdseed, and bits of brass chain, and I can't tell what all! That is what one gets by breeding up a cat! – She had rushed right out by the back door and didn't show her face for twenty-four hours after! And now I don't know where the poor bird will be safe.

from a letter to Thomas Woolner in
New Letters and Memorials of Jane Welsh Carlyle

Bona Fidelia and Her Daughters

ROBERT SOUTHEY (1774–1843)

Bona Fidelia was a tortoiseshell cat. She was filiated upon Lord Nelson, others of the same litter having borne the unequivocal stamp of his likeness. It was in her good qualities that she resembled him, for in truth her name rightly bespoke her nature. She approached as nearly as possible in disposition, to the ideal of a perfect cat: he who supposes that animals have not their difference of disposition as well as men, knows very little of animal nature. Having survived her daughter Madame Catalani, she died of extreme old age, universally esteemed and regretted by all who had the pleasure of her acquaintance.

Bona Fidelia left a daughter and a granddaughter; the former I called Madame Bianchi – the latter Pulcheria. It was impossible ever to familiarize Madame Bianchi, though she had been bred in all respects like her gentle mother, in the same place, and with the same persons. The nonsense of that arch-philosophist Helvetius would be sufficiently confuted by this single example, if such rank folly, contradicted as it is by the experience of every family, needed confutation. She was a beautiful and singular creature, white, with a fine tabby tail, and two or three spots of tabby, always delicately clean; and her wild eyes were bright and green as the Duchess de Cadaval's emerald necklace. Pulcheria did not correspond as she grew up to the promise of her kittenhood and her name; but she was as fond as her mother was shy and intractable. Their fate was extraordinary as well as mournful. When good old Mrs Wilson died, who used to feed and indulge them, they immediately forsook the house, nor could they be allured to enter it again, though they continued to wander and moan round it, and came for food. After some weeks Madame Bianchi disappeared, and Pulcheria soon afterwards died of a disease endemic at that time among cats.

from "Memoir of the Cats of Greta Hall" (18 June 1828)

Madame Théophile

THÉOPHILE GAUTIER (1811–72)

"Madame Théophile", a reddish cat with a white breast, a pink nose and blue eyes, so called because she lived with us in an intimacy which was quite conjugal, sleeping at the foot of our bed, dreaming on the arm of our chair while we wrote, going down to the garden in order to follow us in our walks, assisting at our meals, and sometimes even intercepting a tit-bit from our plate to our mouth.

One day a friend of ours who was going away for a few days brought us his parrot to look after during his absence. The bird, feeling himself to be among strangers, had climbed to the top of his perch by the help of his beak, and was rolling his eyes, which were like brass-headed nails, and blinking the white skin which served him for eyelids in a decidedly frightened way.

"Madame Théophile" had never seen a parrot, and this new creature evidently caused her much surprise.

Motionless as an embalmed Egyptian cat in its wrappings she watched the bird with an air of profound meditation, putting together all the notions of natural history which she had been able to gather on the roof, in the yard, or the garden. The shadow of her thoughts passed across her opalescent eyes, and we could read in them this summary of her investigations: "This is decidedly a green chicken."

The parrot followed the cat's movements with feverish anxiety. His instinct told him that this was an enemy meditating some evil deed.

As to the cat's eyes, which were fixed on the bird with fascinating intensity, they said in language which the parrot understood perfectly, for there was nothing ambiguous about it, "Although it is green, this chicken must be good to eat."

We followed this scene with interest, ready to intervene if necessity arose. Madame Théophile had insensibly drawn nearer. Her pink nose quivered, she half closed her eyes, and her contractile claws went in and out. Little shivers ran down her spine. Suddenly her back was bent like a bow, and in one vigorous, elastic bound she alighted on the perch. The parrot, perceiving the danger, promptly exclaimed in a bass voice, as solemn and deep as that of Monsieur Joseph Prud-homme, "As tu *déjeuné, Jacquot?*" This speech caused the cat to spring back in unspeakable terror. All her ornithological ideas were upset.

The parrot continued: "*Et de quoi? De roti du roi.*"

The cat's face clearly expressed: "It is not a bird; it is a gentleman; he is speaking!"

She cast a look full of interrogation at us, and not being satisfied with our reply she went and hid herself under the bed, from where it was impossible to get her out for the rest of the day.

from *La Ménagerie Intime* translated by Lady Chance

My Cat and I

MICHEL DE MONTAIGNE (1533–92)

When my cat and I entertain each other with mutual antics, as playing with a garter, who knows but that I make more sport for her than she makes for me? Shall I conclude her to be simple that has her time to begin or to refuse to play, as freely as I have mine? Nay, who knows but that it is a defect of my not understanding her language (for doubtless cats can talk and reason with one another) that we agree no better; and who knows but that she pities me for being no wiser than to play with her; and laughs, and censures my folly in making sport for her, when we two play together.

The Kitten Mystery

DANIEL DEFOE (1660–1731)

In this season, I was much surprised with the increase of my family. I had been concerned for the loss of one of my cats, who ran away from me, or, as I thought, had been dead, and I heard no more tale or tidings of her, till, to my astonishment, she came home about the end of August with three kittens. This was the

more strange to me, because, though I had killed a wild cat, as I
called it, with my gun, yet I thought it was a quite different kind
from our European cats; yet the young cats were the same kind of
house-breed like the old one; and both my cats being females, I
thought it very strange. But from these three cats I afterwards
came to be so pestered with cats, that I was forced to kill them like
vermin, or wild beasts, and to drive them from my house as much
as possible [...] but at length, when the two old ones I brought
with me were gone, and after some time continually driving
them from me, and letting them have no provision with me, they
all ran wild into the woods, except two or three favourites, which
I kept tame, and whose young, when they had any, I always
drowned; and these were part of my family.

from *Robinson Crusoe* (1719)

The Eagle, the Wild Sow, and the Cat

JEAN DE LA FONTAINE (1621–95)

A certain hollow tree
Was tenanted by three.
An eagle held a lofty bough,
The hollow root a wild wood sow,
A female cat between the two.
All busy with maternal labours,
They lived awhile obliging neighbours.
At last the cat's deceitful tongue
Broke up the peace of old and young.
Up climbing to the eagle's nest,
She said, with whisker'd lips compress'd,
"Our death, or, what as much we mothers fear,
That of our helpless offspring dear,
Is surely drawing near.
Beneath our feet, see you not how
Destruction's plotted by the sow?
Her constant digging, soon or late,

Our proud old castle will uproot.
And then – Oh, sad and shocking fate! –
She'll eat our young ones, as the fruit!
Were there but hope of saving one,
'Twould soothe somewhat my bitter moan."
Thus leaving apprehensions hideous,
Down went the puss perfidious
To where the sow, no longer digging,
Was in the very act of pigging.
"Good friend and neighbour," whisper'd she,
"I warn you on your guard to be.
Your pigs should you but leave a minute,
This eagle here will seize them in it.
Speak not of this, I beg, at all,
Lest on my head her wrath should fall."
Another breast with fear inspired,
With fiendish joy the cat retired.
The eagle ventured no egress
To feed her young, the sow still less.
Fools they, to think that any curse
Than ghastly famine could be worse!
Both staid at home, resolved and obstinate,
To save their young ones from impending fate –
The royal bird for fear of mine,
For fear of royal claws the swine.
All died, at length, with hunger,
The older and the younger;
There staid, of eagle race or boar,
Not one this side of death's dread door;
A sad misfortune, which
The wicked cats made rich.
Oh, what is there of hellish plot
The treacherous tongue dares not!
Of all the ills Pandora's box outpour'd,
Deceit, I think, is most to be abhorr'd.

from *The Fables* (1842) translated by Elizur Wright

A Dying Mother

ANDREW LANG (1844–1912)

If we take the case of cats, they say little, but they think a great
deal; they conduct trains of reasoning. I have read an anecdote
told by Mrs Frederick Harrison. An old lady cat felt that she was
dying, before her kittens were weaned. She could hardly walk,
but she disappeared one morning, carrying a kitten, and came
back without it. Next day, quite exhausted, she did this with
her two other kittens, and then died. She had carried each
kitten to a separate cat, each of which was nourishing a family,
and accepted the new fosterling. Can anything be wiser or
more touching? This poor old cat had memory, reflection,
reason. Though wordless, she was as much a thinking creature
as any man who makes his last will and testament.

The Retired Cat

WILLIAM COWPER (1731–1800)

A poet's cat, sedate and grave,
As poet well could wish to have,
Was much addicted to inquire
For nooks, to which she might retire,
And where, secure as mouse in chink,
She might repose, or sit and think.
I know not where she caught the trick –
Nature perhaps herself had cast her
In such a mould *philosophique*,
Or else she learn'd it of her master.
Sometimes ascending, debonair,
An apple-tree or lofty pear,
Lodg'd with convenience in the fork,
She watched the gard'ner at his work;
Sometimes her ease and solace sought

In an old empty wat'ring pot,
There wanting nothing, save a fan,
To seem some nymph in her sedan,
Apparell'd in exactest sort,
And ready to be borne to court.

But love of change it seems has place
Not only in our wiser race;
Cats also feel as well as we
That passion's force, and so did she.
Her climbing, she began to find,
Expos'd her too much to the wind,
And the old utensil of tin
Was cold and comfortless within:
She therefore wish'd instead of those,
Some place of more serene repose,
Where neither cold might come, nor air
Too rudely wanton with her hair,
And sought it in the likeliest mode
Within her master's snug abode.

A draw'r – it chanc'd, at bottom lin'd
With linen of the softest kind,
With such as merchants introduce
From India, for the ladies' use –
A draw'r impending o'er the rest,
Half open in the topmost chest,
Of depth enough, and none to spare,
Invited her to slumber there.
Puss with delight beyond expression,
Survey'd the scene, and took possession.
Recumbent at her ease ere long,
And lull'd by her own hum-drum song,
She left the cares of life behind,
And slept as she would sleep her last,
When in came, housewifely inclin'd,
The chambermaid, and shut it fast,

By no malignity impell'd,
But all unconscious whom it held.

Awaken'd by the shock (cried puss)
Was ever cat attended thus!
The open draw'r was left, I see,
Merely to prove a nest for me,
For soon as I was well compos'd,
Then came the maid, and it was closed:
How smooth these 'kerchiefs, and how sweet,
Oh what a delicate retreat!
I will resign myself to rest
Till Sol, declining in the west,
Shall call to supper; when, no doubt,
Susan will come and let me out.

The evening came, the sun descended,
And puss remain'd still unattended.
The night roll'd tardily away,
(With her indeed 'twas never day)
The sprightly morn her course renew'd,
The evening grey again ensued,
And puss came into mind no more
Than if entomb'd the day before.
With hunger pinch'd, and pinch'd for room,
She now presag'd approaching doom,
Not slept a single wink, or purr'd,

Conscious of jeopardy incurr'd.

That night, by chance, the poet watching,
Heard an inexplicable scratching,
His noble heart went pit-a-pat,
And to himself he said – what's that?
He drew the curtain at his side,
And forth he peep'd, but nothing spied.
Yet, by his ear directed, guess'd

Something imprison'd in the chest,
And doubtful what, with prudent care,
Resolv'd it should continue there.
At length a voice, which well he knew,
A long and melancholy mew,
Saluting his poetic ears,
Consol'd him, and dispell'd his fears;
He left his bed, he trod the floor,
He 'gan in haste the draw'rs explore,
The lowest first, and without stop,
The rest in order to the top.
For 'tis a truth well known to most,
That whatsoever thing is lost,
We seek it, ere it come to light,
In ev'ry cranny but the right.
Forth skipp'd the cat; not now replete
As erst with airy self-conceit,
Nor in her own fond apprehension,
A theme for all the world's attention,
But modest, sober, cur'd of all
Her notions hyberbolical,
And wishing for a place of rest
Anything rather than a chest:
Then stept the poet into bed,
With this reflexion in his head:

MORAL

Beware of too sublime a sense
Of your own worth and consequence!
The man who dreams himself so great,
And his importance of such weight,
That all around, in all that's done,
Must move and act for him alone,
Will learn, in school of tribulation,
The folly of his expectation.

A Conversation with a Cat

HILAIRE BELLOC (1870–1953)

The other day I went into the bar of a railway station and, taking a glass of beer, I sat down at a little table by myself to meditate upon the necessary but tragic isolation of the human soul. I began my meditation by consoling myself with the truth that something in common runs through all nature, but I went on to consider that this cut no ice, and that the heart needed something more. I might by long research have discovered some third term a little less hackneyed than these two, when fate, or some fostering star, sent me a tawny, silky, long-haired cat.

If it be true that nations have the cats they deserve, then the English people deserve well in cats, for there are none so prosperous or so friendly in the world. But even for an English cat this cat was exceptionally friendly and fine – especially friendly. It leapt at one graceful bound into my lap, nestled there, put out an engaging right front paw to touch my arm with a pretty timidity by way of introduction, rolled up at me an eye of bright but innocent affection, and then smiled a secret smile of approval.

No man could be so timid after such an approach as not to make some manner of response. So did I. I even took the liberty of stroking Amathea (for by that name did I receive this vision), and though I began this gesture in a respectful fashion, after the best models of polite deportment with strangers, I was soon lending it some warmth, for I was touched to find that I had a friend; yes, even here, at the ends of the tubes in S.W.99. I proceeded (as is right) from caress to speech, and said, "Amathea, most beautiful of cats, why have you deigned to single me out for so much favour? Did you recognize in me a friend to all that breathes, or were you yourself suffering from loneliness (though I take it you are near your own dear home), or is there pity in the hearts of animals as there is in the hearts of some humans? What, then, was your motive? Or am I, indeed, foolish to ask, and not rather to take whatever good comes to me in whatever way from the gods?"

To these questions Amathea answered with a loud purring noise, expressing with closed eyes of ecstasy her delight in the encounter.

"I am more than flattered, Amathea," said I, by way of answer; "I am consoled. I did not know that there was in the world anything breathing and moving, let alone so tawny-perfect, who would give companionship for its own sake and seek out, through deep feeling, some one companion out of all living kind. If you do not address me in words I know the reason and I commend it; for in words lie the seeds of all dissension, and love at its most profound is silent. At least, I read that in a book, Amathea; yes, only the other day. But I confess that the book told me nothing of those gestures which are better than words, or of that caress which I continue to bestow upon you with all the gratitude of my poor heart."

To this Amathea made a slight gesture of acknowledgment – not disdainful – wagging her head a little, and then settling it down in deep content.

"Oh, beautiful-haired Amathea, many have praised you before you found me to praise you, and many will praise you, some in your own tongue, when I am no longer held in the bonds of your presence. But none will praise you more sincerely. For there is not a man living who knows better than I that the four charms of a cat lie in its closed eyes, its long and lovely hair, its silence, and even its affected love."

But at the word "affected" Amathea raised her head, looked up at me tenderly, once more put forth her paw to touch my arm, and then settled down again to a purring beatitude.

"You are secure," said I sadly; "mortality is not before you. There is in your complacency no foreknowledge of death nor even of separation. And for that reason, Cat, I welcome you the more. For if there has been given to your kind this repose in common living, why, then, we men also may find it by following your example and not considering too much what may be to come and not remembering too much what has been and will never return. Also, I thank you, for this, Amathea, my sweet Euplokamos" (for I was becoming a little familiar through an acquaintance of a full five minutes and from the absence of all recalcitrance), "that you have reminded me of my youth, and in a sort of shadowy way, a momentary way, have restored it to me. For there is an age, a blessed youthful age (O my Cat) even with the miserable race of men, when all things are consonant with the life of the body, when sleep is regular and long and deep, when enmities are either unknown or a subject for rejoicing and when the whole of being is lapped in hope as you are now lapped on my lap, Amathea. Yes, we also, we of the doomed race, know peace. But whereas you possess it from blind kittenhood to that last dark day so mercifully short with you, we grasp it only for a very little while. But I would not sadden you by the mortal plaint. That would be treason indeed, and a vile return for your goodness. What! When you have chosen me out of seven London millions upon whom to confer the tender solace of the heart, when you have proclaimed yourself so suddenly to be my dear, shall I introduce you to the sufferings of those of whom you know nothing save that they feed you, house you and pass you by? At least you do not take us for gods, as do the dogs, and the more am I humbly beholden to you for this little service of recognition – and something more."

Amathea slowly raised herself upon her four feet, arched her back, yawned, looked up at me with a smile sweeter than ever and then went round and round, preparing for herself a new couch upon my coat, whereon she settled and began once more to purr in settled ecstasy.

Already had I made sure that a rooted and anchored affection had come to me from out the emptiness and nothingness of the world and was to feed my soul henceforward; already had I changed the mood of long years and felt a conversion towards the life of things, an appreciation, a cousinship with the created light – and all that through one new link of loving kindness – when whatever it is that dashes the cup of bliss from the lips of mortal man (Tupper) up and dashed it good and hard. It was the Ancient Enemy who put the fatal sentence into my heart, for we are the playthings of the greater powers, and surely some of them are evil.

"You will never leave me, Amathea," I said; "I will respect your sleep and we will sit here together through all uncounted time, I holding you in my arms and you dreaming of the fields of paradise. Nor shall anything part us, Amathea; you are my cat and I am your human. Now and onwards into the fullness of peace."

Then it was that Amathea lifted herself once more, and with delicate, discreet, unweighted movement of perfect limbs leapt lightly to the floor as lovely as a wave. She walked slowly away from me without so much as looking back over her shoulder; she had another purpose in her mind; and as she so gracefully and so majestically neared the door which she was seeking, a short, unpleasant man standing at the bar said "Puss, Puss, Puss!" and stooped to scratch her gently behind the ear. With what a wealth of singular affection, pure and profound, did she not gaze up at him, and then rub herself against his leg in token and external expression of a sacramental friendship that should never die.

At the Zoo

MARK TWAIN (1835–1910)

In the great Zoological Gardens [of Marseille] we found specimens of all the animals the world produces, I think . . . The boon companion of the colossal elephant was a common cat! This cat had a fashion of climbing up the elephant's hind legs, and roosting on his back. She would sit up there, with her paws curved under her breast, and sleep in the sun half the afternoon. It used to annoy the elephant at first and he would reach up and take her down, but she would go aft and climb up again. She persisted until she finally conquered the elephant's prejudices, and now they are inseparable friends. The cat plays about her comrade's forefeet or his trunk often, until dogs approach, and then she goes aloft out of danger. The elephant has annihilated several dogs lately, that pressed his companion too closely.

The Cat that Waltzed

MRS HUMPHRY WARD (1851–1920)

Chattie jumped up on the window-sill, with her usual stealthy *aplomb*, and rubbed herself against the girl's face.

"Oh, Chattie!" cried Rose, throwing her arms around the cat, "if Catherine'll *only* marry Mr Elsmere, my dear, and be happy ever afterwards, and set me free to live my own life a bit, I'll be *so* good, you won't know me, Chattie. And you shall have a new collar, my beauty, and cream till you die of it!"

And springing up she dragged in the cat, and snatching a scarlet anemone from a bunch on the table, stood opposite Chattie, who stood slowly waving her magnificent tail from side to side, and glaring as though it were not at all to her taste to be hustled and bustled in this way.

"Now, Chattie, listen! Will she?"

A leaf of the flower dropped on Chattie's nose.

"Won't she? Will she? Won't she? Will – Tiresome flower, why did Nature give it such a beggarly few petals? If I'd had a daisy it would have all come right. Come, Chattie, waltz; and let's forget this wicked world!"

And, snatching up her violin, the girl broke into a Strauss waltz, dancing to it the while, her cotton skirts flying, her pretty feet twinkling, till her eyes glowed, and her cheeks blazed with a double intoxication – the intoxication of movement, and the intoxication of sound – the cat meanwhile following her with little mincing perplexed steps as though not knowing what to make of her.

"Rose, you madcap!" cried Agnes, opening the door.

"Not at all, my dear," said Rose calmly, stopping to take

breath. "Excellent practice and uncommonly difficult. Try if you can do it, and see!"

from *Robert Elsmere* (1888)

Love Letters of Clerical Cats

ERASMUS DARWIN (1731–1802)
AND ANNA SEWARD (1747–1809)

[*From the Persian Snow, at Dr Darwin's, to Miss Po Felina, at the Palace, Lichfield, who had been broken of her propensity to kill birds, and lived several years without molesting a dove, a tame lark, and a redbreast, all of which used to fly about the room where the cat was daily admitted. The dove frequently sat on pussy's back, and the little birds would peck fearlessly from the plate in which she was eating.*]

Lichfield Vicarage
7 September 1780

Dear Miss Pussey,
As I sat, the other day, basking myself in the Dean's Walk, I saw you, in your stately palace, washing your beautiful round face, and elegantly brindled ears, with your velvet paws, and whisking about, with graceful sinuosity, your meandering tail. That treacherous hedgehog, Cupid, concealed himself behind your tabby beauties, and darting one of his too well aimed quills, pierced, O cruel imp! my fluttering heart.

Ever since that fatal hour have I watched, day and night, in my balcony, hoping that the stillness of the starlight evenings might induce you to take the air on the leads of the palace. Many serenades have I sung under your windows; and, when you failed to appear, with the sound of my voice made the vicarage re-echo through all its winding lanes and dirty alleys. All heard me but my cruel Fair-one, she, wrapped in fur, sat purring with contented insensibility, or slept with untroubled dreams.

Though I cannot boast those delicate varieties of melody with which you sometimes ravish the ear of night, and stay the listening stars; though you sleep hourly on the lap of the favourite of the muses, and are patted by those fingers which hold the pen of science; and every day, with her permission, dip your white whiskers in delicious cream; yet am I not destitute of all advantages of birth, education, and beauty. Derived from Persian kings, my snowy fur yet retains the whiteness and splendour of their ermine.

This morning, as I sat upon the Doctor's tea-table, and saw my reflected features in the slop-basin, my long white whiskers, ivory teeth, and topaz eyes, I felt an agreeable presentiment of my suit; and certainly the slop-basin did not flatter me, which shews the azure flowers upon its borders less beauteous than they are.

You know not, dear Miss Pussey Po, the value of the address you neglect. New milk have I, in flowing abundance, and mice pent up in twenty garrets, for your food and amusement.

Permit me, this afternoon, to lay at your divine feet the head of an enormous Norway rat, which has even now stained my paws with its gore. If you will do me the honour to sing the following song, which I have taken the liberty to write, as expressing the sentiments I wish you to entertain, I will bring a band of catgut and catcall, to accompany you in chorus.

(Air: *Spirituosi*)
Cats I scorn, who sleek and fat,
Shiver at a Norway rat;

Rough and hardy, bold and free,
Be the cat that's made for me!
He, whose nervous paws can take
My lady's lapdog by the neck;
With furious hiss attack the hen,
And snatch a chicken from the pen.
If the treacherous swain should prove
Rebellious to my tender love,
My scorn the vengeful paw shall dart,
Shall tear his fur, and pierce his heart.

Chorus
Qu-ow wow, quall, wawl, moon.

Deign, most adorable charmer, to purr your assent to this my request, and believe me to be with the profoundest respect, your true admirer,

Snow

From Miss Po Felina to Mr Snow.

Palace, Lichfield
8 September 1780

I am but too sensible of the charms of Mr Snow; but while I admire the spotless whiteness of his ermine, and the tyger-strength of his commanding form, I sigh in secret, that he, who sucked the milk of benevolence and philosophy, should yet retain the extreme of that fierceness, too justly imputed to the grimalkin race. Our hereditary violence is perhaps commendable when we exert it against the foes of our protectors, but deserves much blame when it annoys their friends.

The happiness of a refined education was mine; yet, dear Mr Snow, my advantages in that respect were not equal to what yours might have been; but, while you give unbounded indulgence to your carnivorous desires, I have so far subdued mine, that the lark pours his mattin song, the canarybird warbles wild and loud, and the robin pipes his farewell song to the setting sun, unmolested in my presence; nay, the plump and tempting dove has reposed securely upon my soft back, and bent her glossy neck in graceful curves as she walked around me.

But let me hasten to tell thee how my sensibilities in thy favour were, last month, unfortunately repressed. Once, in the noon of one of its most beautiful nights. I was invited abroad by the serenity of the amorous hour, secretly stimulated by the hope of meeting my admired Persian. With silent steps I paced around the dimly gleaming leads of the palace. I had acquired a taste for scenic beauty and poetic imagery, by listening to ingenious observations upon their nature from the lips of thy own lord, as I lay purring at the feet of my mistress.

I admired the lovely scene, and breathed my sighs for thee to the listening moon. She threw the long shadows of the majestic cathedral upon the silvered lawn. I beheld the pearly meadows of Stow Valley, and the lake in its bosom, which, reflecting the lunar rays, seemed a sheet of diamonds. The trees of the Dean's Walk, which the hand of Dulness had been restrained from torturing into trim and detestable regularity, met each other in a thousand various and beautiful forms. Their liberated boughs danced on the midnight gale, and the edges of their leaves were whitened by the moonbeams. I descended to the lawn, that I might throw the beauties of the valley into perspective through the graceful arches, formed by their meeting branches. Suddenly my ear was startled, not by the voice of my lover, but by the loud and dissonant noise of the war-song, which six black grimalkins were raising in honour of the numerous victories obtained by the Persian, Snow; compared with which, they acknowledged those of English cats had little brilliance, eclipsed, like the unimportant victories of the Howes, by the puissant Clinton and Arbuthnot, and the still more puissant Cornwallis. It sung that thou didst owe thy matchless might to thy lineal descent from the invincible Alexander, as he derived his more than mortal valour from his mother Olympia's illicit commerce with Jupiter. They sang that, amid the renowned siege of Persepolis, while Roxana and Statira were contending for the honour of his attentions, the conqueror of the world deigned to bestow them upon a large white female cat, thy grandmother, warlike Mr Snow, in the ten thousandth and ninety-ninth ascent.

Thus far their triumphant din was music to my ear; and even when it sung that lakes of milk ran curdling into whey, within the ebon conclave of their pancheons, with terror at thine approach; that mice squealed from all the neighbouring garrets; and that whole armies of Norway rats, crying out amain, 'The devil take the hindmost,' ran violently into the minster-pool, at the first gleam of thy white mail through the shrubs of Mr Howard's garden.

But O! when they sang, or rather yelled, of larks warbling on sun-beams, fascinated suddenly by the glare of thine eyes, and falling into thy remorseless talons; of robins, warbling soft and solitary upon the leafless branch, till the pale cheek of winter dimpled into joy; of hundreds of those bright-breasted songsters, torn from their barren sprays by thy pitiless fangs! – Alas! my heart died within me at the idea of so preposterous a union!

Marry you, Mr Snow, I am afraid I cannot; since, though the laws of our community might not oppose our connection, yet those of principle, of delicacy, of duty to my mistress, do very powerfully oppose it.

As to presiding at your concert, if you extremely wish it, I may perhaps grant your request; but then you must allow me to sing a song of my own composition, applicable to our present situation, and set to music by my sister Sophy at Mr Brown's the organist's, thus:

(Air: *Affettuoso*)
He, whom Pussey Po detains
A captive in her silken chains,
Must curb the furious thirst of prey,
Nor rend the warbler from his spray!
Nor let his wild, ungenerous rage
An unprotected foe engage.

Oh, should cat of Darwin prove
Foe to pity, foe to love!
Cat, that listens day by day,
To mercy's mild and honied lay,
Too surely would the dire disgrace
More deeply brand our future race,
The stigma fix, where'er they range,
That cats can ne'er their nature change.

Should I consent with thee to wed,
These sanguine crimes upon thy head,
And ere the wish'd reform I see,
Adieu to lapping Seward's tea!
Adieu to purring gentle praise
Charm'd as she quotes thy master's lays! —
Could I, alas! our kittens bring
Where sweet her plumy favourites sing,
Would not the watchful nymph espy
Their father's fierceness in their eye,

And drive us far and wide away,
In cold and lonely barn to stray?
Where the dark owl, with hideous scream,
Shall mock our yells for forfeit cream,
As on starv'd mice we swearing dine,
And grumble that our lives are nine.

Chorus (Largo)
Waal, woee, trone, moan, mall, oll, moule.

The still too much admired Mr Snow will have the goodness to pardon the freedom of these expostulations, and excuse their imperfections. The morning, O Snow! had been devoted to this my correspondence with thee, but I was interrupted in that employment by the visit of two females of our species, who fed my ill-starved passion by praising thy wit and endowments, exemplified by thy elegant letter to which the delicacy of my sentiments obliges me to send so inauspicious a reply.

I am, dear Mr Snow
Your ever obliged
Po Felina

Do Cats Eat Bats?

LEWIS CARROLL (1832–98)

Down, down, down. There was nothing else to do, so Alice soon began talking again. "Dinah'll miss me very much to-night. I should think!" (Dinah was the cat.) "I hope they'll remember her saucer of milk at tea-time. Dinah, my dear, I wish you were down here with me! There are no mice in the air, I'm afraid, but you might catch a bat, and that's very like a mouse, you know. But do cats eat bats, I wonder?" And here Alice began to get rather sleepy, and went on saying to herself, in a dreamy sort of way, "Do cats eat bats? Do cats eat bats?" and sometimes, "Do bats eat cats?" for, you see, as she couldn't answer either question, it didn't much matter which way she put it. She felt that she was dozing off, and had just begun to dream that she was walking hand in hand with Dinah, and was saying to her very earnestly, "Now, Dinah, tell me the truth: did you ever eat a bat?" when suddenly, thump! thump! down she came upon a heap of sticks and dry leaves, and the fall was over.

from *Alice's Adventures in Wonderland* (1865)

A Terrible Mistake

ELIZABETH GASKELL (1810–65)

Of course, your ladyship knows that such lace must never be starched or ironed. Some people wash it in sugar and water, and some in coffee, to make it the right yellow colour, but I myself have a very good receipt for washing it in milk, which stiffens it enough and gives it a very good creamy colour. Well, ma'am, I had tacked it together (and the beauty of this fine lace is that, when it is wet, it goes into a very little space), and put it to soak in milk, when, unfortunately, I left the room; on my return I found pussy on the table, looking very like a thief, but gulping very uncomfortably, as if she was half-choked with something she wanted to swallow and could not. And would you believe it? At first I pitied her, and said "Poor pussy! Poor pussy!" till, all at once, I looked and saw the cup of milk empty – cleaned out! "You naughty cat!" said I; and I believe I was provoked enough to give her a slap, which did no good, but only helped the lace down – just as one slaps a choking child on the back. I could have cried, I was so vexed; but I determined I would not give the lace up without a struggle for it. I hoped the lace might disagree with her, at any rate; but it would have been too much for Job, if he had seen, as I did, that cat come in, quite placid and purring, not a quarter of an hour after, and almost expecting to be stroked. "No, pussy!" said I, "if you have any conscience you ought not to expect that!" And then a thought struck me; and I rang the bell for my maid, and sent her to Mr Hoggins, with my compliments, and would he be kind enough to lend me one of his top-boots for an hour? I did not think there was anything odd in the message; but Jenny said the young men in the surgery laughed as if they would be ill at my wanting a top-boot. When it came, Jenny and I put pussy in, with her fore-feet straight down, so that they were fastened, and could not scratch, and we gave her a teaspoonful of currant-jelly in which (your ladyship must excuse me) I had mixed some tartar emetic. I shall never forget how anxious I was for the next half-hour. I took pussy to my own room, and spread a clean towel on the floor. I could have kissed her when she returned the lace to sight, very much as it had gone down. Jenny had boiling water ready, and we soaked it and soaked it, and spread it on a lavender-bush in the sun before I could touch it again, even to put it in milk. But now your ladyship would never guess that it had been in pussy's inside.

from *Cranford* (1853)

The White Cat

COUNTESS D'AULNOY (*c.* 1651–1705)

Once upon a time there was a king who had three brave and handsome sons. He feared they might be seized with the desire of reigning before his death. Certain rumours were abroad that they were trying to gain adherents to assist them in depriving him of his kingdom. The king was old, but as vigorous in mind as ever, and had no desire to yield them a position he filled so worthily. He thought, therefore, the best way of living in peace was to divert them by promises he could always escape fulfilling.

He summoned them to his closet, and after speaking kindly, added: "You will agree with me, my dear children, that my advanced age does not permit me to attend to state affairs so closely as formerly; I fear my subjects may suffer, and wish therefore to give one of you my crown, but it is only fair that in return for such a gift you should seek ways of making my intention of retiring into the country pleasing to me. It seems to me that a clever, pretty, and faithful little dog would be a pleasant companion for me; so without choosing my eldest son rather than my youngest, I declare that whichever of the three brings me the most beautiful dog shall be my heir." The princes were surprised at their father's desire for a little dog, but the two youngest thought they could turn it to their advantage, and gladly accepted the commission; the eldest was too timid and too respectful to press his rights. They took leave of the king; he gave them money and jewels, adding that in a year, without fail, they must return, and on the same day, and at the same hour bring him their little dogs.

Before their departure they repaired to a castle about a league from the town; there they brought their most intimate friends, and gave a great feast, at which the three brothers swore eternal friendship, that they would conduct the matter in hand without jealousy and annoyance, and that the successful one should share his fortune with the others. At length they set out, deciding that on their return they would meet at the same castle, and go together to the king; they would take no attendants with them, and changed their names in order not to be recognized.

Each took a different route. The two eldest had many adventures, but I shall only relate those of the youngest. He was handsome, and of a gay and merry disposition; he had a well-shaped head, great stature, regular features, beautiful teeth, and was very skilful in all exercises befitting a prince. He sang pleasantly, and played charmingly on the lute and theorbo. He could also paint; in short, he was extremely accomplished, and his valour reached almost to rashness.

A day scarcely passed that he did not buy dogs – big, little, greyhounds, bulldogs, boar-hounds, harriers, spaniels, poodles, lap-dogs; as soon as he had a very fine one, he found one still finer, and therefore let the first go and kept the other: for it would have been impossible to take about with him, quite alone, thirty or forty thousand dogs, and he did not wish to have gentlemen-in-waiting, valets or pages in his suite. He was walking on without knowing where he was going, when night, accompanied by thunder and rain, overtook him in a forest where he could no longer see the paths.

He took the first road that offered, and after he had walked for a long time, saw a light, and felt sure there was a house near in which he could take shelter till the next day. Guided by the light, he came to the gates of a castle, the most magnificent imaginable. The gate was of gold covered with carbuncles, whose bright and pure brilliancy lighted up all the surroundings. That was the light the prince had seen from afar; the walls were of transparent porcelain painted in many colours, illustrating the history of the fairies from the creation of the world: the famous adventures of Peau d'Ane, of Finette, of Orange Tree, of Gracieuse, of the Sleeping Beauty in the Wood, of Green Serpent, and a hundred others were not omitted. He was delighted to recognize Prince Lutin, who was a sort of Scotch uncle. The rain and the bad weather prevented him remaining longer in a place where he was getting wet through, and besides, in those places where the light of the carbuncles did not reach, he could not see at all.

He returned to the gold door; he saw a stag's foot fastened to a diamond chain: he admired its magnificence, and the security in which the inhabitants of the castle must live; for he said: "What is there to keep thieves from cutting the chain and tearing out the carbuncles? They would be rich for ever."

He pulled the stag's foot and heard a bell ring, and from its sound judged it to be of gold or silver; in an instant the door was opened, he saw a dozen hands in the air, each holding a torch. He was so astonished that he hesitated to enter, when he felt other hands pushing him from behind somewhat violently. He walked on very uneasily and at great risk; he put his hand on his sword hilt. On entering a vestibule incrusted with porphyry and lapis lazuli, he heard two enchanting voices singing these words:

> Within the bounds of this bright place
> Is nought to fear and nought to flee.
> Save the enchantment of a face,
> If you would live still fancy-free.

He could not imagine that if harm was intended to him later, so kind an invitation should be given now, and feeling himself pushed towards a big coral door that opened as soon as he approached it, he entered a saloon of mother-of-pearl, and then several rooms variously decorated, but so rich in paintings and precious stones that he was as if enchanted. Thousands and thousands of lights, hanging from the roof of the room, lighted some of the other apartments, which contained just the same lustres, girandoles and shelves full of wax candles; indeed, such was the magnificence that it is difficult to believe it possible.

After passing through sixty rooms, the hands that were guiding him stopped; he saw a big and commodious armchair approach the fireplace quite alone. At the same moment the fire was lighted, and the hands, which seemed to him very beautiful, white, small, plump and well-proportioned, undressed him, for, as I already said, he was wet, and they feared he might take cold. He was presented, without seeing anyone, with a shirt beautiful enough for a wedding day, with a dressing-gown of some material frosted with gold, embroidered with small emeralds to form monograms. The bodiless hands pushed to a table where everything necessary for the toilet was set out. Nothing could be more magnificent. They combed his hair with a lightness and skill that were delightful. Then they dressed him, but not in his own clothes; they brought him others much richer. He silently wondered at all that was taking place, and sometimes could not quite control a certain impulse of fear.

When he was powdered, curled, perfumed, adorned and made more beautiful than Adonis, the hands led him into a hall resplendent with gildings and furniture. Looking round you saw the histories of the most famous cats: Rodillardus hung up by the feet at the Council of Rats, Puss in Boots, Marquis of Carabas, the cat who wrote, the cat who became a woman, the sorcerers who became cats, their nocturnal revels and all their ceremonies; nothing could be more curious than these pictures.

The table was laid for two, with gold knife, fork and spoon for each; the sideboard was magnificent with a number of rock-crystal vases and a thousand precious stones. The prince did not know for whom the two covers were intended; he perceived cats taking their places in a little orchestra built on purpose; one held a book in which was written the most extraordinary music imaginable, another a roll of paper with which he beat time, and the rest had small guitars. Suddenly each began to mew in a different key, and to strike the strings of their guitars with their sharp claws; it was the strangest music ever heard. The prince would have thought himself in hell, if the palace had not been too wonderful to give probability to such a thought, but he stuffed up his ears and laughed heartily at the different postures and grimaces of the novel musicians.

He was thinking over his various adventures since his entrance into the castle, when he saw a little figure no bigger than your arm enter the hall. The little creature was shrouded in a long, black crape veil. Two cats conducted her; they were in mourning, with cloaks and swords at their sides; a numerous procession of cats followed; some carried rat-traps full of rats and others mice in cages.

The prince was more astonished than ever; he did not know what to think. The little black figure approached him, and raising her veil, he saw the most beautiful white cat that ever was or ever will be. She looked very young and sad; she began to mew so softly and prettily that it went straight to the heart. She said to the prince: "King's son, you are welcome; my cat-like majesty is glad to see you."

"Madam Cat," said the prince, "it is very kind of you to receive me so cordially, but you do not appear an ordinary animal; your gift of speech and your magnificent castle are strong proofs to the contrary."

"King's son," replied White Cat, "I beg you to leave off making me compliments; I am very simple in speech and manner, but I have a kind heart. Come," she continued, "let supper be served and the musicians cease, because the prince does not understand what they say."

"Are they singing anything, madam?" he replied.

"Certainly," she went on, "we have excellent poets here, and if you stay with us a little while you will be convinced of it."

"It is only necessary to hear you to believe it," said the prince, politely; "you seem to be a most rare cat."

Supper was brought, the bodiless hands waited at table. First two dishes were put on the tables, one of young pigeons and the other of fat mice. The sight of the one prevented the prince from eating the other, imagining that the same cook had prepared them both. But the little cat, guessing by his expression what was passing in his mind, assured him that his kitchen was separate, and that he might eat what was given him without fear of its being rats or mice.

There was no need to repeat it; the prince felt quite sure the beautiful little cat would not deceive him. He was surprised to see that on her paw she wore a miniature. He asked her to show it him, thinking it would be Master Minagrobis. He was astonished to see a young man so handsome that it was scarcely creditable nature could have formed one like him and who resembled him so closely that it would not have been possible to paint his portrait better. She sighed, and becoming more melancholy, remained perfectly silent. The prince saw there was something extraordinary beneath; however, fearing to displease or annoy the cat, he dared not ask. He told her all the news he could think of, and found her well informed about the various interests of princes, and other things that happened in the world.

After supper White Cat invited her guest to enter a hall containing a stage on which twelve cats and twelve monkeys danced a ballet. The former were dressed as Moors and the latter as Chinese. Their leaps and capers may easily be imagined, and now and again they exchanged blows with their paws. Thus the evening ended. White Cat bade her guest goodnight; the hands which had been his guides all along took charge of him again, and led him to an apartment just opposite the one he had seen. It was less magnificent than elegant. It was carpeted with butterflies' wings, whose varied colours formed a thousand different flowers. There were also very rare birds' feathers, never seen perhaps except in this place. The beds were of gauze, fastened by a thousand knots of ribbons. There were large mirrors reaching from the ceiling to the floor, and the chased gold frames represented a thousand little Cupids.

The prince went to bed in silence, for he could not carry on a conversation with the hands; he did not sleep well and was awakened by a confused noise. The hands took him out of bed, and dressed him in hunting costume. He looked out into the courtyard, and saw more than five hundred cats, some of whom led hounds in the leash, others sounded the horn; it was a great fête. White Cat was going hunting and wished the prince to join her. The helpful hands gave him a wooden horse, which galloped at full speed, and stepped grandly. He made some difficulty about mounting, saying that he was far from being a knight-errant like Don Quixote; but his resistance was of no avail, and he was put on the wooden horse. It had housings and saddle of gold and diamond embroidery. White Cat was mounted on the handsomest and finest monkey ever seen. She did not wear her long veil, but a dragoon hat, which lent her such a determined expression that all the mice of the neighbourhood were in terror. Never was there a pleasanter hunt; the cats ran quicker than the rabbits and the hares, so that when they caught them White Cat had the quarry made in front of her, and a thousand skilful and delightful tricks were done. The birds, too, were scarcely safe, for the cats climbed the trees, and the wonderful monkey carried White Cat even into the eagles' nests, so that she might dispose of the eaglets according to her pleasure.

The hunt ended, she blew a horn about a finger's length, but with so loud and clear a sound that it could easily be heard ten leagues off. When she had blown it two or three times, she was surrounded by all the cats of the country: some were in the air driving chariots, others in boats came by water; never had so many been seen before. They were all dressed differently. White Cat returned to the castle with the pompous procession, and begged the prince to come too. He was most willing, although it seemed to him that so many cats savoured somewhat of uproar and sorcery, and the cat who could speak astonished him more than all the rest.

As soon as she reached home she put on her long black veil; she supped with the prince. He was hungry and ate with a good appetite; liqueurs were served him which he drank with great pleasure, and immediately forgot the little dog he was to take the king. He only thought of mewing with the White Cat, that is, to keep her pleasant and faithful company; the days passed in pleasant fêtes, fishing, hunting, ballets, feasts, and many other ways in which he amused himself capitally; sometimes the White Cat composed verses and songs of so passionate a character that it seemed she must have a tender heart, and that she could not speak as she did without loving; but her secretary, an elderly cat, wrote so badly that although her works have been preserved, it is impossible to read them.

The prince had forgotten even his country. The hands of which I spoke continued to serve him. He sometimes regretted he was not a cat, in order that he might spend his life in that pleasant company. "Alas!" he said to White Cat, "how grieved I shall be to leave you, I love you so dearly! Either become a woman or make me a cat." She was much amused at his wish, and made mysterious answers of which he understood nothing.

A year passes so quickly when you have neither cares nor troubles, and are in good health. White Cat knew when he ought to return, and as he had quite forgotten it, she reminded him. "Do you know," she said, "that you have only three days in which to find the little dog your father wants, and your brothers have found beauties?"

The prince then remembered, and astonished at his carelessness, exclaimed: "By what secret charm have I forgotten the thing more important to me than anything in the world? Unless I procure a dog wonderful enough to win me a kingdom, and a horse speedy enough to travel so long a distance in time, it is all up with my fame and fortune." He began to feel very anxious and distressed.

White Cat to comfort him said: "King's son, do not vex yourself, I am your friend. You can stay here another day, and although it is five hundred leagues from here to your country, the wooden horse will take you there in less than twelve hours."

"I thank you, beautiful cat," said the prince; "but it is not enough to return to my father: I must take him a little dog."

"Stay," said White Cat, "here is an acorn which contains one more beautiful than the dogstar."

"Oh!" said the prince, "Madam Cat, you are laughing at me."

"Put the acorn to your ear," she continued, "you will hear it bark."

He obeyed, and heard the little dog say bow-wow; the prince was overjoyed, because a dog that could get into an acorn must be very tiny. He was so anxious to see it that he wanted to open it, but White Cat told him it might be cold on the journey, and it would therefore be better to wait till he was with his father. He thanked her a thousand times, and bade her a tender farewell. "I assure you," he added, "time has passed so quickly with you that I somewhat regret leaving you, and although you are queen here, and the cats who form your court are more intelligent and more gallant than ours, I cannot help inviting you to come with me." The cat's only reply to this was a deep sigh.

They parted; the prince was the first to arrive at the castle where the meeting with his brothers had been arranged to take place. They joined him very soon, and were surprised to see a wooden horse in the courtyard that leaped better than all those in the riding schools.

The prince came to meet them. They embraced each other affectionately, and related their adventures; but our prince did not tell his brothers his real adventures, and showed them a wretched dog which served as turnspit, saying he considered it so pretty that it was the one he destined for the king. No matter how they loved one another, the two eldest were secretly glad of the youngest's foolish choice; being at dinner, one trod on the other's foot as if to say there was nothing to fear on that score.

The next day they went on together in the same coach. The king's two eldest sons brought little dogs in baskets, so beautiful and delicate that one scarcely dared to touch them; the youngest brought the miserable turnspit, which was so dirty that no one could bear it. When they reached the palace, they were greeted and welcomed by all; they entered the king's rooms. He did not know in whose favour to decide, for the dogs brought by his two eldest sons were almost equally beautiful, and they were already disputing the succession, when the youngest brought them into harmony by drawing out of his pocket the acorn White Cat had given him. He quickly opened it, and they saw a little dog lying on cotton wool. He passed through a ring without touching it. The prince put him on the ground, and he began to dance with castanets as lightly as the most famous Spanish girl. He was of a thousand different colours, his silky hair and ears dragged on the ground. The king was greatly puzzled, for it was impossible to find anything to say against the beauty of the little dog.

But he had not the least desire to give away his crown. The tiniest gem of it was dearer to him than all the dogs in the world. He told his children he was pleased with their labours, and they had succeeded so well in the first thing he had asked of them that he wished to prove their skill further before fulfilling his promise; so that he gave them a year to look by sea and land for a piece of linen so fine that it would pass through the eye of a needle used for making Venice point-lace. They were all vastly distressed to be obliged to go on a new quest. The two princes, whose dogs were not so beautiful as that of the youngest, agreed. Each departed his own way without so much affection as the former time, because the turnspit had greatly cooled their love.

Our prince mounted his wooden horse again, and without caring to find other help than that he might hope from White Cat's friendliness, he speedily departed, and returned to the castle where he had been so kindly entertained. He found all the doors open, the windows, roofs, towers and walls were lighted by a hundred thousand lamps that produced a marvellous effect. The hands that had waited on him so well came to meet him, took the bridle of the wooden horse and led it to the stable, while the prince entered White Cat's room.

She was lying in a little basket on a very nice white satin mattress. Her toilette was neglected and she looked out of spirits; but when she saw the prince, she leaped and jumped to show him her joy. "Whatever reason I had," she said, "to hope that you would return, king's son, I dared not expect too much, and I am usually so unfortunate in the things I wish that this event surprises me." The grateful prince caressed her; he related the success of his journey, which she knew probably better than he, and that the king wanted a piece of linen fine enough to go through a needle's eye; that in truth he thought the thing impossible, but he intended to rely on her friendship and help. White Cat, looking serious, said she would think over the matter; fortunately, there were cats in the castle who spun excellently; she would see that what he wanted was prepared, thus he would have no need to go further afield in search of what he could more easily procure in her palace than in any other place in the world.

The hands appeared, carrying torches, and the prince and White Cat following them, entered a magnificent gallery that extended along the bank of a river, where a splendid display of fireworks took place. Four cats, who had been duly tried with all the usual formalities, were to be burned. They were accused of eating the roast meat provided for White Cat's supper, her cheese, her milk, and of having plotted against her person with Martafax and L'Hermite, famous rats of the country, and held as such by La Fontaine, a truthful writer; but all the same it was known that there was a good deal of treachery in the matter, and that most of the witnesses were bribed. However it might have been, the prince obtained their pardon. The fireworks did no one any harm, and there never were more beautiful rockets.

A very excellent supper was afterwards served, which pleased the prince more than the fireworks, for he was very hungry, and his wooden horse travelled at the greatest speed possible. The days that followed were spent in the same way as those that preceded, with a thousand different fêtes devised by White Cat's ingenuity to amuse the prince. He is perhaps the first man who entertained himself so well in the company of cats.

It is true that White Cat had a charming, flexible and versatile mind. She was more learned than cats usually are. The prince was sometimes astonished. "No," he said, "what I see so surprising in you is not a natural thing; if you love me, charming puss, tell me by what miracle you think and speak so correctly that you would be received into the most famous academies of learned men?"

"Cease to ask questions, king's son," she said, "I am not allowed to reply: you can carry your conjectures as far as you please, I shall not oppose them; be contented that I never show my claws to you, and take a tender interest in all that concerns you."

The second year passed as quickly as the first; everything the prince wished for was immediately brought him by the hands; whether it was books, jewels, pictures, antique medals, he had only to say I want such and such a jewel that is in the cabinet of the Mogul or of the King of Persia, such a statue from Corinth or Greece, and he immediately saw before him what he desired, without knowing who brought it or whence it came. That was not without its charms, and it is sometimes a pleasant diversion to become possessed of the most beautiful treasures of the earth.

White Cat, who never ceased to watch over the prince's interests, warned him that the time of his departure was drawing near, that he need not be anxious about the linen he wanted, since she had had made for him a most wonderful piece; she added that she wished this time to give him an equipage worthy of his rank, and without awaiting his reply, she made him look out into the courtyard. He saw an open barouche enamelled with flame-coloured gold, with a thousand elegant devices that pleased the intelligence as well as the eye. Twelve snow-white horses yoked together in fours drew it, harnessed in flame-coloured velvet embroidered with diamonds, and decorated with gold plates. The inside of the barouche was equally magnificent, and a hundred coaches, with eight horses, filled with nobles of fine appearance, superbly dressed, accompanied the barouche. It was also attended by a thousand bodyguards, whose coats were so thickly embroidered that you could not see the material; and what was strangest, White Cat's portrait appeared everywhere: in the decoration of the barouche, on the coats of the guards, or fastened with a ribbon, like an order, round the necks of those who formed the procession.

"Go," she said to the prince, "appear at your father's court in so sumptuous a manner that your magnificence may impress him with awe, so that he will not refuse you the crown you deserve. Here is a walnut; do not crack it until you are before him; it contains the piece of linen you asked of me."

"Good White Cat," he said, "I confess I am so deeply sensible of your kindness that if you would consent, I would rather spend my life with you than amid all the glory I have reason to expect elsewhere."

"King's son," she replied, "I am convinced of your good heart, a very rare commodity among princes; they want to be loved by all without loving anything or anyone themselves, but you are the exception that proves the rule. I shall not forget the affection you show for a little white cat, who is good for nothing but to catch mice." The prince kissed her paw and departed.

It would be difficult to understand the speed at which he travelled, if we did not know already that the wooden horse had taken less than two days to do the five hundred leagues to the castle, so that the same power that animated that horse worked in the others, and they were only twenty-four hours on the road. They halted nowhere until they reached the king's palace, where the two eldest brothers had already repaired, so that not seeing the youngest they applauded his forgetfulness and whispered: "This is very fortunate; he is either dead or sick, he will not be our rival in this important business." They exhibited their pieces of linen, which were indeed so fine that they went through the eye of a big needle, but could not get through that of a small one, and the king, glad of the pretext, showed them the particular needle he meant, and which the magistrates by his orders brought from the treasury of the town, where it had been carefully preserved.

There was much grumbling over this. The princes' friends, and particularly those of the oldest – for his piece of linen was the best – said that it was open chicanery, in which there was great cunning and evasion. The king's supporters upheld that he was not compelled to keep to the proposed conditions. At length, to make them all agree, a delightful sound of trumpets, drums, and hautboys was heard; it was the arrival of the prince and his fine equipment. The king and his two sons were all vastly astonished at its magnificence.

After greeting his father very respectfully and embracing his brothers, he took the walnut out of a box ornamented with rubies, and cracked it, thinking to find in it the famous piece of linen, but instead there was a hazel nut; he cracked that, and was surprised to see a cherry stone. They looked at each other; the king smiled and laughed at his son for being credulous enough to believe a walnut could contain a piece of linen; but why should he not have believed it, since he had already found a little dog contained in an acorn? He cracked the cherry stone, which contained its kernel; then a loud murmur arose in the room, and nothing could be heard but that the youngest prince had been duped. He made no reply to the courtiers' jests; he opened the kernel and found a grain of wheat, and in the grain of wheat a millet seed. In truth, he began to get distrustful, and murmured between his teeth: "Why, cat, White Cat, you have made game of me." He felt at that moment a cat's claw on his hand, which scratched him so severely that he bled. He did not know if this was to encourage him or to make him lose heart. However, he opened the millet seed, and the people were no little astonished when he drew from it a piece of linen four hundred ells long, so wonderful that all the birds, beasts, and fishes were painted on it, with trees, fruits, and plants of the earth, the rocks, the curiosities and shells of the sea, the sun, moon, stars and planets of the heavens; further, there were the portraits of the kings and other sovereigns that had reigned in the world, those of their wives, mistresses, children and sub-jects, not omitting the least important of them. Each in his condition assumed the character that suited him best, and wore the costume of his country. When the king saw the piece of linen, he became as pale as the prince was red from his prolonged efforts to find it. The needle was brought, the piece of linen passed backwards and forwards through the eye six times. The king and the two eldest princes preserved a dismal silence, although the beauty and rarity of the linen compelled them to say that nothing in the world could be compared to it.

The king uttered a deep sigh, and turning to his children, said: "Nothing consoles me more in my old age than your deference to my wishes. I therefore desire to put you to a further proof. Go and travel for a year, and at the end of that time he who brings back the most beautiful girl shall marry her and be crowned king on his wedding day. It is absolutely necessary that my successor should marry. I swear, I promise that I will not again put off the reward."

Our prince strongly felt the injustice. The little dog and the piece of linen deserved ten kingdoms rather than one, but he was too well-bred to oppose his father's will, and without delay got into the barouche again. The whole procession accompanied him, and he returned to his beloved White Cat. She knew the day and hour of his arrival. The road was strewed with flowers, a thousand perfume burners smoked on all sides, and especially in the castle. She was seated on a Persian carpet, under a canopy of cloth of gold, in a gallery whence she could see him coming. He was received by the hands that had always waited on him. All the cats climbed up to the gutters in order to welcome him with a terrible mewing.

"Well, king's son," she said, "you have again returned without a crown?"

"Madam," he replied, "your kindness has certainly given me the best chance of gaining it, but I am convinced that the king would have more trouble in giving it away than I should have pleasure in possessing it."

"No matter," she said, "you must neglect nothing that can make you deserve it. I will help you this time, and since you must take a beautiful girl to your father's court, I will find you one who will cause you to win the prize. Now let us amuse ourselves; I have ordered a naval combat between my cats and the terrible rats of the country. My cats will doubtless be uncomfortable, for they fear the water, but otherwise they would have had too great an advantage, and things ought before all to be fair." The prince admired Madam Puss's prudence; he praised her highly, and accompanied her to a terrace that looked on the sea.

The cats' ships consisted of big pieces of cork, on which they floated comfortably enough. The rats had joined together several eggshells to form their vessels. The combat was obstinately kept up; the rats threw themselves into the water, and swam far better than the cats; so that twenty times they were conquerors and conquered, but Minagrobis, admiral of the cats' fleet, reduced the rats to the extremity of despair. He greedily ate up the leader of their fleet, an old experienced rat, who had been thrice round the world in good vessels, where he was neither captain nor sailor, but only a parasite.

White Cat did not wish those poor wretches to be entirely destroyed. She knew how to rule her people, and thought that if there should be no more rats or mice in the land, her subjects would live in an idleness very harmful to them. The prince spent that year like the others in hunting, fishing and games, for White Cat played chess extremely well. Now and again he could not help asking her fresh questions as to the miracle by which she was able to speak. He asked her if she was a fairy, or if she had become a cat by some change of shape. But she always said only what she wanted to say, and replied only what she wished; and she did this by so many phrases that meant nothing at all, that he clearly saw she did not wish to share her secret with him.

Nothing passes more swiftly than days spent without trouble or care, and if the cat had not been wise enough to remember the time for returning to the court, it is certain that the prince would have entirely forgotten it. She told him the evening before that it only rested with him to take to his father one of the most beautiful princesses the world had ever seen; that the time for destroying the fatal work of the fairies had at length arrived, and to do that it was necessary for him to cut off her head and tail, and throw them at once into the fire.

"I," he exclaimed, "White Cat, my love, am I to be cruel enough to kill you? Ah, you doubtless want to prove my heart, but be sure it will never be wanting in the affection and gratitude it owes you."

"No, king's son," she continued, "I do not suspect you of ingratitude, I know your merit; it is neither you nor I who rule our fate in this matter. Do what I wish; we shall both begin to be happy, and you will know on the faith of a rich and honourable cat that I am indeed your friend."

The tears came into the prince's eyes at the mere thought of cutting off his cat's pretty little head. He said everything loving and tender he could think of to dissuade her, but she obstinately replied that she wished to die by his hand, and that it was the only way of preventing his brothers from obtaining the crown; in fact, she urged him so ardently that trembling he drew his sword, and with a shaking hand cut off the head and tail of his good friend, the cat. Immediately the most charming change imaginable took place. White Cat's body grew tall, and suddenly turned into a girl, whose beauty cannot be described; never was there any so perfect. Her eyes enchanted all hearts, and her sweetness captivated them. Her stature was majestic, and her bearing noble and modest; her mind was versatile, her manners attractive; indeed, she was superior to everything that was most amiable.

The prince was so surprised, and so agreeably surprised at the sight, that he thought he must be enchanted. He could not speak, he could only look at her, and his tongue was so tied that he could not express his astonishment; but it was a very different thing when he saw an extraordinary number of lords and ladies enter the room, who, with their cats' skins thrown over their shoulders, bowed low to their queen, and testified their joy at seeing her again in her natural state. She received them with marks of kindness that were enough to prove the character of her disposition. And after holding her court for a few moments, she gave orders that she should be left alone with the prince, and spoke to him thus: "Do not imagine, sir, that I have always been a cat. My father ruled over six kingdoms. He loved my mother dearly, and allowed her to do exactly as she liked. Her ruling passion was travel, so that shortly before I was born she set out to visit a certain mountain, of which she had heard the most wonderful accounts. On the way she was told that near the place where she then was, was an ancient fairy castle of very great beauty, so at least report said, for, as no one had ever entered it, it could not be proved a fact; but it was well known that the fairies' garden contained the best and most delicately flavoured fruits ever eaten.

"The queen was seized with a violent desire to taste them, and turned her steps in the direction of the castle. She reached the gate of the magnificent building that shone with gold and azure on all sides. But she knocked in vain; none appeared, it seemed that everybody was dead. The difficulties only served to increase her desire, and she sent for ladders so that they might get over the garden wall. They would have succeeded if the walls had not visibly increased in height although no one worked at them; they tied the ladders together, but they gave way under the weight of the climbers, who were either crippled for life or killed outright.

"The queen was in despair. She saw big trees loaded with fruits that seemed delicious; she felt she must taste them or die; she ordered sumptuous tents to be pitched before the castle, and she and all her court remained there six weeks. She neither ate nor slept; she did nothing but sigh and talk of the fruit in the inaccessible garden. At length she fell dangerously ill, and no one could cure her, for the inexorable fairies had not as much as appeared since she had established herself near the castle. All her officers were greatly distressed. Only weeping and sighs were heard while the dying queen asked her attendants for fruits, but would only have what was denied her.

"One night, when she was somewhat drowsy, she saw when she woke a little ugly decrepit old woman seated in an armchair by her bedside. She was surprised her attendants should have allowed anyone she did not know to come so near her. The old dame said: 'We consider your majesty very importunate in wishing so obstinately to eat of our fruits, but since your life is in danger my sisters and I have agreed to give you as many as you can carry away, and as many as you like while you remain here, provided you make us a present.'

" 'Ah! my dear mother,' exclaimed the queen, 'speak; I will give you my realms, my heart, my soul, provided I may have the fruit; no price is too great for it!'

" 'We desire your majesty,' she said, 'to give us the daughter shortly to be born to you; at her birth we shall come and fetch her away and bring her up among us. We shall endow her with all the virtues, with beauty and knowledge; in short, she will be our child; we shall make her happy, but remember you will see her no more until she is married. If you like the proposal I will cure you at once and take you to our orchards; although it is night, you will be able to see clearly enough to choose what you please. If you do not like what I have said – well, good-evening, madam, I shall go home to bed.'

" 'Although the conditions you impose on me are very hard, I accept them rather than die, for it is certain I have not a day to live. Cure me, wise fairy,' she continued, 'and do not let me be a moment longer without enjoying the privilege you have just granted me.'

"The fairy touched her with a small gold wand, saying: 'May your majesty be freed from the sufferings that keep you in this bed!' It seemed to her immediately as though she had put off a very heavy and uncomfortable gown, which had oppressed her. In some places, seemingly where her malady had been most acute, the burden still weighed upon her. She called her ladies-in-waiting, and told them with cheerful looks that she felt extremely well, was going to get up, and that the gates of the fairy palace, so fast bolted and barricaded, would be open for her to eat and carry away as much of the fruit as she pleased.

"The ladies thought the queen was delirious, and dreaming of the fruits she longed for; instead therefore of answering her, they began to cry and awoke the physicians to come and see in what a condition she was. The delay exasperated the queen: she asked for her clothes and was refused; she got angry and became very flushed. They thought it was the effect of the fever.

However, the physicians felt her pulse, went through the usual formalities and could not deny that she was in perfect health. Her ladies, seeing the fault their zeal had made them commit, tried to mend it by dressing her quickly. They asked her pardon and were forgiven: she hastened to follow the old fairy, who had been waiting for her all the time.

"She entered the palace, where nothing was wanting to make it the most beautiful place in the world. This you will easily believe, sir," said Queen White Cat, "when I tell you it is the very castle in which we are; two other fairies, a little younger than my mother's guide, received them at the door and welcomed them kindly. She begged them to take her at once into the garden, and show her the trees on which she would find the best fruit. 'They are all equally good,' they told her, 'and if you were not so anxious to pluck them yourself, we have merely to bid them come!'

" 'I entreat you, ladies,' said the queen, 'give me the pleasure of seeing so extraordinary a thing.'

"The oldest put her fingers to her mouth, and whistled three times; then she shouted: 'Apricots, peaches, nectarines, cherries, plums, pears, white-heart cherries, melons, grapes, apples, oranges, lemons, currants, strawberries, raspberries, come at my bidding!'

" 'But,' said the queen, 'those you summon, ripen at different seasons.'

" 'It is not so in our orchard,' they said. 'We have all the fruits the earth produces always ripe, always good; they never go bad!'

"Directly they all came, rolling, creeping along, pell-mell, without getting bruised or harmed; so that the queen, eager to satisfy her longing, took the first that offered, and rather devoured than ate them.

"When she was somewhat satisfied, she asked the fairies to let her go to the trees that she might have the pleasure of choosing the fruit with her eye, before plucking it. 'We willingly consent,' said the three fairies, 'but remember your promise. You can no longer go back from it.'

" 'I am sure,' she replied, 'it is very pleasant here, and if I did not love my husband so dearly, I should ask you to let me live here too; so that you need have no fear I shall retract.' The fairies, extremely pleased, opened all their gardens and enclosures; the queen stayed with them three days and three nights without wishing to go, so delicious was the fruit. She gathered some to take with her, and as it never spoiled she loaded four thousand mules with it. The fairies added to the fruit gold baskets of exquisite workmanship to put it in, and several curiosities of great value. They promised to give me the education of a princess, to make me perfect, choose a husband for me, and to inform my mother of the day of the wedding, to which they hoped she would come.

"The king was delighted at the queen's return; the whole court rejoiced with him. There were balls, masquerades, running at the ring, and banquets, where the queen's fruits were served as a delicious feast. The king ate them in preference to everything else that was offered him. He did not know the treaty she had made with the fairies, and he often asked her the name of the land from which she had brought such good things. She told him they were to be found on an almost inaccessible mountain; at another time, that they came from the valleys, then from a garden, or a big forest. So many contradictions surprised the king. He questioned those who had accompanied her, but as she had forbidden them to tell the adventure to anyone, they dared not speak of it. As the time of my birth drew nearer, the queen, anxious about her promise to the fairies, fell into a terrible melancholy; she sighed every moment and changed colour rapidly. The king grew very uneasy, and urged the queen to tell him what distressed her. With great difficulty she told him what had passed between her and the fairies, and how she had promised her daughter to them. 'What!' exclaimed the king, 'we are to have no children; you know how I long for them, and for the sake of eating two or three apples you were capable of promising your daughter. You cannot have any affection for me.' He overwhelmed her with a thousand reproaches, which nearly caused my mother to die of grief; but he was not content with that: he shut her up in a tower and surrounded it with guards to prevent her having communication with anybody but the servants who waited on her, and changed those who had been with her at the fairy castle.

"The bad feeling between the king and queen threw the court into great consternation. Everybody put off his rich clothes in order to don those suitable to the general grief. The king, on his part, seemed inexorable; he never saw his wife, and directly I was born, had me brought to his palace to be fed and cared for, while the queen remained a most unhappy prisoner. The fairies knew everything that was going on; they became angry, they wanted to gain possession of me; they looked upon me as their property, and that it was a theft from them to keep me. Before seeking a revenge in proportion to their anger, they sent an embassy to the king, asking him to set the queen at liberty, and take her into favour again, and to give me to their ambassadors in order to be brought up by them. The ambassadors were so small, and so deformed – they were ugly dwarfs – that they had not the gift of persuading the king to do what they wished. He refused roughly, and if they had not speedily departed worse might have befallen them.

"When the fairies learned my father's course of action, they became very indignant; and after inflicting the most desolating evils on his six kingdoms, they let loose a terrible dragon which poisoned all the places he passed through, devoured men and children, and killed the trees and plants by breathing on them.

"The king was in the depths of despair; he consulted all the wise men in the kingdom about what he ought to do to secure his subjects from these overwhelming misfortunes. They advised him to seek through all the world for the cleverest physicians, and the most excellent remedies, and to promise life to all the condemned criminals who would fight the dragon. The king, pleased with the counsel, followed it, but without result, for the mortality continued, and everyone who went against the dragon was devoured; then he had recourse to a fairy who had protected him from his earliest youth. She was very old, and scarcely ever left her bed; he went to her and reproached her for permitting fate to persecute him thus, and for not coming to his assistance. 'What do you want me to do?' she said; 'you have annoyed my sisters; they are as powerful as I am, and we seldom act against each other. Appease them by giving them your daughter; the little princess belongs to them You have closely imprisoned the queen; what has she done that you should treat so amiable a woman so badly? Fulfil the promise she gave, and I undertake that good shall come of it.'

"My father loved me dearly, but seeing no other way of saving his kingdoms, and delivering himself from the fatal dragon, he told his friend that he would trust her, and give me to the fairies since she declared I should be cherished, and treated as became a princess of my rank; that he would set the queen free, and that she had only to tell him who was to carry me to the fairy castle. 'You must carry her in her cradle,' said his fairy friend, 'to the mountain of flowers; you can even remain near and see what will happen.' The king told her that in a week he would go with the queen; meanwhile she might inform her sisters of his decision, that they might make what preparations they thought proper.

"When he returned to the palace, he released the queen with as much affection and ceremony as he had made her prisoner in anger and rage. She was so dejected and changed that he would hardly have recognized her if his heart had not assured him that it was the same woman he had so deeply loved. He entreated her with tears in his eyes to forget the troubles he had caused her, assuring her that they would be the last she would experience from him. She replied that she had brought them on herself by her imprudence in promising her daughter to the fairies, and if anything could excuse her, it was her present condition. The king then told her he intended to deliver me to their keeping. It was now the queen who objected; it seemed to be fated that I was always to be a subject for discord between my father and mother. She wept and groaned without obtaining her desire, for the king was too well aware of the fatal consequences, and our subjects continued to die as if they had been guilty of the faults of our family. At length she consented, and everything was prepared for the ceremony.

"I was put into a mother-of-pearl cradle ornamented with everything pretty that art could imagine. It was hung with wreaths and festoons of flowers made of precious stones, and the different colours catching the sun's rays became so dazzling that you could not look at them. The magnificence of my clothing surpassed that of the cradle. All the fastenings of my robes were composed of big pearls, and twenty-four princesses of the blood carried me on a sort of light litter; their ornaments were not ordinary, and they were only allowed to wear white, as befitted my innocence. The whole court accompanied me, each in his rank.

"While they were ascending the mountain, the sound of a melodious symphony was heard coming nearer, and at length the fairies, thirty in number, appeared. They had asked their good friend to accompany them; each was seated in a pearly shell bigger than that in which Venus rose from the sea; and the shells were drawn by walruses that moved uneasily on dry land. The fairies were more magnificently escorted than great queens, but they were exceedingly old and ugly. They carried an olive branch to signify to the king that his submission found favour with them, and they covered me with such extraordinary caresses that it seemed they intended to live only to make me happy.

"The dragon who had avenged them on my father followed them fastened in diamond chains. They took me in their arms, kissed me, endowed me with many precious qualities, and then began the fairy dance. It was very merry, and it is incredible how those old ladies leaped and sprang; and the dragon, who had eaten so many people, approached crawling. The three fairies, to whom my mother had promised me, seated themselves on him and placed my cradle in their midst, and struck the dragon with a wand. He unfolded his big, scaly wings, finer than crape, and of a thousand different colours; thus they repaired to the castle. My mother, seeing me in the air at the mercy of the furious dragon, could not help uttering loud cries. The king consoled her with the assurance given him by his good friend that no harm should come to me, and that I should be as well taken care of as if I had remained in the palace. She became calmer, although it was very sad to lose me for so long, and to be herself the cause of such a misfortune, for if she had not desired to eat the fruit in the garden, I should have remained in my father's kingdoms and should not have suffered all the misfortunes I have still to relate to you.

"Learn then, king's son, that my guardians had purposely built a tower in which were a thousand beautiful apartments for all the seasons of the year, magnificent furniture, interesting books, but no door, and you had to get in by the windows, which were extremely high up. On the tower was a beautiful garden adorned with flowers, fountains and arbours which procured shade even in the hottest season. Here the fairies brought me up with a care that surpassed everything they had promised the queen. My clothes were always in the fashion, and so splendid that if anyone had seen me they would have thought it was my wedding day. They taught me everything that belonged to my age and rank. I did not give them much trouble, for there was scarcely anything I did not understand with the greatest ease; they liked my gentleness, and as I had never seen anyone except them I might have lived contented with them for the rest of my life.

"They always visited me, mounted on the furious dragon I have already mentioned; they never spoke of the king or queen; they called me their daughter, and I thought I was. No one lived with me in the tower except a parrot and a little dog they had given me for my amusement, for the animals were endowed with reason, and spoke perfectly.

"One of the sides of the castle was built on a deep road, so full of ruts and trees that it was almost impassable, so that since I had lived in the tower I had never seen anyone there. But one day when I was at the window chatting with the parrot and dog I heard a noise. I looked all round and saw a young knight who had stopped to listen to our conversation; I had never seen anyone like him, except in pictures. I was not sorry that an unexpected meeting should afford me such an opportunity, and having no idea of the danger that is attached to the satisfaction of contemplating a pleasant thing, I came forward to look at him, and the longer I looked, the more pleasure I felt. He made me a low bow, and fixed his eyes on me, and seemed greatly troubled to know how he might speak to me; for my window was very high, and he feared to be overheard, well knowing that I was in the fairy castle.

"Night suddenly came on, or to speak more correctly, it came without our perceiving it. He sounded his horn two or three times very prettily and then departed: it was so dark that I could not see which way he went. I was in a dream and no longer took the same pleasure as before in chatting with my parrot and dog. They told me the prettiest things imaginable, for fairy animals are intelligent, but I was preoccupied and knew not how to dissemble. Parrot noticed it; he was cunning and did not betray what was passing in his mind.

"I did not fail to rise with the dawn. I ran to my window and was agreeably surprised to see the young knight at the foot of the town. He was magnificently dressed. I flattered myself that it was somewhat on my account, and I was not mistaken. He talked to me through a kind of speaking trumpet, and by its aid told me that, having been hitherto insensible to all the beauties he had seen, he was suddenly so impressed with me, that unless he saw me every day of his life he should die. I was charmed with the compliment, and much distressed at not daring to reply to it, for it would have been necessary to shout with all my might, and so risk being better heard by the fairies than by him. I threw him some flowers I had in my hands: he received them as a marked favour, kissed them several times and thanked me. He then asked me if I should like him to come every day at the same time to my windows, and, if so, I was to throw him something. I took a turquoise ring from my finger and hastily threw it him, signing him to go away quickly because I heard the Fairy Violent mounting her dragon to bring me my breakfast.

"The first words she said on entering the room were: 'I smell the voice of a man here; search for him, dragon.' Imagine my feelings. I was paralyzed with fear lest he should go out by the other window and follow the knight in whom I was already greatly interested.

" 'My dear mamma' (for it was thus the old fairy liked me to call her), 'you are joking when you say you smell a man's voice: has a voice any smell? and even if it has, who is the mortal daring enough to ascend this tower?'

" 'What you say is true, my daughter,' she replied; 'I am delighted you argue so nicely, and I suppose it must be the hatred I have for men which sometimes makes me think they are not far from me.' She gave me my breakfast and my distaff. 'When you have finished eating, spin,' she said, 'for you are very idle and my sisters will be angry.' I had been so taken up with my unknown knight that I had found it impossible to spin.

"As soon as she was gone, I saucily threw the distaff on the ground, and ascended the terrace to see farther over the country. I had an excellent spy-glass; nothing impeded my view; I looked on all sides, and discovered my knight on the top of a mountain. He was resting under a rich pavilion of some gold material, and was surrounded by a large court. I supposed he must be the son of some king who was a neighbour of the fairies' palace. As I feared if he returned to the tower he would be discovered by the terrible dragon, I told my parrot to fly to the mountain, seek out the man who had spoken to me, and beg him on my behalf not to return, because I dreaded my guardians' vigilance, and that they might do him some mischief.

"Parrot acquitted himself of the mission like a parrot of intelligence. It surprised everybody to see him come swiftly and perch on the prince's shoulder and whisper in his ear. The prince felt both pleasure and pain at the message; my anxiety for his welfare flattered him, but the difficulty of seeing and speaking to me overwhelmed him, without, however, turning him from his purpose of pleasing me. He asked Parrot a hundred questions, and Parrot in his turn asked him a hundred, for he was curious by nature. The prince entrusted him with a ring for me instead of my turquoise; it was formed of the same stones, but was much more beautiful than mine; it was cut in the shape of a heart, and ornamented with diamonds. 'It is only right,' he added, 'that I should treat you as an ambassador; here is my portrait, only show it to your charming mistress.' He fastened the portrait under his wing and brought the ring in his beak.

"I awaited my little messenger's return with an impatience I had never before felt. He told me my knight was a great king; that he had received him most kindly, and that I might rest assured he only wished to live for me; that in spite of the danger he ran in coming to my tower, he was determined to risk everything rather than give up the pleasure of seeing me. That news worried me greatly, and I began to weep. Parrot and Bow-wow consoled me as well as they could, for they loved me dearly; then Parrot gave me the prince's ring and showed me the portrait. I confess I was extremely glad to be able to examine closely the man I had only seen in the distance. He seemed even more charming than I had imagined; a thousand thoughts, some pleasant, others sad, came into my mind, and gave me an extraordinary look of anxiety. The fairies perceived it, and said to each other that doubtless I was feeling bored, and they must, therefore, think about finding me a husband of fairy race. They spoke of several, and fixed on the little King Migonnet, whose kingdom was five hundred thousand leagues from their palace, but that was of no consequence. Parrot overheard this fine advice, and told me of it. 'Ah !' he said, 'I pity you, my dear mistress, if you become Migonnet's queen; his appearance is enough to frighten anyone. I regret to say it, but truly the king who loves you would not have him for a footman.'

" 'Have you seen him, Parrot?' I asked.

" 'I should think so,' continued he; 'I have been on a branch with him.'

" 'What! on a branch?' I replied.

" 'Yes,' he said; 'he has the claws of an eagle.'

"Such a tale distressed me strangely. I looked at the charming portrait of the king: I thought he could only have given it to

Parrot so that I might have an opportunity of seeing him, and when I compared him with Migonnet I could hope for nothing more in life, and determined to die rather than marry him.

"I did not sleep the whole night through. Parrot and Bow-wow talked to me. I slept a little towards morning; and as my dog had a keen scent he smelt that the king was at the bottom of the tower. He woke Parrot. 'I bet,' he said, 'the king is down below.'

"Parrot replied: 'Be quiet, chatterbox; because your eyes are always open and your ear on the alert, you object to others resting.'

" 'But let us bet,' said Bow-wow again; 'I know he is there.'

"Parrot replied: 'And I know very well he is not; did I not carry a message from my mistress forbidding him to come?'

" 'Truly, you're imposing nicely on me with your prohibitions,' exclaimed the dog. 'A passionate man only consults his heart'; and thereupon he began to pull his wings about so roughly that Parrot grew angry. Their cries awoke me; they told me the cause of the dispute: I ran, or rather flew, to the window. I saw the king, who stretched out his arms, and told me, by means of his trumpet, that he could not live without me, and implored me to find means to get out of the tower, or for him to enter it; he called all the gods and the elements to witness that he would marry me and make me one of the greatest queens in the world.

"I told Parrot to go and tell him that what he hoped seemed to me almost impossible; but that relying on the promise he had made me and on his oaths, I would attempt to do what he wished. But I implored him not to come every day, because he might be seen, and the fairies would give no quarter.

"He went away greatly rejoiced at the hope I held out; but when I thought over what I had just promised, I was in the greatest possible embarrassment. How to get out of a tower that had no doors, the only assistance being Parrot and Bow-wow! to be so young, inexperienced, and timid! I therefore determined not to attempt a thing in which I could never succeed, and sent Parrot to tell the king so. He almost killed himself then and there; but at length he ordered him to persuade me either to come and see him die, or to console him. 'Sire,' exclaimed the feathered ambassador, 'my mistress has the will but lacks the power.'

"When he related to me all that had taken place I was more distressed than ever. Fairy Violent came and found my eyes red and swollen; she declared I had been crying, and that if I did not tell her the reason she would burn me, for her threats were always terrible. I replied, trembling, that I was tired of spinning, and that I wanted some small nets to catch the little birds that pecked the fruit in my garden. 'What you desire,' she said, 'need cost you no more tears. I will bring you as much twine as you like'; and in fact I had it the same evening; but she advised me to think less of working than of making myself beautiful, because King Migonnet was expected shortly. I shuddered at the terrible news and said nothing.

"When she was gone, I began to make two or three pieces of netting; but what I really worked at was a rope ladder, and, although I had never seen one, it was very well made. The fairy did not provide me with as much twine as I wanted, and continually said: 'But, my daughter, your work is like Penelope's, it never advances, and you are never tired of asking me for more material.'

" 'Oh ! my dear mamma,' I said, 'it is all very well to talk, but don't you see that I am not very skilful, and burn it all? Are you afraid I shall ruin you in twine?' My look of simplicity rejoiced her, although she was of a very disagreeable and cruel disposition.

"I sent Parrot to tell the king to come one evening under the windows of the tower, that he would find a ladder there, and would know the rest when he arrived. I made it fast; determined to fly with him; but when he saw it he did not wait for me to come down but eagerly ascended it, and rushed into my room just as I was preparing for my flight.

"I was so delighted to see him that I forgot the danger we were in. He repeated his oaths, and implored me not to delay making him my husband. Parrot and Bow-wow were witnesses of our marriage; never was a wedding between people of such high rank concluded with less splendour and fuss, and never was any couple happier than we were.

"Day had scarcely dawned when the king left me: I told him the fairies' terrible plan of marrying me to the little Migonnet; I described his appearance, and he was as horrified as I was. After his departure the hours seemed to me as long as years. I ran to the window, I followed him with my eyes in spite of the darkness, but what was my astonishment to see in the air a fiery chariot drawn by winged salamanders who travelled at such speed that the eye could scarcely follow them. The chariot was accompanied by several guards mounted on ostriches. I had not leisure enough to examine the creature which thus traversed the air; but I imagined it must be a fairy or a sorcerer.

"Soon after Fairy Violent entered my room. 'I bring you good news,' she said; 'your lover has been here for some hours; prepare to receive him; here are clothes and jewels.'

" 'Who told you,' I exclaimed, 'that I wanted to be married? it is not at all my desire; send King Migonnet away. I shall not put on a pin more, whether he thinks me beautiful or ugly; I am not for him.'

" 'Oh ! indeed,' said the fairy, 'what a little rebel ! what a little idiot! I do not permit such conduct, and I will make you . . .'

" 'What will you do to me?' I asked, quite red with the names she had called me. 'Could anyone be worse treated than I was, in a tower with a parrot and a dog, seeing every day the hideous and terrible dragon?'

" 'Oh ! you ungrateful little thing,' said the fairy, 'did you deserve so much care and trouble? I have often told my sisters we should have a poor reward.' She sought them and told them our dispute; they were all greatly surprised.

"Parrot and Bow-wow remonstrated with me, and said if I persisted in rebelling, they foresaw that bitter misfortunes would happen to me. I was so proud of possessing the heart of a great king that I despised the fairies, and the advice of my poor little companions. I did not dress myself, and did my hair all crooked so that Migonnet might find me unpleasing. Our interview took place on the terrace. He came there in his fiery chariot. Never since there were dwarfs had one so small been seen. He walked on his eagle's feet and on his knees all at the same time, because he had no bones in his legs, and he supported himself on diamond crutches. His royal cloak was only half-an-ell long, and a third of it dragged along the ground. His head was as big as a bushel measure, and his nose so big that he carried a dozen birds on it, in whose chirping he delighted. His beard was so tremendous that canaries made their nests in it, and his ear projected an arm's length beyond his head, but it was scarcely noticed because of a high, pointed crown he wore to make himself appear taller. The flame of his chariot roasted the fruits, and dried up the flowers and fountains of my garden. He came to me, arms open to embrace me; I held myself so upright that his chief squire had to lift him up, but directly he was near me I fled into my room, shut the door and windows, so that Migonnet went back to the fairies very angry with me.

"They asked him to forgive my rudeness, and to appease him – for he was to be feared – they determined to bring him into my room at night while I was asleep, to tie my hands and feet, and put me with him into his burning chariot, so that he might take me away with him. The matter once decided, they scarcely scolded me for my rudeness; they only said I must think how to make up for it. Parrot and Bow-wow were surprised at this gentleness. 'Do you know, my mistress,' said the dog, 'I do not augur well from it; the fairies are strange creatures, and very violent.' I laughed at these fears, and awaited my beloved husband most impatiently; he was too anxious to see me to be late. I let down the rope ladder, fully resolved to return with him; he ascended with light step, and spoke to me so tenderly that I dare not recall to memory what he said.

"While we were talking with as much security as if we had been in his palace, suddenly the windows of the room were darkened. The fairies entered on their horrible dragon, Migonnet followed in his fiery chariot, with all his guards and their ostriches. The king, without fear, laid hold of his sword, and only thought of protecting me from the most horrible calamity, for, shall I tell you, sir? the savage creatures set their dragon on him, and it devoured him before my very eyes.

"In despair at his misfortune and mine, I threw myself into the horrid monster's mouth, wishing him to swallow me as he had just swallowed all I loved best in the world. He was very willing, but not so the fairies, who were more cruel than he was. 'We must reserve her,' they said, 'for longer torment; a speedy death is too good for that unworthy girl.' They touched me and I at once became a white cat. They brought me to this magnificent palace, which belonged to my father. They changed all the lords and ladies into cats; of some they allowed only the hands to be seen, and reduced me to the deplorable condition in which you found me, informing me of my rank, of the death of my father and mother, and that I could only be delivered from my cat-form by a prince who should exactly resemble the husband they had torn from me. You, sir, possess that likeness," she continued, "the same features, same expression, the same tone of voice. I was struck by it directly I saw you. I was informed of all that had happened and will happen; my troubles are at an end."

"And mine, beautiful queen," said the prince, throwing himself at her feet, "will they be of long duration?"

"I already love you more than my life, sir," said the queen. "We must go to your father and see what he thinks of me, and if he will consent to what you desire."

She went out, the prince took her hand, and she stepped into a chariot more magnificent than those he had hitherto seen. The rest of the equipment equalled it in such a degree that all the horses' shoes were of emerald with diamond nails. Probably that is the only time such a thing was seen. I do not relate the pleasant conversation of the queen and the prince; it was unique in its charm and intelligence, and the young prince was as perfect as she was: so that their thoughts were most beautiful.

When they were near the castle where the prince was to

meet his two eldest brothers, the queen went inside a little crystal rock whose points were all adorned with rubies and gold. It had curtains all round, so that you could not see it, and it was carried by handsome young men magnificently attired. The prince remained in the chariot, and perceived his brothers walking with very beautiful princesses. When they recognized him they drew near to receive him, and asked him if he had brought a mistress with him. He said he had been unfortunate enough during all his travels only to meet very ugly women, and the most beautiful thing he had brought was a little white cat. They began to laugh at his simplicity. "A cat!" they said; "are you afraid that our palace will be eaten up by mice?" The prince replied that he was certainly not wise to make his father such a present, and each then took his way to the town.

The elder princes and their princesses got into barouches of gold and azure, the horses wore feathers and aigrettes on their heads, and nothing could have been more brilliant than the cavalcade. Our young prince followed, and then the crystal rock that everybody looked at with admiration.

The courtiers hastened to tell the king that the three princes had arrived. "Do they bring beautiful women with them?" asked the king. "It is impossible that they should be surpassed," was their reply. He seemed vexed at the answer. The two princes eagerly entered with their wonderful princesses. The king welcomed them kindly, and did not know to which to award the prize. He looked at the youngest, and said: "This time you come alone?"

"Your majesty will see in that rock a little white cat," replied the prince, "which mews so prettily and is so gentle that she will charm you."

The king smiled, and himself opened the rock, but, as he approached it, the queen by a spring shattered it to pieces, and appeared like the sun which has been for some time hidden by a cloud; her fair hair was flowing over her shoulders, and fell in long curls to her feet; her head was encircled with flowers; her gown was of a light white gauze, lined with pink silk; she rose and made the king a low curtsey, who, in the excess of his admiration, could not help exclaiming: "This is the matchless woman who deserves my crown."

"Sire," she said, "I am not come to take from you a throne you fill so worthily. I possess, by inheritance, six kingdoms: allow me to offer you one, and give the same to each of your sons. As a reward, I only ask for your affection, and this young prince for my husband. We shall have quite enough with three kingdoms." The king and the court uttered cries of joy and astonishment. The marriage was celebrated at once, and also the marriage of the two princes, so that the court spent many months in amusements and delights. Then each went to rule his own kingdom. The beautiful White Cat was immortalized as much by her goodness and generosity as by her rare merit and beauty.

CATS AND DOGS

"The visionary chooses a cat; the man of concrete
a dog. Hamlet must have kept a cat."
Anonymous

A Cat's Conscience

ANONYMOUS

A Dog will often steal a bone,
But conscience lets him not alone,
And by his tail his guilt is known.

But cats consider theft a game,
And, howsoever you may blame,
Refuse the slightest sign of shame.

When food mysteriously goes,
The chances are that Pussy knows
More than she leads you to suppose.

And hence there is no need for you,
If Puss declines a meal or two,
To feel her pulse and make ado.

Abner of the Porch

GEOFFREY HOUSEHOLD (b. 1900)

When my voice broke, even Abner and MacGillivray understood my grief. I did not expect sympathy from MacGillivray, for he had no reason to like me. But he knew what it was to be excluded from cathedral ceremonies. He was the bishop's dog.

Abner was masterless. I would not claim that he appreciated the alto's solo in the 'Magnificat' when the organ was hushed and there was no other sound in the million and a half cubic feet of the cathedral but the slender purity of a boy's voice; yet he would patronize me after such occasions with the air of the master alto which he might have been. Though not a full tom, he knew the ancestral songs which resemble our own. To our ears the scale of cats is distasteful, but one cannot deny them sustained notes of singular loveliness and clarity.

Abner's career had followed a common human pattern. My father was the gardener, responsible for the shaven lawns and discreet flowerbeds of the cathedral close. Some three years earlier he had suffered from an invasion of moles – creatures of ecclesiastical subtlety who avoided all the crude traps set for them by a mere layman. The cat, appearing from nowhere, took an interest. After a week he had caught the lot, laying out his game-bag each morning upon the tarpaulin which covered the mower.

Fed and praised by my father, he began to pay some attention to public relations and attracted the attention of visitors. Officially recognized as an ornament of the cathedral when his photograph appeared in the local paper, he ventured to advance from the lawns and tombstones to the porch. There he captivated the dean, always politely rising from the stone bench and thrusting his noble flanks against the gaitered leg. He was most gracious to the bishop and the higher clergy, but he would only stroke the dean. He knew very well from bearing and tone of voice, gentle though they were, that the cathedral belonged to him. It was the dean who christened him Abner.

To such a personage the dog of our new bishop was a disaster. MacGillivray was of respectable middle age, and had on occasion a sense of dignity; but when dignity was not called for he behaved like any other Aberdeen terrier and would race joyously round the cathedral or across the close, defying whatever human being was in charge of him to catch the lead which bounced and flew behind.

His first meeting with his rival set the future tone of their relations. He ventured with appalling temerity to make sport of the cathedral cat. Abner stretched himself, yawned, allowed MacGillivray's charge to approach within a yard, leaped to the narrow and rounded top of a tombstone and, draping himself over it, went ostentatiously to sleep. MacGillivray jumped and yapped at the tail tip which graciously waved for him, and then realized that he was being treated as a puppy. After that, the two passed each other politely but without remark. In our closed world of the cathedral such coolness between servants of dean and servants of bishop was familiar.

MacGillivray considered that he should be on permanent duty with his master. Since he was black, small and ingenious, it was difficult to prevent him. So devoted a friend could not be cruelly chained – and in summer the French windows of the Bishop's Palace were always open.

He first endeared himself to choir and clergy at the ceremony of the bishop's installation. Magnificent in mitre and full robes, the bishop at the head of his procession knocked with his crozier upon the cathedral door to demand admission. Mac-Gillivray, observing that his master was shut out and in need of help, hurtled across the close, bounced at the door and added his excited barks to the formal solemnity of the bishop's order.

Led away in disapproving silence, he took the enormity of his crime more seriously than we did. On his next appearance he behaved with decent humility, following the unconscious bishop down the chancel and into the pulpit with bowed head and tail well below horizontal.

Such anxious piety was even more embarrassing than bounce. It became my duty, laid upon me by the bishop in person, to ensure on all formal occasions that MacGillivray had not evaded the butler and was safely confined. I was even empowered to tie him up to the railings on the north side of the close in cases of emergency.

I do not think the bishop ever realized what was troubling his friend and erring brother, MacGillivray – normally a dog of sense who could mind his own business however great his affection for his master. When he accompanied the bishop around the diocese he never committed the solecism of entering a parish church and never used the vicar's cat as an objective for assault practice.

His indiscipline at home was, we were all sure, due to jealousy of Abner. He resented with Scottish obstinacy the fact that he was ejected in disgrace from the cathedral whereas

Abner was not. He could not be expected to understand that Abner's discreet movements were beyond human control.

The dean could and did quite honestly declare that he had never seen that cat in the cathedral. Younger eyes, however, which knew where to look, had often distinguished Abner curled up on the ornate stone canopy over the tomb of a seventeenth-century admiral. In winter, he would sometimes sleep upon the left arm of a stone crusader in the cavity between shield and mailed shirt – a dank spot, I thought, until I discovered that it captured a current of warm air from the grating beside the effigy. In both his resting-places he was, if he chose to be, invisible. He was half Persian, tiger-striped with brownish grey on lighter grey, and he matched the stone of the cathedral.

As the summer went by, the feud between Abner and MacGillivray became more subtle. Both scored points. Mac-Gillivary, if he woke up feeling youthful, used to chase the tame pigeons in the close. One morning, to the surprise of both dog and bird, a pigeon failed to get out of the way in time and broke a wing. MacGillivray was embarrassed. He sniffed the pigeon, wagged his tail to show that there was no ill-feeling and sat down to think.

Abner strolled from the porch and held down the pigeon with a firm, gentle paw. He picked it up in his mouth and presented it with liquid and appealing eyes to an elegant American tourist who was musing sentimentally in the close. She swore that the cat had asked her to heal the bird – which, by remaining a whole week in our town in and out of the vet's consulting room, she did. Personally, I think that Abner was attracted by the feline grace of her walk and was suggesting that, as the pigeon could be of no more use to the cathedral, she might as well eat it. But whatever his motives, he had again made MacGillivray look a clumsy and impulsive fool.

MacGillivray's revenge was a little primitive. He deposited bones and offal in dark corners of the porch and pretended that Abner had put them there. That was the second worst crime he knew – to leave on a human floor the inedible portion of his meals.

The verger was deceived and submitted a grave complaint in writing to the dean. The dean, however, knew very well that Abner had no interest in mutton bones, old or new. He was familiar with the cat's tastes. Indeed, it was rumoured from the deanery that he secreted a little box in his pocket at meals, into which he would drop such delicacies as the head of a small trout or the liver of a roast duck.

I cannot remember all the incidents of the cold war. And, anyway, I could not swear to their truth. My father and the dean read into the animals' behaviour motives which were highly unlikely and then shamelessly embroidered them, creating a whole miscellany of private legend for the canons and the choir. So I will only repeat the triumph of MacGillivray and its sequel, both of which I saw myself.

That fulfilment of every dog's dream appeared at first final and overwhelming victory. It was 1 September, the feast of St Giles, our patron saint. Evensong was a full choral and instrumental service, traditional, exquisite, and attracting a congregation whose interest was in music rather than religion. The bishop was to preach. Perhaps the effort of composition, of appealing to well-read intellectuals without offending the simpler clergy, had created an atmosphere of hard work and anxiety in the bishop's study. At any rate, MacGillivray was nervous and mischievous.

While I was ensuring his comfort before shutting him up, he twitched the lead out of my hand and was off on his quarter-mile course round the cathedral looking for a private entrance. When at last I caught him, the changes of the bells had stopped. I had only five minutes before the processional entry of the choir. There wasn't even time to race across the close and tie him up to the railings.

I rushed into the north transept with MacGillivray under my arm, pushed him down the stairs into the crypt and shut the door behind him. I knew that he could not get out. Our Norman crypt was closed to visitors during the service, and no one on a summer evening would have reason to go down to the masons' and carpenters' stores, the strong-room or the boilers. All I feared was that MacGillivray's yaps might be heard through the gratings in the cathedral floor.

I dived into my ruffled surplice and took my place in the procession, earning the blackest possible looks from the choirmaster. I just had time to explain to him that it was the fault of MacGillivray. I was not forgiven, but the grin exchanged between choir-master and precentor suggested that I probably would be – if I wasn't still panting by the time that the alto had to praise all famous men and our fathers that begat us.

St Giles, if he still had any taste for earthly music, must have approved his servants that evening. The bishop, always an effective preacher, surpassed himself. His sinewy arguments were of course beyond me, but I had my eye – vain little beast that I was – on the music critics from the London papers, and I could see that several of them were so interested that they were bursting to take over the pulpit and reply.

Only once did he falter, when the barking of MacGillivray, hardly perceptible to anyone but his master and me, caught the episcopal ear. Even then his momentary hesitation was put down to a search for the right word.

I felt that my desperate disposal of MacGillivray might not be appreciated. He must have been audible to any of the congregation sitting near the gratings of the northern aisle. So I shot down to release him immediately after the recessional. The noise was startling as soon as I opened the door. MacGillivray was holding the stairs against a stranger in the crypt.

The man was good-dogging him and trying to make him shut up. He had a small suitcase by his side. When two sturdy vergers, attracted by the noise, appeared hot on my heels, the intruder tried to bolt – dragging behind him MacGillivray with teeth closed on the turn-ups of his trousers. We detained him and opened the suitcase. It contained twenty pounds' weight of the cathedral silver. During the long service our massive but primitive strong-room door had been expertly opened.

The congregation was dispersing, but bishop, dean, archdeacon and innumerable canons were still in the cathedral. They attended the excitement just as any other crowd. Under the circumstances, MacGillivray was the centre of the most complimentary fuss. The canons would have genially petted any dog. But this was the bishop's dog. The wings of gowns and surplices flowed over him like those of exclamatory seagulls descending upon a stranded fish.

Dignity was represented only by our local superintendent of police and the terrier himself. When the thief had been led away, MacGillivray reverently followed his master out of the cathedral; his whole attitude reproached us for ever dreaming that he might take advantage of his popularity.

At the porch, however, he turned round and loosed one short, triumphant bark into the empty nave. The bishop's chaplain unctuously suggested that it was a little voice of thanksgiving. So it was – but far from pious. I noticed where MacGillivray's muzzle was pointing. That bark was for a softness of outline, a shadow, a striping of small stone pinnacles upon the canopy of the Admiral's Tomb.

For several days – all of ten I should say – Abner deserted both the cathedral and its porch. He then returned to his first friend, helping my father to make the last autumn cut of the grass and offering his catch of small game for approval. The dean suggested that he was in need of sunshine. My father shook his head and said nothing. It was obvious to both of us that for Abner the cathedral had been momentarily defiled. He reminded me of an old verger who gave in his resignation – it was long overdue anyway – after discovering a family party eating lunch from paper bags in the Lady Chapel.

He went back to the porch a little before the harvest festival, for he always enjoyed that. During a whole week while the decorations were in place he could find a number of discreet lairs where it was impossible to detect his presence. There may also have been a little hunting in the night. We did not attempt to fill the vastness of the cathedral with all the garden produce dear to a parish church, but the dean was fond of fat sheaves of wheat, oats and barley, bound round the middle like sheaves on a heraldic shield.

It was his own festival in his own cathedral, so that he, not the bishop, conducted it. He had made the ritual as enjoyable as that of Christmas, reviving ancient customs for which he was always ready to quote authority. I suspect that medieval deans would have denied his interpretation of their scanty records, but they would have recognized a master of stage management.

His most effective revival was a procession of cathedral tenants and benefactors, each bearing some offering in kind which the dean received on the altar steps. Fruit, honey and cakes were common, always with some touch of magnificence in the quality, quantity or container. On one occasion, the landlord of the Pilgrim's Inn presented a roasted peacock set in jelly with tail feathers erect. There was some argument about this on the grounds that it ran close to advertisement. But the dean would not be dissuaded. He insisted that any craftsman had the right to present a unique specimen of his skill.

That year the gifts were more humble. My father, as always, led the procession with a basket tray upon which was a two-foot bunch of black grapes from the vinery in the canons' garden. A most original participant was a dear old nursery gardener who presented a plant of his new dwarf camellia which had been the botanical sensation of the year and could not yet be bought for money. There was also a noble milk-pan of Alpine strawberries and cream – which, we hoped, the cathedral school would share next day with the alms houses.

While the file of some twenty persons advanced into the chancel, the choir full-bloodedly sang the 65th Psalm to the joyous score of our own organist. The dean's sense of theatre was as faultless as ever. Lavish in ritual and his own vestments, he then played his part with the utmost simplicity. He thanked and blessed each giver almost conversationally.

Last in the procession were four boys of the cathedral school bearing a great silver bowl of nuts gathered in the hedgerows. The gift and their movements were traditional. As they separated, two to the right and two to the left, leaving the dean alone upon the altar steps, a shadow appeared at his feet and vanished so swiftly that by the time our eyes had registered its true, soft shape it was no longer there.

The dean bent down and picked up a dead field-mouse. He

was not put out of countenance for a moment. He laid it reverently with the other gifts. No one was present to be thanked; but when the dean left the cathedral after service and stopped in the porch to talk to Abner he was – to the surprise of the general public – still wearing his full vestments, stiff, gorgeous and suggesting the power of the Church to protect and armour with its blessing the most humble of its servants.

from *The Europe That Was*

The Farmer, the Spaniel and the Cat

EDWARD MOORE (1712–57)

As at his board a farmer sat,
Replenish'd by his homely treat,
His favourite Spaniel near him stood,
And with his master shar'd the food;
The crackling bones his jaws devour'd,
His lapping tongue the trenchers scour'd,
Till sated, now supine he lay,
And snor'd the rising fumes away.

The hungry Cat in turn drew near,
And humbly crav'd a servant's share;
Her modest worth the Master knew,
And straight the fattening morsel threw;
Enrag'd the snarling Cur awoke,
And this with spiteful envy spoke:

"They only claim a right to eat
Who earn by services their meat:
Me zeal and industry inflame
To scour the fields and spring the game,
Or plunging in the wintry wave
For man the wounded bird to save.
With watchful diligence I keep

From prowling wolves his fleecy sheep,
At home his midnight hours secure,
And drive the robber from the door:
For this his breast with kindness glows,
For this his hand the food bestows;
And shall thy indolence impart
A warmer friendship to his heart,
That thus he robs me of my due,
To pamper such vile things as you?"

"I own (with meekness Puss replied)
Superior merit on your side;
Nor does my breast with envy swell
To find it recompens'd so well;
Yet I, in what my nature can,
Contribute to the good of man.
Whose claws destroy the pilfering mouse?
Who drives the vermin from the house?
Or, watchful for the labouring swain,
From lurking rats secures the grain?
From hence if he rewards bestow,
Why should your heart with gall o'erflow?
Why pine my happiness to see,
Since there's enough for you and me?"

"Thy words are just," the Farmer cried,
And spurn'd the snarler from his side.

On Cats and Dogs

JEROME K. JEROME (1859–1927)

Yet, in general, I like cats and dogs very much indeed. What jolly chaps they are! They are much superior to human beings as companions. They do not quarrel or argue with you. They never talk about themselves, but listen to you while you talk about yourself, and keep up an appearance of being interested in the conversation. They never make stupid remarks. They never observe to Miss Brown across a dinner-table, that they always understood she was very sweet on Mr Jones (who has just married Miss Robinson). They never mistake your wife's cousin for her husband, and fancy that you are the father-in-law. And they never ask a young author with fourteen tragedies, sixteen comedies, seven farces, and a couple of burlesques in his desk, why he doesn't write a play.

They never say unkind things. They never tell us of our faults, "merely for our own good". They do not, at inconvenient moments, mildly remind us of our past follies and mistakes. They do not say, "Oh yes, a lot of use *you* are, if you are ever really wanted" – sarcastic like. They never inform us, as our *inamoratas* sometimes do, that we are not nearly so nice as we used to be. We are always the same to them.

They are always glad to see us. They are with us in all our humours. They are merry when we are glad, sober when we feel solemn, sad when we are sorrowful.

"Hulloa! happy, and want a lark! Right you are; I'm your man. Here I am, frisking round you, leaping, barking, pirouetting, ready for any amount of fun and mischief. Look at my eyes, if you doubt me. What shall it be? A romp in the drawing-room, and never mind the furniture, or a scamper in the fresh, cool air, a scud across the fields, and down the hill, and won't we let old Gaffer Goggles's geese know what time o' day it is, neither. Whoop! come along."

Or you'd like to be quiet and think. Very well. Pussy can sit on the arm of the chair, and purr, and Montmorency will curl himself up on the rug, and blink at the fire, yet keeping one eye on you the while, in case you are seized with any sudden desire in the direction of rats.

And when we bury our face in our hands and wish we had never been born, they don't sit up very straight, and observe that we have brought it all upon ourselves. They don't even hope it will be a warning to us. But they come up softly; and shove their heads against us. If it is a cat, she stands on your shoulder, rumples your hair, and says, "Lor', I am sorry for you, old man," as plain as words can speak; and if it is a dog, he looks up at you with his big, true eyes, and says with them, "Well, you've always got me, you know. We'll go through the world together, and always stand by each other, won't we?"

from *Idle Thoughts of an Idle Fellow* (1886)

The Vain Cat

AMBROSE BIERCE (1842–1914)

Remarked a Tortoise to a Cat:
"Your speed's a thing to marvel at!
I saw you as you flitted by,
And wished I were one-half so spry."
The Cat said, humbly: "Why, indeed
I was not showing then my speed –
That was a poor performance." Then
She said exultantly (as when
The condor feels his bosom thrill
Remembering Chimborazo's hill,
And how he soared so high above,
It looked a valley, he a dove):
" 'Twould fire your very carapace
To see me with a dog in chase!"
Its snout in any kind of swill,
Pride, like a pig, will suck its fill.

Mother Tabbyskins

ELIZABETH ANNA HART (1822–*c.* 1888)

Sitting at a window
In her cloak and hat,
I saw Mother Tabbyskins,

The *real* old cat!
Very old, very old,
Crumplety and lame;
Teaching kittens how to scold –
Is it not a shame?

Kittens in the garden
Looking in her face,
Learning how to spit and swear –
Oh, what a disgrace!
Very wrong, very wrong,
Very wrong and bad;
Such a subject for our song,
Makes us all too sad.

Old Mother Tabbyskins,
Sticking out her head,
Gave a howl, and then a yowl,
Hobbled off to bed.
Very sick, very sick,
Very savage, too;
Pray send for a doctor quick –
Any one will do!

Doctor Mouse came creeping,
Creeping to her bed;
Lanced her gums and felt her pulse,
Whispered she was dead.
Very sly, very sly,
The *real* old cat
Open kept her weather eye –
Mouse! beware of that!

Old Mother Tabbyskins,
Saying "Serves him right",
Gobbled up the doctor, with
Infinite delight.

Very fast, very fast,
Very pleasant, too —
"What a pity it can't last!
Bring another, do!"

Doctor Dog comes running,
Just to see her begs;
Round his neck a comforter,
Trousers on his legs.
Very grand, very grand —
Golden-headed cane
Swinging gaily from his hand,
Mischief in his brain!

"Dear Mother Tabbyskins,
And how are you now?
Let me feel your pulse — so, so;
Show your tongue — bow, wow!
Very ill, very ill,
Please attempt to purr;
Will you take a draught or pill?
Which do you prefer?"

Ah, Mother Tabbyskins,
Who is now afraid?
Of poor little Doctor Mouse
You a mouthful made.
Very nice, very nice
Little doctor he;
But for Doctor Dog's advice
You must pay the fee.

Doctor Dog comes nearer,
Says she must be bled;
I heard Mother Tabbyskins
Screaming in her bed.
Very near, very near,

Scuffling out and in;
Doctor Dog looks full and queer –
Where is Tabbyskin?

I will tell the Moral
Without any fuss:
Those who lead the young astray
Always suffer thus.
Very nice, very nice,
Let our conduct be;
For all doctors are not mice,
Some are dogs, you see!

Hinse the Cat

WASHINGTON IRVING (1783–1859)

Among the other important and privileged members of the
household who figured in attendance at the dinner, was a large
grey cat, who I observed was regaled from time to time with
tit-bits from the table. This sage grimalkin was a favourite of
both master and mistress and slept at night in their room. And
Scott laughingly observed that one of the least wise parts of
their establishment was, that the window was left open at night
for puss to go in and out. The cat assumed a kind of ascendancy
among the quadrupeds; sitting in state in Scott's armchair, and
occasionally stationing himself on a chair beside the door as if to
review his subjects as they passed, giving each dog a cuff beside
the ears as he went by. This clapperclawing was always taken in
good part; it appeared to be, in fact, a mere act of sovereignty
on the part of grimalkin to remind the others of their vassalage;
which they acknowledged, by the most perfect acquiescence. A
general harmony prevailed between sovereign and subjects, and
they would all sleep together in the sunshine.

from "Abbotsford" in *The Crayon Miscellamy* (1849)

Cat Sayings

VARIOUS

If a dog jumps up into your lap, it is because he is fond of you; but if a cat does the same thing, it is because your lap is warmer.

A.N. Whitehead

Cat: a pygmy lion who loves mice, hates dogs, and patronizes human beings.

Oliver Herford

The cat is an anarchist, while the dog is a socialist. He is an aristocratic, tyrannical anarchist, at that.

Carl van Vechten

Somebody once said that a dog looked up to a man as its superior, that a horse regarded a man as its equal, and that a cat looked down on him as its inferior.

Sir Compton Mackenzie

Dog, Cats, Books and the Average Man

ANONYMOUS (1896)

I hope you will not suspect me of making a bid for his affection, when I remark that the Average Man loves the Obvious. By consequence (for, like all unthinking creatures, the duffer's logical), by consequence, his attitude towards the Subtle, the Elusive, when not an attitude of mere torpid indifference, is an attitude of positive distrust and dislike.

Of this ignoble fact, pretty nearly everything – from the popularity of beer and skittles, to the popularity of Mr Hall Caine's novels; from the general's distaste for caviar, to the general's neglect of Mr Henry James's tales – pretty nearly everything is a reminder. But, to go no further afield, for the moment, than his own hearthrug, may I ask you to consider a little the relative positions occupied in the Average Man's regard by the Dog and the Cat?

The Average Man ostentatiously loves the Dog.

The Average Man, when he is not torpidly indifferent to that princely animal, positively distrusts and dislikes the Cat.

I have used the epithet "princely" with intention, in speaking of the near relative of the King of Beasts. The Cat is a Princess of the Blood. Yes, my dear, always a Princess, though the Average Man, with his unerring instinct for the malappropriate word, sometimes names her Thomas. The Cat is always a Princess, because everything nice in this world, everything fine, sensitive, distinguished, everything beautiful, everything worth while, is of essence Feminine, though it may be male by the accident of sex; and that's as true as gospel, let Mr W. E. Henley's lusty young disciples shout their loudest in celebration of the Virile. The Cat is a Princess.

The Dog, on the contrary, is not even a gentleman. Far otherwise: his admirers may do what they will to forget it, the circumstance remains, writ large in every Natural History, that the Dog is sprung from quite the meanest family of the Quadrupeds. That coward thief the wolf is his bastard brother; the carrion hyena is his cousin-german. And in his person, as in his character, bears he not an hundred marks of his base descent? In his rough coat (contrast it with the silken mantle of the Cat); in his harsh, monotonous voice (contrast it with the flexible organ of the Cat, her versatile mewings, chirpings, and purrings, and their innumerable shades and modulations); in the stiff-jointed clumsiness of his movements (compare them to the inexpressible grace and suppleness of the Cat's); briefly, in the all-pervading plebeian commonness that hangs about him like an atmosphere (compare it to the high-bred reserve and dignity that invest the Cat). The wolf's brother, is the Dog not himself a coward? Watch him when, emulating the ruffian who insults an unprotected lady, he puts a Cat to flight in the streets: watch him when the lady halts and turns. Faugh, the craven! with his wild show of savagery so long as there is not the slightest danger

347

– and his sudden chopfallen drawing back when the lady halts and turns! The hyena's cousin, is he not himself of carrion an impassioned amateur? At Constantinople he serves ('tis a labour of love; he receives no stipend) he serves as Public Scavenger, swallowing with greed the ordures cast by the Turk. Scripture tells us to what he returneth: who has failed to observe that he returneth not to his own alone? And the other day, strolling upon the sands by the illimitable sea, I came upon a friend and her pet terrier. She was holding the little beggar by the scruff of his neck, and giving him repeated sousing in a pool. I stood a pleased spectator of this exercise, for the terrier kicked and spluttered and appeared to be unhappy. "He found a decaying jellyfish below there, and rolled in it," my friend pathetically explained. I should like to see the Cat who could be induced to roll in a decaying jellyfish. The Cat's fastidiousness, her meticulous cleanliness, the time and the pains she bestows upon her toilet, and her almost morbid delicacy about certain more private errands, are among the material indications of her patrician nature. It were needless to allude to the vile habits and impudicity of the Dog.

Have you ever met a Dog who wasn't a bounder? Have you ever met a Dog who wasn't a bully, a sycophant, and a snob? Have you ever met a Cat who was? Have you ever met a Cat who would half frighten a timid little girl to death, by rushing at her and barking? Have you ever met a Cat who, left alone with a visitor in your drawing-room, would truculently growl and show her teeth, as often as that visitor ventured to stir in his chair? Have you ever met a Cat who would snarl and snap at the servants, Master's back being turned? Have you ever met a Cat who would cringe to you and fawn to you, and kiss the hand that smote her?

Conscious of her high lineage, the Cat understands and accepts the responsibilities that attach to it. She knows what she owes to herself, to her rank, to the Royal Idea. Therefore, it is you who must be the courtier. The Dog, poor-spirited today, will study your eye to divine your mood, and slavishly adapt his own mood and his behaviour to it. Not so the Cat. As between you and her, it is you who must do the toadying. A guest in the house, never a dependent, she remembers always the courtesy and the consideration that are her due. You must respect her pleasure. Is it her pleasure to slumber, and do you disturb her: note the disdainful melancholy with which she silently comments your rudeness. Is it her pleasure to be grave: tempt her to frolic, you will tempt in vain. It is her pleasure to be cold: nothing in human possibility can win a caress from her. Is it her pleasure to be rid of your presence: only the physical influence of a closed door will persuade her to remain in the room with you. It is you who must be the courtier, and wait upon her desire.

But then!

When, in her own good time, she chooses to unbend, how graciously, how entrancingly, she does it! Oh, the thousand wonderful lovelinesses and surprises of her play! The wit, the humour, the imagination, that inform it! Her ruses, her false leads, her sudden triumphs, her feigned despairs! And the topazes and emeralds that sparkle in her eyes; the satiny lustre of her apparel; the delicious sinuousities of her body! And her parenthetic interruptions of the game: to stride in regal progress round the apartment, flourishing her tail like a banner: or coquettishly to throw herself in some en-ravishing posture at length upon the carpet at your feet: or (if she loves you) to leap upon your shoulder, and press her cheek to yours, and murmur rapturous assurances of her passion! To be loved by a Princess! Whosoever, from the Marquis de Carabas down, has been loved by a Cat, has savoured that felicity. My own particular treasure of a Cat, at this particular moment is lying wreathed about my neck, watching my pen as it moves along the paper, and purring approbation of my views. But when, from time to time, I chance to use a word that doesn't strike her altogether as the fittest, she reaches down her little velvet paw, and dabs it out. I should like to see the Dog who could do that.

But – the Cat is subtle, the Cat is elusive, the Cat is not to be read at a glance, the Cat is not a simple equation. And so the Average Man, gross mutton-devouring, money-grubbing mechanism that he is, when he doesn't just torpidly tolerate her, distrusts her and dislikes her. A great soul, misappreciated, misunderstood, she sits neglected in his chimney-corner; and the fatuous idgit never guesses how she scorns him.

But – the Dog is obvious Any fool can grasp the meaning of the Dog. And the Average Man, accordingly, recreant for once to the snobbism which is his religion, hugs the hyena's cousin to his bosom.

What of it?

Only this: that in the Average Man's sentimental attitude towards the Dog and the Cat, we have a formula, a symbol, for his sentimental attitude towards many things, especially for his sentimental attitude towards Books.

Some books, in their uncouthness, their awkwardness, their boisterousness, in their violation of the decencies of art, in their low truckling to the tastes of the purchaser, in their commonness, their vulgarity, in their total lack of suppleness and distinction, are the very Dogs of Bookland. The Average Man loves 'em. Such as they are, they're obvious.

And other books, by reason of their beauties and their virtues, their graces and refinements; because they are considered finished; because they are delicate, distinguished, aristocratic; because their touch is light, their movement deft and fleet; because they proceed by omission, by implication and suggestion; because they employ the *demi-mot* and the *nuance*; because, in fine, they are Subtle – other books are the Cats of Bookland. And the Average Man hates them or ignores them.

from *The Yellow Book* (1896)

Cats and Aesthetics

ANONYMOUS

To respect the cat is the beginning of the aesthetic sense. At a stage of culture when utility governs all its judgments, mankind prefers the dog . . . There will yet arise a philosopher who will conceive the Absolute as a gigantic and self-satisfied cat, purring as it clasps in comfortable round its own perfection, and uttering as it purrs that line of Edmund Spenser's about the cosmos – "It loved itself because itself was fair."

from *The Nation*

Chattie

MRS HUMPHRY WARD (1851–1920)

Rose sat fanning herself with a portentous hat, which when in its proper place served her, apparently, both as hat and as parasol. She seemed to have been running races with a fine collie, who lay at her feet panting, but studying her with his bright eyes, and evidently ready to be off again at the first indication that his playmate had recovered her wind. Chattie was coming lazily over the lawn, stretching each leg behind her as she walked, tail arched, green eyes flaming in the sun, a model of treacherous beauty.

"Chattie, you fiend, come here!" cried Rose, holding out a hand to her; "if Miss Barks were ever pretty she must have looked like you at this moment."

"I won't have Chattie put upon," said Agnes, establishing herself at the other side of the little tea-table; "she has done you no harm. Come to me, beastie. I won't compare you to disagreeable old maids."

The cat looked from one sister to the other, blinking; then with a sudden magnificent spring leaped on to Agnes's lap and curled herself up there.

"Nothing but cupboard love," said Rose scornfully, in answer to Agnes's laugh; "she knows you will give her bread and butter and I won't, out of a double regard for my skirts and her morals."

from *Robert Elsmere* (1888)

Dog and Cat

WILLIAM SHAKESPEARE (1564–1616)

I think Crab my dog be the sourest-natured dog that lives: my mother weeping, my father wailing, my sister crying, our maid howling, our cat wringing her hands, and all our house in a great perplexity, yet did not this cruel-hearted cur shed one tear.

Cats as Faithful as Dogs?

JEROME K. JEROME (1859–1927)

Cats have the credit of being more worldly wise than dogs – of looking more after their own interests, and being less blindly devoted to those of their friends. And we men and women are naturally shocked at such selfishness. Cats certainly do love a family that has a carpet in the kitchen more than a family that has not; and if there are many children about, they prefer to spend their leisure time next door. But, taken altogether, cats are libelled. Make a friend of one, and she will stick to you through thick and thin. All the cats that I have had have been most firm comrades.

from "On Cats and Dogs" in *Idle Thoughts of an Idle Fellow* (1886)

Cheese and Biscuits

EMILE ZOLA (1840–1902)

When the cheese and biscuits were put upon the table, Matthew's sudden appearance caused a boisterous commotion. Until then he had been lying asleep under the table. But the arrival of the biscuits had awakened him. He seemed to have scented them in his sleep. Every evening, just at this stage of the meal, it was his custom to get up and shake himself and make the round of the table, questioning the faces of the diners to see if they were charitably disposed. Usually it was Lazare who first took pity upon him, but that evening Matthew, on his second circuit of the table, halted by Pauline's side and gazed up at her earnestly with his honest human-like eyes; and then, divining in her a friend both of man and beast, he laid his huge head on her little knee, without dropping his glance of mild supplication.

"Oh, what a shameful beggar you are!" said Madame Chanteau. "Aren't you ashamed of yourself, Matthew, to be so greedy?"

The dog swallowed at a single gulp the piece of biscuit which Pauline offered him, and then again laid his head on her little knee, asking for another piece, with his eyes constantly fixed on those of his new friend. She laughed at him and kissed him and found him very amusing, with his flattened ears and the black spot under his left eye, the only spot of colour that marked his rough white hairy coat. Then there came a diversion of another character. Minouche, growing jealous, leapt lightly upon the edge of the table, and began to purr and rub her head against the little girl's chin, swaying her supple body the while with all the grace of a young kid. To poke one with her cold nose and kiss one lightly with her sharp teeth, while she pounded about with her feet like a baker kneading dough, was her feline way of caressing. Pauline was now quite delighted between the two animals. The cat on her left, the dog on her right, took possession of her and worried her shamefully in order to secure all her biscuits.

"Send them away," said her aunt. "They will leave you nothing for yourself."

"Oh! that doesn't matter," she placidly replied, feeling quite happy in being despoiled.

They finished, and Véronique removed the dishes. The two animals, seeing the table quite bare, gave their lips a last lick and then took themselves off, without even saying "thank you".

from *The Joy of Life*

Matthew Arnold's Dogs and Cats

MRS HUMPHRY WARD (1851–1920)

His visits to Russell Square, and our expeditions to Cobham where he lived, in the pretty cottage beside the Mole, are marked in memory with a very white stone. The only drawback to the Cobham visits were the "dear, dear boys"! – i.e. the dachshunds, Max and Geist, who, however adorable in themselves, had no taste for visitors and no intention of letting such intruding creatures interfere with their possession of their master. One would go down to Cobham, eager to talk to "Uncle Matt" about a book or an article – covetous at any rate of *some* talk with him undisturbed. And it would all end in a breathless chase after Max, through field after field where the little wretch was harrying either sheep or cows, with the dear poet, hoarse with shouting, at his heels. The dogs were always *in the party*, talked to, caressed, or scolded exactly like spoilt children; and the cat of the house was almost equally dear. Once, at Harrow, the then ruling cat – a tom – broke his leg, and the house was in lamentation. The vet was called in, and hurt him horribly. Then Uncle Matt ran up to town, met Professor Huxley at the Athenaeum, and anxiously consulted him. "I'll go down with you," said Huxley. The two travelled back instanter to Harrow, and while Uncle Matt held the cat, Huxley – who had begun life, let it be remembered, as Surgeon to the *Rattlesnake!* – examined him, the two black heads together. There is a rumour that Charles Kingsley was included in the consultation. Finally the limb was put in splints, and left to nature. All went well.

from *A Writer's Recollections* (1918)

The Cat

VICOMTE DE CHATEAUBRIAND (1768–1848)

I value in the cat the independent and almost ungrateful spirit which prevents her from attaching herself to anyone, the indifference with which she passes from the salon to the housetop. When we caress her, she stretches herself and arches her back responsively; but this is because she feels an agreeable sensation, not because she takes a silly satisfaction, like the dog, in faithfully loving a thankless master. The cat lives alone, has no need of society, obeys only when she pleases, pretends to sleep that she may see the more clearly, and scratches everything on which she can lay her paw.

My Pets

SIR RICHARD STEELE (1672–1729)

They both of them sit by my fire every Evening and wait with Impatience; and, at my Entrance, never fail of running up to me, and bidding me Welcome, each of them in its proper Language. As they have been bred up together from Infancy, and have seen no other Company, they have acquired each other's Manners; so that the Dog gives himself the Airs of a Cat, and the Cat, in several of her Motions and Gestures, affects the Behaviour of the little Dog.

from *The Tatler* (1711)

The Cat and the Money

EMILE ZOLA (1840–1902)

Just then Matthew appeared to have smelt the tea in his dreams, for he gave himself a shake, and again came and thrust his big head upon the edge of the table. Minouche, too, got up and stretched herself and yawned, and, when she was quite awake, she craned out her neck to sniff at the packet of papers in the greasy covers. As the Chanteaus glanced at Pauline, they saw that her eyes were also open and fixed upon the scrip and the old ledger binding.

"Ah! she knows very well what is inside there," said Madame Chanteau. "Don't you, my dear? I showed them all to you in Paris. That is what your poor father and mother have left you." Tears trickled down the child's face. Her grief often recurred in April-like showers. But she soon smiled again through her tears, feeling amused at Minouche, who had for a long time smelt at the papers and was doubtless attracted by their odour, for she began to purr and rub her head against the corners of the ledger.

"Come away, Minouche!" cried Madame Chanteau. "Money isn't to be made a plaything of!"

Chanteau laughed, and so did Lazare. With his head resting on the edge of the table, Matthew was becoming quite excited. Looking eagerly with his flaming eyes at the packet of papers which he must have taken for some great delicacy, he began to bark at the cat. Then all the family grew lively. Pauline caught up Minouche and fondled her in her arms as though she were a doll.

from *The Joy of Life*

Little Puss

ANONYMOUS

As Pussy sat upon the step,
    Taking the nice fresh air,
A neighbour's little dog came by,
    "Ah, Pussy, are you there?
Good morning, Mistress Pussy Cat,
    Come, tell me how you do?"
"Quite well, I thank you," Puss replied;
    "Now tell me how are you?"

from *Little Rhymes for Little Folks* (1823)

A Superior Cat

SIR WALTER SCOTT (1771–1832)

I have added a romantic inmate to my family – a large bloodhound, allowed to be the finest dog of the kind in Scotland, perfectly gentle, affectionate, good-natured, and the darling of all the children. He is between the deer-greyhound and mastiff, with a shaggy mane like a lion, and always sits beside me at dinner, his head as high as the back of my chair; yet it will gratify you to know that a favourite cat keeps him in the greatest possible order, insists upon all rights of precedence, and scratches with impunity the nose of an animal who would make no bones of a wolf, and pulls down a red deer without fear or difficulty. I heard my friend set up some most piteous howls (and I assure you the noise was no joke), all occasioned by his fear of passing Puss, who had stationed himself on the stairs.

from a letter to Joanna Baillie

Montmorency's Bad Day

JEROME K. JEROME (1859–1927)

We got up tolerably early on the Monday morning at Marlow, and went for a bathe before breakfast; and, coming back, Montmorency made an awful ass of himself. The only subject on which Montmorency and I have any serious difference of opinion is cats. I like cats; Montmorency does not.

When I meet a cat, I say, "Poor Pussy!" and stoop down and tickle the side of its head; and the cat sticks up its tail in a rigid, cast-iron manner, arches its back, and wipes its nose up against my trousers; and all is gentleness and peace. When Montmorency meets a cat, the whole street knows about it; and there is enough bad language wasted in ten seconds to last an ordinary respectable man all his life, with care.

357

I do not blame the dog (contenting myself, as a rule, with merely clouting his head or throwing stones at him), because I take it that it is his nature. Fox-terriers are born with about four times as much original sin in them as other dogs are, and it will take years and years of patient effort on the part of us Christians to bring about any appreciable reformation in the rowdiness of the fox-terrier nature . . .

Such is the nature of fox-terriers; and, therefore, I do not blame Montmorency for his tendency to row with cats; but he wished he had not given way to it that morning.

We were, as I have said, returning from a dip, and halfway up the High Street a cat darted out from one of the houses in front of us, and began to trot across the road. Montmorency gave a cry of joy – the cry of a stern warrior who sees his enemy given over to his hands – the sort of cry Cromwell might have uttered when the Scots came down the hill – and flew after his prey.

His victim was a large black tom. I never saw a larger cat, nor a more disreputable-looking cat. It had lost half its tail, one of its ears, and a fairly appreciable proportion of its nose. It was a long, sinewy-looking animal. It had a calm, contented air about it.

Montmorency went for that poor cat at the rate of twenty miles an hour; but the cat did not hurry up – did not seem to have grasped the idea that its life was in danger. It trotted quietly on until its would-be assassin was within a yard of it, and then it turned round and sat down in the middle of the road, and looked at Montmorency with a gentle, inquiring expression, that said: "Yes! You want me?"

Montmorency does not lack pluck; but there was something about the look of that cat that might have chilled the heart of the boldest dog. He stopped abruptly, and looked back at Tom.

Neither spoke; but the conversation that one could imagine was clearly as follows:

THE CAT: "Can I do anything for you?"

MONTMORENCY: "No – no, thanks."

THE CAT: "Don't you mind speaking if you really want anything, you know."

MONTMORENCY (*backing down the High Street*): "Oh, no – not at all – certainly – don't you trouble. I – I am afraid I've made a mistake. I thought I knew you. Sorry I disturbed you."

THE CAT: "Not at all – quite a pleasure. Sure you don't want anything, now?"

MONTMORENCY (*still backing*): "Not at all, thanks – not at all – very kind of you. Good morning."

THE CAT: "Good morning."

Then the cat rose, and continued his trot; and Montmorency, fitting what he calls his tail carefully into its groove, came back to us, and took up an unimportant position in the rear.

To this day, if you say the word "Cats!" to Montmorency, he will visibly shrink and look up piteously at you, as if to say: "Please don't."

from *Three Men in a Boat* (1889)

The Cat's Pilgrimage

JAMES ANTHONY FROUDE (1818–94)

I

"It is all very fine," said the Cat, yawning, and stretching herself against the fender, "but it is rather a bore; I don't see the use of it." She raised herself, and arranging her tail into a ring, and seating herself in the middle of it, with her forepaws in a straight line from her shoulders, at right angles to the hearth rug, she looked pensively at the fire. "It is very odd," she went on. "There is my poor Tom; he is gone. I saw him stretched out in the yard. I spoke to him, and he took no notice of me. He won't, I suppose, ever any more, for they put him under the earth. Nice fellow he was. It is wonderful how little one cares about it. So many jolly evenings we spent together; and now I seem to get on quite as well without him. I wonder what has become of him; and my last children, too, what has become of them. What are we here for? I would ask the men, only they are so conceited and stupid they can't understand what we say. I hear them droning away, teaching their little ones every day; telling them to be good, and to do what they are bid, and all that. Nobody ever tells me to do anything; if they do I don't do it, and I am not very good. I wonder whether I should be any better if I minded more. I'll ask the Dog.

"Dog," said she, to a little fat spaniel coiled up on a mat, like a lady's muff with a head and tail stuck on to it, "Dog, what do you make of it all?"

The Dog faintly opened his languid eyes, looked sleepily at the Cat for a moment, and dropped them again.

"Dog," she said, "I want to talk to you; don't go to sleep. Can't you answer a civil question?"

"Don't bother me," said the Dog, "I am tired. I stood on my hind legs ten minutes this morning before I could get my breakfast, and it hasn't agreed with me."

"Who told you to do it?" said the Cat.

"Why, the lady I have to take care of me," replied the Dog.

"Do you feel any better for it, Dog, after you have been standing on your legs?" asked she.

"Haven't I told you, you stupid Cat, that it hasn't agreed with me? Let me go to sleep and don't plague me."

"But I mean," persisted the Cat, "do you feel improved, as the men call it? They tell their children that if they do what they are told they will improve, and grow good and great. Do you feel good and great?"

"What do I know?" said the Dog. "I eat my breakfast and am happy. Let me alone."

"Do you never think, O Dog without a soul! Do you never wonder what dogs are, and what this world is?"

The Dog stretched himself, and rolled his eyes lazily round the room. "I conceive," he said, "that the world is for dogs, and men and women are put into it to take care of dogs; women to take care of little dogs like me, and men for the big dogs like those in the yard – and cats," he continued, "are to know their place, and not to be troublesome."

"They beat you sometimes," said the Cat. "Why do they do that? They never beat me."

"If they forget their places, and beat me," snarled the Dog, "I bite them, and they don't do it again. I should like to bite you, too, you nasty Cat; you have woken me up."

"There may be truth in what you say," said the Cat, calmly; "but I think your view is limited. If you listened like me you would hear the men say it was all made for them, and you and I were made to amuse them."

"They don't dare to say so?" said the Dog.

"They do, indeed," said the Cat. "I hear many things which you lose by sleeping so much. They think I am asleep, and so they are not afraid to talk before me; but my ears are open when my eyes are shut."

"You surprise me," said the Dog. "I never listen to them, expect when I take notice of them, and then they never talk of anything except of me."

"I could tell you a thing or two about yourself which you don't know," said the Cat. "You have never heard, I dare say, that once upon a time your fathers lived in a temple, and that people prayed to them?"

"Prayed! what is that?"

"Why, they went on their knees to you to ask you to give them good things, just as you stand on your toes to them now to ask for your breakfast. You don't know either that you have got one of those bright things we see up in the air at night called after you?"

"Well, it is just what I said," answered the Dog. "I told you it was all made for us. They never did anything of that sort for you."

"Didn't they? Why, there was a whole city where the people did nothing else, and as soon as we got stiff and couldn't move about any more, instead of being put under the ground like poor Tom, we used to be stuffed full of all sorts of nice things, and kept better than we were when we were alive."

"You are a very wise Cat," answered her companion, "but what good is it knowing all this?"

"Why, don't you see?" said she. "They don't do it any more. We are going down in the world, we are, and that is why living on this way is such an unsatisfactory sort of thing. I don't mean to complain for myself, and you needn't, Dog; we have a quite life of it; but a quiet life is not the thing, and if there is nothing to be done except sleep and eat, and eat and sleep, why, as I said before, I don't see the use of it. There is something more in it than that; there was once, and there will be again, and I sha'n't be happy till I find it out. It is a shame, Dog, I say. The men have been here only a few thousand years, and we – why, we have been here hundreds of thousands. If we are older, we ought to be wiser. I'll go and ask the creatures in the wood."

"You'll learn more from the men," said the Dog.

"They are stupid, and they don't know what I say to them; besides, they are so conceited they care for nothing except themselves. No, I shall try what I can do in the woods. I'd as soon go after poor Tom as stay living any longer like this."

"And where is poor Tom?" yawned the Dog.

"That is just one of the things I want to know," answered she. "Poor Tom is lying under the yard, or the skin of him, but whether that is the whole I don't feel so sure. They didn't think so in the city I told you about. It is a beautiful day, Dog; you won't take a trot out with me?" she added wistfully.

"Who? I?" said the Dog. "Not quite."

"You may get so wise," said she.

"Wisdom is good," said the Dog; "but so is the hearth rug, thank you!"

"But you may be free," said she.

"I shall have to hunt for my own dinner," said he.

"But, Dog, they may pray to you again," said she.

"But I sha'n't have a softer mat to sleep upon, Cat, and as I am rather delicate, that is a consideration."

II

So the Dog wouldn't go, and the Cat set off by herself to learn how to be happy, and to be all that a cat could be. It was a fine sunny morning. She determined to try the meadow first, and, after an hour or two, if she had not succeeded, then to go off to the wood. A Blackbird was piping away on a thornbush as if his heart was running over with happiness. The Cat had breakfasted, and so was able to listen without any mixture of feeling. She didn't sneak. She walked boldly up under the bush, and the bird, seeing she had no bad purpose, sat still and sung on.

"Good morning, Blackbird; you seem to be enjoying yourself this fine day."

"Good morning, Cat."

"Blackbird, it is an odd question, perhaps. What ought one to do to be as happy as you?"

"Do your duty, Cat."

"But what is my duty, Blackbird?"

"Take care of your little ones, Cat."

"I haven't any," said she.

"Then sing to your mate," said the bird.

"Tom is dead," said she.

"Poor Cat!" said the bird. "Then sing over his grave. If your song is sad, you will find your heart grow lighter for it."

Mercy! thought the Cat. I could do a little singing with a living lover, but I never heard of singing for a dead one. "But you see, bird, it isn't cats' nature. When I am cross, I mew. When I am pleased, I purr; but I must be pleased first. I can't purr myself into happiness."

"I am afraid there is something the matter with your heart, my Cat. It wants warming; goodbye."

The Blackbird flew away. The Cat looked sadly after him. "He thinks I am like him; and he doesn't know that a cat is a cat," said she. "As it happens, now, I feel a great deal for a cat. If I hadn't got a heart I shouldn't be unhappy. I won't be angry. I'll try that great fat fellow."

The Ox lay placidly chewing, with content beaming out of his eyes and playing on his mouth.

"Ox," she said, "what is the way to be happy?"

"Do your duty," said the Ox.

"Bother," said the Cat, "duty again. What is it, Ox?"

"Get your dinner," said the Ox.

"But it is got for me, Ox; and I have nothing to do but to eat it."

"Well, eat it, then, like me."

"So I do; but I am not happy for all that."

"Then you are a very wicked, ungrateful Cat."

The Ox munched away. A Bee buzzed into a buttercup under the Cat's nose.

"I beg your pardon," said the Cat, "it isn't curiosity – what are you doing?"

"Doing my duty; don't stop me, Cat."

"But, Bee, what is your duty?"

"Making honey," said the Bee.

"I wish I could make honey," sighed the Cat.

"Do you mean to say you can't?" said the Bee. "How stupid you must be. What do you do, then?"

"I do nothing, Bee. I can't get anything to do."

"You won't get anything to do, you mean, you lazy Cat! You are a good-for-nothing drone. Do you know what we do to our drones? We kill them; and that is all they are fit for."

"Well, I am sure," said the Cat, "they are treating me civilly! I had better have stopped at home at this rate. Stroke my whiskers! Heartless! wicked! good-for-nothing! stupid! and only fit to be killed! This is a pleasant beginning, anyhow. I must look for some wiser creatures than these are. What shall I do? I know. I know where I will go."

It was in the middle of the wood. The bush was very dark, but she found him by his wonderful eye. Presently, as she got used to the light, she distinguished a sloping roll of feathers, a rounded breast, surmounted by a round head, set close to the body, without an inch of neck intervening. "How wise he looks!" she said; "what a brain; what a forehead! His head is not long, but what an expanse! and what a depth of earnestness!"

The Owl sloped his head a little on one side; the Cat slanted hers upon the other. The Owl set it straight again, the Cat did the same. They stood looking in this way for some minutes; at last, in a whispering voice, the Owl said, "What are you, who presume to look into my repose? Pass on upon your way, and carry elsewhere those prying eyes."

"O wonderful Owl," said the Cat, "you are wise, and I want to be wise; and I am come to you to teach me."

A film floated backwards and forwards over the Owl's eyes; it was his way of showing that he was pleased.

"I have heard in our schoolroom," went on the Cat, "that you sat on the shoulder of Pallas, and she told you all about it."

"And what would you know, O my daughter?" said the Owl.

"Everything," said the Cat, "everything. First of all, how to be happy."

"Mice content you not, my child, even as they content not me," said the Owl. "It is good."

"Mice indeed!" said the Cat; "no, parlour cats don't eat mice. I have better than mice, and no trouble to get it; but I want something more."

"The body's meat is provided. You would now fill your soul?"

"I want to improve," said the Cat. "I want something to do. I want to find out what the creatures call my duty."

"You would learn how to employ those happy hours of your leisure? – rather, how to make them happy by a worthy use? Meditate, O Cat! meditate! meditate!"

"That is the very thing," said she. "Meditate! that is what I like above all things. Only I want to know how: I want something to meditate about. Tell me, Owl, and I will bless you every hour of the day as I sit by the parlour fire."

"I will tell you," answered the Owl, "what I have been thinking of ever since the moon changed. You shall take it home with you and think about it too; and the next full moon you shall come again to me: we will compare our conclusions."

"Delightful! delightful!" said the Cat. "What is it? I will try this minute."

"From the beginning," replied the Owl, "our race have been considering which first existed, the Owl or the egg. The Owl comes from the egg, but likewise the egg from the Owl."

"Mercy!" said the Cat.

"From sunrise to sunset I ponder on it, O Cat! When I reflect on the beauty of the complete Owl I think that must have been first as the cause is greater than the effect. When I remember my own childhood I incline the other way."

"Well, but how are we going to find out?" said the Cat.

"Find out!" said the Owl. "We can never find out. The beauty of the question is, that its solution is impossible. What would become of all our delightful reasonings, O unwise Cat, if we were so unhappy as to know?"

"But what in the world is the good of thinking about it, if you can't, O Owl?"

"My child, that is a foolish question. It is good, in order that the thoughts on these things may stimulate wonder. It is in wonder that the Owl is great."

"Then you don't know anything at all," said the Cat. "What did you sit on Pallas's shoulder for? You must have gone to sleep."

"Your tone is over-flippant, Cat, for philosophy. The highest of all knowledge is to know that we know nothing."

The Cat made two great arches with her back and her tail.

"Bless the mother that laid you," said she. "You were dropped by mistake in a goose nest. You won't do. I don't know much, but I am not such a creature as you, anyhow. A great white thing!"

She straightened her body, stuck her tail up on end, and marched off with much dignity. But, though she respected herself rather more than before, she was not on the way to the end of her difficulties. She tried all the creatures she met without advancing a step. They had all the old story, "Do your duty." But each had its own, and no one could tell her what hers was. Only one point they all agreed upon – the duty of getting their dinner when they were hungry. The day wore on, and she began to think she would like hers. Her meals came so regularly at home that she scarcely knew what hunger was; but now the sensation came over her very palpably, and she experienced quite new emotions as the hares and rabbits skipped about her, or as she spied a bird upon a tree. For a moment she thought she would go back and eat the Owl – he was the most useless creature she had seen; but on second thoughts she didn't fancy he would be nice: besides that, his claws were sharp and his beak too. Presently, however, as she sauntered down the path, she came on a little open patch of green, in the middle of which a fine fat Rabbit was sitting. There was no escape. The path ended there, and the bushes were so thick on each side that he couldn't get away except through her paws.

"Really," said the Cat, "I don't wish to be troublesome; I wouldn't do it if I could help it; but I am very hungry; I am afraid I must eat you. It is very unpleasant, I assure you, to me as well as to you."

The poor Rabbit begged for mercy.

"Well," said she, "I think it is hard; I do really – and, if the law could be altered, I should be the first to welcome it. But what can a cat do? You eat the grass; I eat you. But, Rabbit, I wish you would do me a favour."

"Anything to save my life," said the Rabbit.

"It is not exactly that," said the Cat; "but I haven't been used to killing my own food, and it is disagreeable. Couldn't you die? I shall hurt you dreadfully if I kill you."

"Oh!" said the Rabbit, "you are a kind Cat; I see it in your eyes, and your whiskers don't curl like those of the cats in the woods. I am sure you will spare me."

"But, Rabbit, it is a question of principle. I have to do my duty; and the only duty I have, as far as I can make out, is to get my dinner."

"If you kill me, Cat, to do your duty, I sha'n't be able to do mine."

It was a doubtful point, and the Cat was new to casuistry. "What is your duty?" said she.

"I have seven little ones at home – seven little ones, and they will all die without me. Pray let me go."

"What! do you take care of your children?" said the Cat. "How interesting! I should like to see that; take me."

"Oh! you would eat them, you would," said the Rabbit. "No! better eat me than them. No, no."

"Well, well," said the Cat, "I don't know; I suppose I couldn't answer for myself. I don't think I am right, for duty is pleasant, and it is very unpleasant to be so hungry; but I suppose you must go. You seem a good Rabbit. Are you happy, Rabbit?"

"Happy! oh, dear beautiful Cat! if you spare me to my poor babies!"

"Pooh, pooh!" said the Cat, peevishly; "I don't want fine speeches; I meant whether you thought it worth while to be alive? Of course you do! It don't matter. Go, and keep out of my way; for, if I don't find something to eat, you may not get off another time. Get along, Rabbit."

III

It was a day in the Fox's cave. The eldest cub had the night before brought home his first goose, and they were just sitting down to it as the Cat came by.

"Ah, my young lady! what, you in the woods? Bad feeding at home, eh? Come out to hunt for yourself?"

The goose smelt excellent; the Cat couldn't help a wistful look. She was only come, she said, to pay her respects to her wild friends.

"Just in time," said the Fox. "Sit down and take a bit of meat; I see you want it. Make room, you cubs; place a seat for the lady."

"Why, thank you," said the Cat, "yes; I acknowledge it is not unwelcome. Pray, don't disturb yourselves, young Foxes. I am hungry. I met a rabbit on my way here. I was going to eat him, but he talked so prettily I let him go."

The cubs looked up from their plates, and burst out laughing.

"For shame, young rascals," said their father. "Where are your manners? Mind your business, and don't be rude."

"Fox," she said, when it was over, and the cubs were gone to play, "you are very clever. The other creatures are all stupid." The Fox bowed. "Your family were always clever," she continued. "I have heard about them in the books they use in our schoolroom. It is many years since your ancestor stole the crow's dinner."

"Don't say *stole*, Cat; it is not pretty. Obtained by superior ability."

"I beg your pardon," said the Cat; "it is all living with those men. That is not the point. Well, but I want to know whether you are any wiser or any better than Foxes were then."

"Really," said the Fox, "I am what Nature made me. I don't know. I am proud of my ancestors, and do my best to keep up the credit of the family."

"Well, but, Fox, I mean, do you improve? do I? do any of you? The men are always talking about doing their duty, and that, they say, is the way to improve, and to be happy. And as I was not happy I thought that had, perhaps, something to do with it, so I came out to talk to the creatures. They also had the old chant – duty, duty, duty; but none of them could tell me what mine was, or whether I had any."

The Fox smiled. "Another leaf out of your schoolroom," said he. "Can't they tell you there?"

"Indeed," she said, "they are very absurd. They say a great deal about themselves, but they only speak disrespectfully of us. If such creatures as they can do their duty, and improve, and be happy, why can't we?"

"They say they do, do they?" said the Fox. "What do they say of me?"

The Cat hesitated.

"Don't be afraid of hurting my feelings, Cat. Out with it."

"They do all justice to your abilities, Fox," said she; "but your morality, they say, is not high. They say you are a rogue."

"Morality!" said the Fox. "Very moral and good they are. And you really believe all that? What do they mean by calling me a rogue?"

"They mean, you take whatever you can get, without caring whether it is just or not."

"My dear Cat, it is very well for a man, if he can't bear his own face, to paint a pretty one on a panel and call it a looking glass; but you don't mean that it takes *you* in?"

"Teach me," said the Cat. "I fear I am weak."

"Who get justice from the men unless they can force it? Ask the sheep that are cut into mutton. Ask the horses that draw their ploughs. I don't mean it is wrong of the men to do as they do; but they needn't lie about it."

"You surprise me," said the Cat.

"My good Cat, there is but one law in the world. The weakest goes to the wall. The men are sharper-witted than the creatures, and so they get the better of them and use them. They may call it just, if they like; but when a tiger eats a man I guess he has just as much justice on his side as the man when he eats a sheep."

"And that is the whole of it," said the Cat. "Well, it is very sad. What do you do with yourself?"

"My duty, to be sure," said the Fox; "use my wits and enjoy myself. My dear friend, you and I are on the lucky side. We eat and are not eaten."

"Except by the hounds now and then," said the Cat.

"Yes, by brutes that forget their nature, and sell their freedom to the man," said the Fox, bitterly. "In the meantime my wits have kept my skin whole hitherto, and I bless nature for making me a Fox and not a goose."

"And are you happy, Fox?"

"Happy? Yes, of course. So would you be if you would do like me, and use your wits. My good Cat, I should be as miserable as you if I found my geese every day at the cave's mouth. I have to hunt for them, lie for them, sneak for them, fight for them; cheat those old fat farmers, and bring out what there is inside me; and then I am happy – of course I am. And then, Cat, think of my feelings as a father last night, when my dear boy came home with the very young gosling which was marked for the Michaelmas dinner! Old Reinke himself wasn't more than a match for that young Fox at his years. You know our epic?"

"A little of it, Fox. They don't read it in our schoolroom. They say it is not moral; but I have heard pieces of it. I hope it is not all quite true."

"Pack of stuff! it is the only true book that ever was written. If it is not, it ought to be. Why, that book is the law of the world – *la carrière aux talents* – and writing it was the honestest thing ever done by a man. That fellow knew a thing or two, and wasn't ashamed of himself when he did know. They are all like him, too, if they would only say so. There never was one of them yet who wasn't more ashamed of being called ugly than of being called a rogue, and of being called stupid than of being called naughty."

"It has a roughish end, this life of yours, if you keep clear of the hounds, Fox," said the Cat.

"What! a rope in the yard? Well, it must end some day; and when the farmer catches me I shall be getting old, and my brains will be taking leave of me; so the sooner I go the better, that I may disgrace myself the less. Better be jolly while it lasts, than sit mewing out your life and grumbling at it as a bore."

"Well," said the Cat, "I am very much obliged to you. I suppose I may even get home again. I shall not find a wiser friend than you, and perhaps I shall not find another good-natured enough to entertain me so handsomely. But it is very sad."

"Think of what I have said," answered the Fox. "I'll call at your house some night; you will take me a walk round the yard, and then I'll show you."

Not quite, thought the Cat, as she trotted off. One good turn deserves another, that is true; and you have given me a dinner. But they have given me many at home, and I mean to take a few more of them; so I think you mustn't go round our yard.

IV

The next morning, when the Dog came down to breakfast, he found his old friend sitting in her usual place on the hearth rug.

"Oh! so you have come back?" said he. "How d'ye do? You don't look as if you had had a very pleasant journey."

"I have learnt something," said the Cat. "Knowledge is never pleasant."

"Then it is better to be without it," said the Dog.

"Especially better to be without knowing how to stand on one's hind legs, Dog," said the Cat; "still, you see, you are proud of it; but I have learnt a great deal, Dog. They won't worship you any more, and it is better for you; you wouldn't be any happier. What did you do yesterday?"

"Indeed," said the Dog, "I hardly remember. I slept after you went away. In the afternoon I took a drive in the carriage. Then I had my dinner. My maid washed me and put me to bed. There is the difference between you and me; you have to wash yourself and put yourself to bed."

"And you really don't find it a bore, living like this? Wouldn't you like something to do? Wouldn't you like some children to play with? The Fox seemed to find it very pleasant."

"Children, indeed!" said the Dog, "when I have got men and women. Children are well enough for foxes and wild creatures; refined dogs know better; and, for doing – can't I stand on my toes? can't I dance? at least, couldn't I before I was so fat?"

"Ah! I see everybody likes what he was bred to," sighed the Cat. "I was bred to do nothing, and I must like that. Train the cat as the cat should go, and the cat will be happy and ask no questions. Never seek for impossibilities, Dog. That is the secret."

"And you have spent a day in the woods to learn that?" said he. "I could have taught you that. Why, Cat, one day when you were sitting scratching your nose before the fire, I thought you looked so pretty that I should have liked to marry you; but I knew I couldn't, so I didn't make myself miserable."

The Cat looked at him with her odd green eyes. "I never wished to marry you, Dog; I shouldn't have presumed. But it was wise of you not to fret about it. Listen to me, Dog – listen. I met many creatures in the wood, all sorts of creatures, beasts and birds. They were all happy; they didn't find it a bore. They went about their work, and did it, and enjoyed it, and yet none of them had the same story to tell. Some did one thing, some another; and, except the Fox, each had got a sort of notion of doing its duty. The Fox was a rogue, he said he was; but yet he was not unhappy. His conscience never troubled him. Your work is standing on your toes, and you are happy. I have none, and this is why I am unhappy. When I came to think about it, I found every creature out in the wood had to get its own living. I tried to get mine, but I didn't like it, because I wasn't used to it; and as for knowing, the Fox, who didn't care to know anything except how to cheat greater fools than himself was the cleverest fellow I came across. Oh! the Owl, Dog – you should have heard the Owl. But I came to this, that it was no use trying to know, and the only way to be jolly was to go about one's own business like a decent Cat. Cats' business seems to be killing rabbits and such-like, and it is not the pleasantest possible; so the sooner one is bred to it the better. As for me, that have been bred to do nothing, why, as I said before, I must try to like that; but I consider myself an unfortunate Cat."

"So, don't I consider myself an unfortunate Dog?" said her companion.

"Very likely you do not," said the Cat.

By this time their breakfast was come in. The Cat ate hers, the Dog did penance for his; and if one might judge by the purring on the hearth rug, the Cat, if not the happier of the two, at least was not exceedingly miserable.

DEMONIC
CATS

"Those who'll play with cats must expect to be scratched."
Miguel de Cervantes Saavedra (1547–1616)

The Black Cat

EDGAR ALLAN POE (1809–49)

For the most wild yet most homely narrative which I am about to pen, I neither expect nor solicit belief. Mad indeed would I be to expect it, in a case where my very senses reject their own evidence. Yet mad am I not – and very surely do I not dream. But tomorrow I die, and today I would unburden my soul. My immediate purpose is to place before the world, plainly, succinctly, and without comment, a series of mere household events. In their consequences, these events have terrified – have tortured – have destroyed me. Yet I will not attempt to expound them. To me, they have presented little but horror – to many they will seem less terrible than *baroques*. Hereafter, perhaps, some intellect may be found which will reduce my phantasm to the commonplace – some intellect more calm, more logical, and far less excitable than my own, which will perceive, in the circumstances I detail with awe, nothing more than an ordinary succession of very natural causes and effects.

From my infancy I was noted for the docility and humanity of my disposition. My tenderness of heart was even so conspicuous as to make me the jest of my companions. I was especially fond of animals, and was indulged by my parents with a great variety of pets. With these I spent most of my time, and never was so happy as when feeding and caressing them. This peculiarity of character grew with my growth, and, in my manhood, I derived from it one of my principal sources of pleasure. To those who have cherished an affection for a faithful and sagacious dog, I need hardly be at the trouble of explaining the nature or the intensity of the gratification thus derivable. There is something in the unselfish and self-sacrificing love of a brute, which goes directly to the heart of him who has had frequent occasion to test the paltry friendship and gossamer fidelity of mere *Man*.

I married early, and was happy to find in my wife a disposition not uncongenial with my own. Observing my partiality for domestic pets, she lost no opportunity of procuring those of the most agreeable kind. We had birds, goldfish, a fine dog, rabbits, a small monkey, and a *cat*.

This latter was a remarkable large and beautiful animal, entirely black, and sagacious to an astonishing degree. In speaking of his intelligence, my wife, who at heart was not a little tinctured with superstition, made frequent allusion to the ancient popular notion, which regarded all black cats as witches in disguise. Not that she was ever *serious* upon this point -- and I mention the matter at all for no better reason than that it happens, just now, to be remembered.

Pluto – this was the cat's name – was my favourite pet and playmate. I alone fed him, and he attended me wherever I went about the house. It was even with difficulty that I could prevent him from following me through the streets.

Our friendship lasted, in this manner, for several years, during which my general temperament and character – through the instrumentality of the Fiend Intemperance – had (I blush to confess it) experienced a radical alteration for the worse. I grew, day by day, more moody, more irritable, more regardless of the feelings of others. I suffered myself to use intemperate language to my wife. At length, I even offered her personal violence. My pets, of course, were made to feel the change in my disposition. I not only neglected, but ill-used them. For Pluto, however, I still retained sufficient regard to restrain me from maltreating him, as I made no scruple of maltreating the rabbits, the monkey, or even the dog, when, by accident, or through affection, they came in my way. But my disease grew upon me – for what disease is like Alcohol! – and at length even Pluto, who was now becoming old, and consequently somewhat peevish – even Pluto began to experience the effects of my ill temper.

One night, returning home, much intoxicated, from one of my haunts about town, I fancied that the cat avoided my presence. I seized him; when, in his fright at my violence, he inflicted a slight wound upon my hand with his teeth. The fury of a demon instantly possessed me. I knew myself no longer. My original soul seemed, at once, to take its flight from my body; and a more than fiendish malevolence, gin-nurtured, thrilled every fibre of my frame. I took from my waistcoat pocket a penknife, opened it, grasped the poor beast by the throat, and deliberately cut one of its eyes from the socket! I blush, I burn, I shudder, while I pen the damnable atrocity.

When reason returned with the morning – when I had slept off the fumes of the night's debauch – I experienced a senti-ment half of horror, half of remorse, for the crime of which I had been guilty; but it was, at best, a feeble and equivocal feeling, and the soul remained untouched. I again plunged into excess, and soon drowned in wine all memory of the deed.

In the meantime the cat slowly recovered. The socket of the lost eye presented, it is true, a frightful appearance, but he no longer appeared to suffer any pain. He went about the house as usual, but, as might be expected, fled in extreme terror at my approach. I had so much of my old heart left, as to be at first grieved by this evident dislike on the part of a creature which had once so loved me. But this feeling soon gave place to irritation. And then came, as if to my final and irrevocable overthrow, the spirit of *perverseness*. Of this spirit philosophy takes no account. Yet I am not more sure that my soul lives, than I am that perverseness is one of the primitive impulses of the human heart – one of the indivisible primary faculties, or sentiments, which give direction to the character of Man. Who has not, a hundred times, found himself committing a vile or a stupid action, for no other reason than because he knows he should *not*? Have we not a perpetual inclination, in the teeth of our best judgment, to violate that which is Law, merely because we understand it to be such? This spirit of perverseness, I say, came to my final overthrow. It was this unfathomable longing of the soul to *vex itself* – to offer violence to its own nature – to do wrong for the wrong's sake only – that urged me to continue and finally to consummate the injury I had inflicted upon the unoffending brute. One morning, in cold blood, I slipped a noose about its neck and hung it to the limb of a tree – hung it with the tears streaming from my eyes, and with the bitterest remorse at my heart – hung it *because* I knew that it had loved me, and *because* I felt it had given me no reason of offence – hung it *because* I knew that in so doing I was committing a sin – a deadly sin that would so jeopardize my immortal soul as to place it – if such a thing were possible – even beyond the reach of the infinite mercy of the Most Merciful and Most Terrible God.

On the night of the day on which this most cruel deed was done, I was aroused from sleep by the cry of fire. The curtains of my bed were in flames. The whole house was blazing. It was with great difficulty that my wife, a servant, and myself, made our escape from the conflagration. The destruction was complete. My entire worldly wealth was swallowed up, and I resigned myself thenceforward to despair.

I am above the weakness of seeking to establish a sequence of cause and effect, between the disaster and the atrocity. But I am detailing a chain of facts – and wish not to leave even a possible link imperfect. On the day succeeding the fire, I visited the ruins. The walls, with one exception, had fallen in. This exception was found in a compartment wall, not very thick, which stood about the middle of the house, and against which had rested the head of my bed. The plastering had here, in great measure, resisted the action of the fire – a fact which I attributed to its having been recently spread. About this wall a dense crowd were collected, and many persons seemed to be examining a particular portion of it with very minute and eager attention. The words "strange!" "singular!" and other similar expressions, excited my curiosity. I approached and saw, as if graven in bas-relief upon the white surface, the figure of a gigantic *cat*. The impression was given with an accuracy truly marvellous. There was a rope about the animal's neck.

When I first beheld this apparition – for I could scarcely regard it as less – my wonder and my terror were extreme. But at length reflection came to my aid. The cat, I remembered, had been hung in a garden adjacent to the house. Upon the alarm of fire, this garden had been immediately filled by the crowd – by some one of whom the animal must have been cut from the tree and thrown, through an open window, into my chamber. This had probably been done with the view of arousing me from sleep. The falling of other walls had compressed the victim of my cruelty into the substance of the freshly spread plaster; the lime of which, with the flames, and the ammonia from the carcass, had then accomplished the portraiture as I saw it.

Although I thus readily accounted to my reason, if not altogether to my conscience, for the startling fact just detailed, it did not the less fail to make a deep impression upon my fancy. For months I could not rid myself of the phantasm of the cat; and, during this period, there came back into my spirit a half-sentiment that seemed, but was not, remorse. I went so far as to regret the loss of the animal, and to look about me, among the vile haunts which I now habitually frequented, for another pet of the same species, and of somewhat similar appearance, with which to supply its place.

One night as I sat, half stupefied, in a den of more than infamy, my attention was suddenly drawn to some black object, reposing upon the head of one of the immense hogsheads of gin, or of rum, which constituted the chief furniture of the apartment. I had been looking steadily at the top of this hogshead for some minutes, and what now caused me surprise was the fact that I had not sooner perceived the object thereupon. I approached it, and touched it with my hand. It was a black cat – a very large one – fully as large as Pluto, and closely resembling him in every respect but one. Pluto had not a white hair upon any portion of his body; but this cat had a large, although indefinite splotch of white, covering nearly the whole region of the breast.

Upon my touching him, he immediately arose, purred loudly, rubbed against my hand, and appeared delighted with my notice. This, then, was the very creature of which I was in search. I at once offered to purchase it of the landlord; but this person made no claim to it – knew nothing of it – had never seen it before.

I continued my caresses, and when I prepared to go home, the animal evinced a disposition to accompany me. I permitted it to do so; occasionally stooping and patting it as I proceeded. When it reached the house it domesticated itself at once, and became immediately a great favourite with my wife.

For my own part, I soon found a dislike to it arising within me. This was just the reverse of what I had anticipated; but – I knew not how or why it was – its evident fondness for myself rather disgusted and annoyed me. By slow degrees these feelings of disgust and annoyance rose into the bitterness of hatred. I avoided the creature; a certain sense of shame, and the remembrance of my former deed of cruelty, preventing me from physically abusing it. I did not, for some weeks, strike, or otherwise violently ill use it; but gradually – very gradually – I came to look upon it with unutterable loathing, and to flee silently from its odious presence, as from the breath of a pestilence.

What added, no doubt, to my hatred of the beast, was the discovery, on the morning after I brought it home, that, like Pluto, it also had been deprived of one of its eyes. This circumstance, however, only endeared it to my wife, who, as I have already said, possessed, in a high degree, that humanity of feeling which had once been my distinguishing trait, and the source of many of my simplest and purest pleasures.

With my aversion to this cat, however, its partiality for myself seemed to increase. It followed my footsteps with a pertinacity which it would be difficult to make the reader comprehend. Whenever I sat, it would crouch beneath my chair, or spring upon my knees, covering me with its loathsome caresses. If I arose to walk it would get between my feet and thus nearly throw me down, or, fastening its long and sharp claws in my dress, clamber, in this manner, to my breast. At such times, although I longed to destroy it with a blow, I was yet withheld from so doing, partly by a memory of my former crime, but chiefly – let me confess it at once – by absolute *dread* of the beast.

This dread was not exactly a dread of physical evil – and yet I should be at a loss how otherwise to define it. I am almost ashamed to own – yes, even in this felon's cell, I am almost ashamed to own – that the terror and horror with which the animal inspired me, had been heightened by one of the merest chimeras it would be possible to conceive. My wife had called my attention, more than once, to the character of the mark of white hair, of which I have spoken, and which constituted the sole visible difference between the strange beast and the one I had destroyed. The reader will remember that this mark, although large, had been originally very indefinite; but, by slow degrees – degrees nearly imperceptible, and which for a long time my reason struggled to reject as fanciful – it had, at length, assumed a rigorous distinctness of outline. It was now the representation of an object that I shudder to name – and for this, above all, I loathed, and dreaded, and would have rid myself of the monster *had I dared* – it was now, I say, the image of a hideous – of a ghastly thing – of the *Gallows!* – oh, mournful and terrible engine of Horror and of Crime – of Agony and of Death!

And now was I indeed wretched beyond the wretchedness of mere Humanity. And a *brute beast* – whose fellow I had contemptuously destroyed – *a brute beast* to work out for *me* – for me, a man fashioned in the image of the High God – so much of insufferable woe! Alas! neither by day nor by night knew I the blessing of rest any more! During the former the creature left me no moment alone, and in the latter I started hourly from dreams of unutterable fear to find the hot breath of *the thing* upon my face, and its vast weight – an incarnate nightmare that I had no power to shake off – incumbent eternally upon my *heart!*

Beneath the pressure of torments such as these the feeble remnant of the good within me succumbed. Evil thoughts became my sole intimates – the darkest and most evil of thoughts. The moodiness of my usual temper increased to hatred of all things and of all mankind; while from the sudden, frequent, and ungovernable outbursts of a fury to which I now blindly abandoned myself, my uncomplaining wife, alas, was the most usual and the most patient of sufferers.

One day she accompanied me, upon some household errand, into the cellar of the old building which our poverty compelled us to inhabit. The cat followed me down the steep stairs, and, nearly throwing me headlong, exasperated me to madness. Uplifting an axe, and forgetting in my wrath the childish dread which had hitherto stayed my hand, I aimed a blow at the animal, which, of course, would have proved instantly fatal had it descended as I wished. But this blow was arrested by the hand of my wife. Goaded by the interference into a rage more than demoniacal, I withdrew my arm from her grasp and buried the axe in her brain. She fell dead upon the spot without a groan.

This hideous murder accomplished, I set myself forthwith, and with entire deliberation, to the task of concealing the body. I knew that I could not remove it from the house, either by day or by night, without the risk of being observed by the neighbours. Many projects entered my mind. At one period I thought of cutting the corpse into minute fragments, and destroying them by fire. At another, I resolved to dig a grave for it in the floor of the cellar. Again, I deliberated about casting it in the well in the yard – about packing it in a box, as if merchandise, with the usual arrangements, and so getting a porter to take it from the house. Finally I hit upon what I considered a far better expedient than either of these. I determined to wall it up in the cellar, as the monks of the Middle Ages are recorded to have walled up their victims.

For a purpose such as this the cellar was well adapted. Its walls were loosely constructed, and had lately been plastered throughout with a rough plaster, which the dampness of the atmosphere had prevented from hardening. Moreover, in one of the walls was a projection, caused by a false chimney, or fireplace, that had been filled up and made to resemble the rest of the cellar. I made no doubt that I could readily displace the bricks at this point, insert the corpse, and wall the whole up as before, so that no eye could detect anything suspicious.

And in this calculation I was not deceived. By means of a crowbar I easily dislodged the bricks, and, having carefully deposited the body against the inner wall, I propped it in that position, while with little trouble I relaid the whole structure as it originally stood. Having procured mortar, sand and hair, with every possible precaution, I prepared a plaster which could not be distinguished from the old and with this I very carefully went over the new brickwork. When I had finished, I felt satisfied that all was right. The wall did not present the slightest appearance of having been disturbed. The rubbish on the floor was picked up with the minutest care. I looked around triumphantly, and said to myself: "Here at least, then, my labour has not been in vain."

My next step was to look for the beast which had been the cause of so much wretchedness; for I had, at length, firmly resolved to put it to death. Had I been able to meet with it at the moment, there could have been no doubt of its fate; but it appeared that the crafty animal had been alarmed at the violence of my previous anger, and forbore to present itself in my present mood. It is impossible to describe or to imagine the deep, the blissful sense of relief which the absence of the detested creature occasioned in my bosom. It did not make its appearance during the night; and thus for one night, at least, since its introduction into the house, I soundly and tranquilly slept; aye, *slept* even with the burden of murder upon my soul.

The second and the third day passed, and still my tormentor came not. Once again I breathed as a free man. The monster, in terror, had fled the premises for ever! I should behold it no more! My happiness was supreme! The guilt of my dark deed disturbed me but little. Some few inquiries had been made, but these had been readily answered. Even a search had been instituted – but of course nothing was to be discovered. I looked upon my future felicity as secured.

Upon the fourth day of the assassination, a party of the police came, very unexpectedly, into the house, and proceeded again to make rigorous investigation of the premises. Secure, however, in the inscrutability of my place of concealment, I felt no embarrassment whatever. The officers bade me accompany them in their search. They left no nook or corner unexplored.

At length, for the third or fourth time, they descended into the cellar. I quivered not in a muscle. My heart beat calmly as that of one who slumbers in innocence. I walked the cellar from end to end. I folded my arms upon my bosom, and roamed easily to and fro. The police were thoroughly satisfied and prepared to depart. The glee at my heart was too strong to be restrained. I burned to say if but one word, by way of triumph, and to render doubly sure their assurance of my guiltlessness.

"Gentlemen," I said at last, as the party ascended the steps, "I delight to have allayed your suspicions. I wish you all health and a little more courtesy. By the bye, gentlemen, this – this is a very well-constructed house" (in the rabid desire to say something easily, I scarcely knew what I uttered at all) – "I may say an *excellently* well-constructed house. These walls – are you going, gentleman? – these walls are solidly put together"; and here, through the mere frenzy of bravado, I rapped heavily with a cane which I held in my hand, upon that very portion of the brickwork behind which stood the corpse of the wife of my bosom.

But may God shield and deliver me from the fangs of the Arch-Fiend! No sooner had the reverberation of my blows sunk into silence, than I was answered by a voice from within the tomb! – by a cry, at first muffled and broken, like the sobbing of a child, and then quickly swelling into one long, loud and continuous scream, utterly anomalous and inhuman – a howl – a wailing shriek, half of horror and half of triumph, such as might have arisen only out of hell, conjointly from the throats of the damned in their agony and of the demons that exult in the damnation.

Of my own thoughts it is folly to speak. Swooning, I staggered to the opposite wall. For one instant the party on the stairs remained motionless, through extremity of terror and awe. In the next a dozen stout arms were toiling at the wall. It fell bodily. The corpse, already greatly decayed and clotted with gore, stood erect before the eyes of the spectators. Upon its head, with red extended mouth and solitary eye of fire, sat the hideous beast whose craft had seduced me into murder, and whose informing voice had consigned me to the hangman. I had walled the monster up within the tomb.

from *Works of Edgar Allen Poe* (1874)

The Vampire Cat of Nabéshima

LORD REDESDALE (1837–1916)

There is a tradition in the Nabéshima family that, many years ago, the Prince of Hizen was bewitched and cursed by a cat that had been kept by one of his retainers. This prince had in his house a lady of rare beauty, called O Toyo: amongst all his ladies she was the favourite, and there was none who could rival her charms and accomplishments. One day the Prince went out into the garden with O Toyo, and remained enjoying the fragrance of the flowers until sunset, when they returned to the palace, never noticing that they were being followed by a large cat. Having parted with her lord, O Toyo retired to her own room and went to bed. At midnight she awoke with a start, and became aware of a huge cat that crouched watching her; and when she cried out, the beast sprang on her, and, fixing its cruel teeth in her delicate throat, throttled her to death. What a piteous end for so fair a dame, the darling of her prince's heart, to die suddenly, bitten to death by cat! Then the cat, having scratched out a grave under the verandah, buried the corpse of O Toyo, and assuming her form, began to bewitch the Prince.

But my lord the Prince knew nothing of all this, and little thought that the beautiful creature who caressed and fondled him was an impish and foul beast that had slain his mistress and assumed her shape in order to drain out his life's blood. Day by day, as time went on, the Prince's strength dwindled away; the colour of his face was changed, and became pale and livid; and he was as a man suffering from a deadly sickness. Seeing this, his councillors and his wife became greatly alarmed; so they summoned the physicians, who prescribed various remedies for him; but the more medicine he took, the more serious did his illness appear, and no treatment was of any avail. But most of all did he suffer in the night-time, when his sleep would be troubled and disturbed by hideous dreams. In consequence of this, his councillors nightly appointed a hundred of his retainers to sit up and watch over him, but, strange to say, towards ten o'clock on the very first night that the watch was set, the guard were seized with a sudden and unaccountable drowsiness, which they could not resist, until one by one every man had fallen asleep. Then the false O Toyo came in and harassed the Prince until morning. The following night the same thing occurred, and the Prince was subjected to the imp's tyranny, while his guards slept helplessly around him. Night after night this was repeated, until at last three of the Prince's councillors determined themselves to sit up on guard, and see whether they could overcome this mysterious drowsiness; but they fared no better than the others, and by ten o'clock were fast asleep. The next day the three councillors held a solemn conclave, and their chief, one Isahaya Buzen, said –

'This is a marvellous thing, that a guard of a hundred men should thus be overcome by sleep. Of a surety, the spell that is upon my lord and upon his guard must be the work of witchcraft. Now, as all our efforts are of no avail, let us seek out Ruiten, the chief priest of the temple called Miyô In, and beseech him to put up prayers for the recovery of my lord.'

And the other councillors approving what Isahaya Buzen had said, they went to the priest Ruiten and engaged him to recite litanies that the Prince might be restored to health.

So it came to pass that Ruiten, the chief priest of Miyô In, offered up prayers nightly for the Prince. One night, at the ninth hour (midnight), when he had finished his religious exercises and was preparing to lie down to sleep, he fancied that he heard a noise outside in the garden, as if some one were washing himself as the well. Deeming this passing strange, he looked down from the window; and there in the moonlight he saw a handsome young soldier, some twenty-four years of age, washing himself, who, when he had finished cleaning himself and had put on his clothes, stood before the figure of Buddha

and prayed fervently for the recovery of my lord the Prince.
Ruiten looked on with admiration; and the young man, when
he had made an end of his prayer, was going away; but the
priest stopped him, calling out to him –

"Sir, I pray you to tarry a little: I have something to say to
you."

"At your reverence's service. What may you please to
want?"

"Pray be so good as to step up here, and have a little talk."

"By your reverence's leave;" and with this he went upstairs.
Then Ruiten said –

"Sir, I cannot conceal my admiration that you, being so
young a man, should have so loyal a spirit. I am Ruiten, the
chief priest of this temple, who am engaged in praying for the
recovery of my lord. Pray what is your name?"

"My name, sir, is Itô Sôda, and I am serving in the infantry of
Nabéshima. Since my lord has been sick, my one desire has
been to assist in nursing him; but, being only a simple soldier, I
am not of sufficient rank to come into his presence, so I have no
resource but to pray to the gods of the country and to Buddha
that my lord may regain his health."

When Ruiten heard this, he shed tears in admiration of the
fidelity of Itô Sôda, and said –

"Your purpose is, indeed, a good one; but what a strange
sickness this is that my lord is afflicted with! Every night he
suffers from horrible dreams; and the retainers who sit up with
him are all seized with a mysterious sleep, so that not one can
keep awake. It is very wonderful."

"Yes," replied Sôda, after a moment's reflection, "this
certainly must be witchcraft. If I could but obtain leave to
sit up one night with the Prince, I would fain see whether I
could not resist this drowsiness and detect the goblin."

At last the priest said, "I am in relations of friendship with
Isahaya Buzen, the chief councillor of the Prince. I will speak to
him of you and of your loyalty, and will intercede with him
that you may attain your wish."

"Indeed, sir, I am most thankful. I am not prompted by any

vain thought of self-advancement, should I succeed: all I wish for is the recovery of my lord. I commend myself to your kind favour."

"Well, then, to-morrow night I will take you with me to the councillor's house."

"Thank you, sir, and farewell." And so they parted.

On the following evening Itô Sôda returned to the temple Miyô In, and having found Ruiten, accompanied him to the house of Isahaya Buzen: then the priest, leaving Sôda outside, went in to converse with the councillor, and inquire after the Prince's health.

"And pray, sir, how is my lord? Is he in any better condition since I have been offering up prayers for him?"

"Indeed, no; his illness is very severe. We are certain that he must be the victim of some foul sorcery; but as there are no means of keeping a guard awake after ten o'clock, we cannot catch a sight of the goblin, so we are in the greatest trouble."

"I feel deeply for you: it must be most distressing. However, I have something to tell you. I think that I have found a man who will detect the goblin; and I have brought him with me."

"Indeed! who is the man?"

"Well, he is one of my lord's foot-soldiers, named Itô Sôda, a faithful fellow, and I trust that you will grant his request to be permitted to sit up with my lord."

"Certainly, it is wonderful to find so much loyalty and zeal in a common soldier," replied Isahaya Buzen, after a moment's reflection; "still it is impossible to allow a man of such low rank to perform the office of watching over my lord."

It is true that he is but a common soldier," urged the priest; "but why not raise his rank in consideration of his fidelity, and then let him mount guard?"

"It would be time enough to promote him after my lord's recovery. But come, let me see this Itô Sôda, that I may know what manner of man he is: if he pleases me, I will consult with the other councillors, and perhaps we may grant his request."

"I will bring him in forthwith," replied Ruiten, who thereupon went out to fetch the young man.

When he returned, the priest presented Itô Sôda to the councillor, who looked at him attentively, and, being pleased with his comely and gentle appearance, said --

"So I hear that you are anxious to be permitted to mount guard in my lord's room at night. Well, I must consult with the other councillors, and we will see what can be done for you."

When the young soldier heard this he was greatly elated, and took his leave, after warmly thanking Ruiten, who had helped him to gain his object. The next day the councillors held a meeting, and sent for Itô Sôda, and told him that he might keep watch with the other retainers that very night. So he went his way in high spirits, and at nightfall, having made all his preparations, took his place among the hundred gentlemen who were on duty in the prince's bedroom.

Now the Prince slept in the centre of the room, and the hundred guards around him sat keeping themselves awake with entertaining conversation and pleasant conceits. But, as ten o'clock approached, they began to doze off as they sat; and in spite of all their endeavours to keep one another awake, by degrees they all fell asleep. Itô Sôda all this while felt an irresistible desire to sleep creeping over him, and, though he tried by all sorts of ways to rouse himself, he saw that there was no help for it, but by resorting to an extreme measure, for which he had already made his preparations. Drawing out a piece of oil paper which he had brought with him, and spreading it over the mats, he sat down upon it; then he took the small knife which he carried in the sheath of his dirk, and stuck it into his own thigh. For awhile the pain of the wound kept him awake; but as the slumber by which he was assailed was the work of sorcery, little by little he became drowsy again. Then he twisted the knife round and round in his thigh, so that the pain becoming very violent, he was proof against the feeling of sleepiness, and kept a faithful watch. Now the oil paper which he had spread under his leg was in order to prevent the blood, which might spurt from his wound, from defiling the mats.

So Itô Sôda remained awake, but the rest of the guard slept;

and as he watched, suddenly the sliding-doors oft he Prince's room were drawn open, and he saw a figure coming in stealthily, and, as it drew nearer, the form was that of a marvellously beautiful woman some twenty-three years of age. Cautiously she looked around her; and when she saw that all the guard were asleep, she smiled an ominous smile, and was going up to the Prince's bedside, when she perceived that in one corner of the room there was a man yet awake. This seemed to startle her, but she went up to Sôda and said –

"I am not used to seeing you here. Who are you?"

"My name is Itô Sôda, and this is the first night that I have been on guard."

"A troublesome office, truly! Why, here are all the rest of the guard asleep. How is it that you alone are awake? You are a trusty watchman."

"There is nothing to boast about. I'm alseep myself, fast and sound."

"What is that wound on your knee? It is all red with blood."

"Oh! I felt very sleepy; so I stuck my knife into my thigh, and the pain of it has kept me awake."

"What wondrous loyalty!" said the lady.

"Is it not the duty of a retainer to lay down his life for his master? Is such a scratch as this worth thinking about?"

Then the lady went up to the sleeping prince and said, "How fares it with my lord to-night?" But the Prince, worn out with sickness, made no reply. But Sôda was watching her eagerly, and guessed that it was O Toyo, and made up his mind that if she attempted to harass the Prince he would kill her on the spot. The goblin, however, which in the form of O Toyo had been tormenting the Prince every night, and had come again that night for no other purpose, was defeated by the watchfulness of Itô Sôda; for whenever she drew near to the sick man, thinking to put her spells upon him, she would turn and look behind her, and there she saw Itô Sôda glaring at her; so she had no help for it but to go away again, and leave the Prince undisturbed.

At last the day broke, and the other officers, when they

awoke and opened their eyes, saw that Itô Sôda had kept awake by stabbing himself in the thigh; and they were greatly ashamed, and went home crestfallen.

That morning Itô Sôda went to the house of Isahaya Buzen, and told him all that had occurred the previous night. The councillors were all loud in their praise of Itô Sôda's behaviour, and ordered him to keep watch again that night. At the same hour, the false O Toyo came and looked all round the room, and all the guard were asleep, excepting Itô Sôda, who was wide awake; and so, being again frustrated, she returned to her own apartments.

Now as since Sôda had been on guard the Prince had passed quiet nights, his sickness began to get better, and there was great joy in the palace, and Sôda was promoted and rewarded with an estate. In the meanwhile O Toyo, seeing that her nightly visits bore no fruits, kept away; and from that time forth the night-guard were no longer subject to fits of drowsiness. This coincidence struck Sôda as very strange, so he went to Isahaya Buzen and told him that of a certainty this O Toyo was no other than a goblin. Isahaya Buzen reflected for a while, and said –

"Well, then, how shall we kill the foul thing?"

"I will go to the creature's room, as if nothing were the matter, and try to kill her; but in case she should try to escape, I will beg you to order eight men to stop outside and lie in wait for her."

Having agreed upon this plan, Sôda went at nightfall to O Toyo's apartment, pretending to have been sent with a message from the Prince. When she saw him arrive, she said –

"What message have you brought me from my lord?"

"Oh! nothing in particular. Be so good as to look at this letter;" and as he spoke, he drew near to her, and suddenly drawing his dirk cut at her; but the goblin, springing back, seized a halberd, and glaring fiercely at Sôda, said –

"How dare you behave like this to one of your lord's ladies? I will have you dismissed;" and she tried to strike Sôda with the halberd. But Sôda fought desperately with his dirk; and the

393

goblin, seeing that she was no match for him, threw away the halberd, and from a beautiful woman became suddenly transformed into a cat, which, springing up the sides of the room, jumped on to the roof. Isahaya Buzen and his eight men who were watching outside shot at the cat, but missed it, and the beast made good its escape.

So the cat fled to the mountains, and did much mischief among the surrounding people, until at last the Prince of Hizen ordered a great hunt, and the beast was killed.

But the Prince recovered from his sickness; and Itô Sôda was richly rewarded.

from *Tales of Old Japan* (1871)

The White Mog

ERNEST DUDLEY (b. 1922)

First time he saw it, he could hardly credit his luck.

Latish autumn night it is and Fred Ellis is on his usual prowl. Averaged him seven or eight cats a week it did – which up to £20–30 a time couldn't be bad. He covered different parts of London, different nights of the week. Him and his little van. All the gear you needed was a little van. And a couple of sacks, of course.

So long as the mogs could breathe okay. Might yowl and scratch but no sweat. Needed a dead mog, you did, like a hole in the head. This white cat, it was a real beaut. He'd spotted it in the gardens from St Mary's Church in the square – its owners, he guessed, being the churchwarden and his wife, who lived next door to St Mary's – and even though it'd been only this brief flash, the white cat had made him drool at the thought of it in his sack.

He'd checked the time. Just gone eight thirty.

Next night he'd be there, same time. People mostly put their cats out at the same time every night. Later in the summer, of course.

So next night he's there. On the dot. And suddenly there it is. In the light of the street lamp, it's all gleaming, brilliant white. Made your eyes pop, it was that white. And it looked even bigger. But, same as last time, it was there for only a couple of seconds. Then -- nothing. Fred Ellis wondered what had made it take off like that. He cursed -- then, suddenly again, there it was. A few yards further along the railings towards St Mary's wide steps. It was a bit misty, so perhaps it hadn't seen him.

He went after it, dead cautious, his sack in his left hand, held behind his back.

The cat was a moving, white wraith, and something told Fred Ellis his luck was in as, stealthily, he followed it.

Then the white cat saw him. He stopped, hardly breathing. But it didn't take off. It stood there on the church steps, it did, thick furry tale flicking, eyes glowing greenish-gold. Then -- would you believe it? -- it was *purring* . . . purring an invitation to him! He was only a couple of yards away. It was the moment to pounce.

"Hello, white cat," Fred Ellis said softly. Its pale, pinkish ears twitched. "Come on, puss, we're pals, ain't we?"

But then it turned and went up the steps to St Mary's big, oak doors. For a moment a swirl of mist gave it a ghostly appearance, then it was there again and one of the great doors was slightly open. Fred Ellis could have laughed out loud -- *the cat was about to enter the church*. It was locked at nine thirty. He'd once noticed the churchwarden locking it from inside. The churchwarden also locked the glass doors inside, leading to the nave and the altar beyond. So, once inside the big doors, the cat would be trapped in the space between them and the doors to the nave.

How he knew the layout of the church entrance was because one day he had helped an old girl with two sticks up the wide steps and through the glass doors to the nave. She had been profusely grateful, plus he'd managed to nick the small purse from her handbag -- its lock was faulty, and it had been an open invitation. Inside there were a couple of quid and some silver, but it was all grist to your mill. He returned the purse as he'd pushed the old dear into the nave.

The white cat went in, and Fred Ellis knew it was as good as his – he could feel it, struggling in his sack. He sucked in his breath as the white furry tail disappeared and, letting out the air through his lips in a hiss, he dashed forward. He pulled the big door wide open and, slamming it behind him, reached for his pocket torch.

Then, he froze.

Dozens of pairs of greenish-gold eyes blazed at him in the darkness. His whole body crawled with terror. He spun round. But more eyes blazed at him. The place was alive with cats. He started for the door, but the eyes sprang, yowling, spitting. Cat's claws slashed his face and neck. He could feel the blood spurting. Dreadful claws tore his body.

He let out a frightful shriek as the cats ripped him. Shriek after shriek.

The agonized shrieks reached Dr Havers and his wife who were passing by and they dashed up the steps, pulled the big door open, found the light switch and, in the glare, saw Fred Ellis sprawled on the floor, one hand gripping his sack, the other, which had held the torch but dropped it, outstretched.

Dr Havers bent and felt his pulse. As he straightened up, shaking his head, his wife asked, "What was all that about?"

"Must have had a heart attack," Dr Havers said. He glanced round. A non-committal shrug. Stared down. There wasn't a mark on Fred Ellis's face. Not a mark of a hundred slashing claws, tearing his face to pieces.

Not a mark.

Lady Jane

CHARLES DiCKENS (1812–70)

"Hi, Lady Jane!"

A large grey cat leapt from some neighbouring shelf on his shoulder, and startled us all.

"Hi! show 'em how you scratch. Hi! Tear, my lady!" said her master.

The cat leaped down, and ripped at a bundle of rags with her tigerish claws, with a sound that it set my teeth on edge to hear.

"She'd do as much for anyone I was to set her on," said the old man. "I deal in cat-skins among other general matters, and hers was offered to me. It's a very fine skin, as you may see, but I didn't have it stripped off! *That* warn't like Chancery practice though, says you!"

He had by this time led us across the shop, and now opened a door in the back part of it, leading to the house-entry. As he stood with his hand upon the lock, the little old lady graciously observed to him before passing out: "That will do, Krook. You mean well, but are tiresome." [...]

She lived at the top of the house, in a pretty large room, from which she had a glimpse of Lincoln's Inn Hall. [...] She partly drew aside the curtain of the long low garret-window, and called our attention to a number of birdcages hanging there: some, containing several birds. There were larks, linnets, and gold-finches – I should think at least twenty. [...]

We all draw nearer to the cages, feigning to examine the birds.

"I can't allow them to sing much," said the little old lady, "for (you'll think this curious) I find my mind confused by the idea that they are singing, while I am following the arguments in Court. And my mind requires to be so very clear, you know! Another time, I'll tell you their names. Not at present. On a day of such good omen, they shall sing as much as they like. In honour of youth," a smile and curtsey, "hope", a smile and curtsey, "and beauty", a smile and curtsey. "There! We'll let in the full light."

The birds began to stir and chirp.

"I cannot admit the air freely," said the little old lady – the room was close, and would have been the better for it – "because the cat you saw downstairs – called Lady Jane – is greedy for their lives. She crouches on the parapet outside for hours and hours. I have discovered," whispering mysteriously, "that her natural cruelty is sharpened by a jealous fear of their regaining their liberty. In consequence of the judgment I expect being shortly given. She is sly, and full of malice. I half believe, sometimes, that she is no cat, but the wolf of the old saying. It is so very difficult to keep her from the door." [...]

Passing through the shop on our way out, as we had passed through it on our way in, we found the old man storing a quantity of packets of waste paper, in a kind of well in the floor. He seemed to be working hard, with the perspiration standing on his forehead, and had a piece of chalk by him; with which, as he put each separate package or bundle down, he made a crooked mark on the panelling of the wall.

Richard and Ada, and Miss Jellyby, and the little old lady had gone by him, and I was going, when he touched me on the arm to stay me, and chalked the letter J upon the wall – in a very curious manner, beginning with the end of the letter, and shaping it backward. It was a capital letter, not a printed one, but just such a letter as any clerk in Messrs Kenge and Carboy's office would have made.

"Can you read it?" he asked me with a keen glance.

"Surely," said I. "It's very plain."

"What is it?"

"J."

With another glance at me, and a glance at the door, he rubbed it out, and turned an *a* in its place (not a capital letter this time) and said, "What's that?"

I told him. He then rubbed that out, and turned the letter *r*, and asked me the same question. He went on quickly until he had formed, in the same curious manner, beginning at the ends and bottoms of the letters, the word *Jarndyce*, without once leaving two letters on the wall together.

"What does that spell?" he asked me.

When I told him, he laughed. In the same odd way, yet with the same rapidity, he then produced singly, and rubbed out singly, the letters forming the words *Bleak House*. These, in some astonishment, I also read; and he laughed again.

"Hi!" said the old man, laying aside the chalk, "I have a turn for copying from memory, you see, miss, though I can neither read nor write."

He looked so disagreeable, and his cat looked so wickedly at me, as if I were a blood-relation of the birds upstairs, that I was quite relieved by Richard's appearing at the door and saying: "Miss Summerson, I hope you are not bargaining for the sale of your hair. Don't be tempted. Three sacks below are quite enough for Mr Krook!"

I lost no time in wishing Mr Krook good morning, and joining my friends outside, where we parted with the little old lady, who gave us her blessing with great ceremony, and renewed her assurance of yesterday in reference to her intention of settling estates on Ada and me. Before we finally turned out of those lanes, we looked back, and saw Mr Krook standing at his shop-door, in his spectacles, looking after us, with his cat upon his shoulder, and her tail sticking up on one side of his hairy cap, like a tall feather.

from *Bleak House* (1852–3)

The Sea-Cat

ST BRENDAN (*c.* 484–*c.* 577)

After this they rowed for a while over the ocean in a westerly direction, and found a pleasant little island with a number of fishermen in it. As they were going round it they saw in it a little stone church, in which was an aged man, pale and sorrowful, engaged in prayer. And he had neither flesh nor blood, but merely a thin miserable skin over his hard and yellow bones. Then that elder said: "Flee, Brendan, with all speed," said he. "For there is here now a sea-cat as big as a young ox or a three-year-old horse, which has thriven on the fish of the sea and of this island; beware of it now."

They betake them to their boat, and row over the ocean with all their might. As they were thus, they saw the monstrous sea-cat swimming after them; each of its two eyes was as big as a cauldron, it had tusks like a boar, sharp-pointed bristles, the maw of a leopard, the strength of a lion, and the rage of a mad dog. Then each of them began to pray to God by reason of the great fear which seized them. Then said Brendan: "O God Almighty," said he, "keep off Thy monsters from us, that they may not reach us."

Then a great sea whale rose up between them and the cat-monster, and each of them set to work to try and drown the other in the depths of the sea, and neither of them ever appeared again. Then Brendan and his company gave thanks to God, and turned back again to the place where the elder was. And the elder wept for the greatness of the joy which possessed him, and said: "I am of the men of Erin," said he, "and twelve of us were there when we came on our pilgrimage, and we brought that bestial sea-cat with us, and we were very fond of it; and it grew afterwards enormously, but it never hurt any of us. And now of our original company eleven have died, and I am left alone, waiting for thee to give me the body and blood of Christ, that therewith I may go to heaven."

He revealed to them afterwards the little country which they were seeking, that is the *Land of Promise*. And after receiving the body and blood of Christ, the elder went to heaven. He was buried there beside his brethren with great reverence, and with psalms and hymns, in the name of the Father, and of the Son, and of the Holy Ghost.

The Demon Cat

LADY WILDE (1826–96)

There was a woman in Connemara, the wife of a fisherman; as he had always good luck, she had plenty of fish at all times stored away in the house ready for market. But, to her great annoyance, she found that a great cat used to come in at night and devour all the best and finest fish. So she kept a big stick by her, and determined to watch.

One day, as she and a woman were spinning together, the house suddenly became quite dark; and the door was burst open as if by the blast of the tempest, when in walked a huge black cat, who went straight up to the fire, then turned round and growled at them.

"Why, surely this is the devil," said a young girl, who was by, sorting fish.

"I'll teach you how to call me names," said the cat; and, jumping at her, he scratched her arm till the blood came. "There, now," he said, "you will be more civil another time when a gentleman comes to see you." And with that he walked over to the door and shut it close, to prevent any of them going out, for the poor young girl, while crying loudly from fright and pain, had made a desperate rush to get away.

Just then a man was going by, and hearing the cries, he pushed open the door and tried to get in; but the cat stood on the threshold, and would let no one pass. On this the man attacked him with his stick, and gave him a sound blow; the cat, however, was more than a match in the fight, for it flew at him and tore his face and hands so badly that the man at last took to his heels and ran away as fast as he could.

"Now, it's time for my dinner," said the cat, going up to examine the fish that was laid out on the tables. "I hope the fish is good today. Now, don't disturb me, nor make a fuss; I can help myself." With that he jumped up, and began to devour all the best fish, while he growled at the woman.

"Away, out of this, you wicked beast," she cried, giving it a blow with the tongs that would have broken its back, only it was a devil; "out of this; no fish shall you have today."

But the cat only grinned at her, and went on tearing and spoiling and devouring the fish, evidently not a bit the worse for the blow. On this, both the women attacked it with sticks, and struck hard blows enough to kill it, on which the cat glared at them, and spit fire; then making a leap, it tore their heads and arms till the blood came, and the frightened women rushed shrieking from the house.

But presently the mistress returned, carrying with her a bottle of holy water; and, looking in, she saw the cat still devouring the fish, and not minding. So she crept over quietly and threw holy water on it without a word. No sooner was this done than a dense black smoke filled the place, through which nothing was seen but the two red eyes of the cat, burning like coals of fire. Then the smoke gradually cleared away, and she saw the body of the creature burning slowly till it became shrivelled and black like a cinder, and finally disappeared. And from that time the fish remained untouched and safe from harm, for the power of the evil one was broken, and the demon cat was seen no more.

The Squaw

BRAM STOKER (1847–1912)

Nurnberg at the time was not so much exploited as it has been since then. Irving had not been playing *Faust*, and the very name of the old town was hardly known to the great bulk of the travelling public. My wife and I being in the second week of our honeymoon, naturally wanted someone else to join our party, so that when the cheery stranger, Elias P. Hutcheson, hailing from Isthmian City, Bleeding Gulch, Maple Tree County, Nebraska, turned up at the station at Frankfurt, and casually remarked that he was going on to see the most all-fired old Methuselah of a town in Yurrup, and that he guessed that so much travelling alone was enough to send an intelligent, active citizen into the melancholy ward of a daft house, we took the pretty broad hint and suggested that we should join forces. We found, on comparing notes afterwards, that we had each intended to speak with some diffidence or hesitation so as not to appear too eager, such not being a good compliment to the success of our married life; but the effect was entirely marred by our both beginning to speak at the same instant – stopping simultaneously and then going on together again. Anyhow, no matter how, it was done; and Elias P. Hutcheson became one of our party. Straightway Amelia and I found the pleasant benefit; instead of quarrelling, as we had been doing, we found that the restraining influence of a third party was such that we now took every opportunity of spooning in odd corners. Amelia declares that ever since she has, as the result of that experience, advised all her friends to take a friend on the honeymoon. Well, we "did" Nurnberg together, and much enjoyed the racy remarks of our Transatlantic friend, who, from his quaint speech and his wonderful stock of adventures, might have stepped out of a novel. We kept for the last object of interest in the city to be visited the Burg, and on the day appointed for the visit strolled round the outer wall of the city by the eastern side.

The Burg is seated on a rock dominating the town, and an immensely deep fosse guards it on the northern side. Nurnberg has been happy in that it was never sacked: had it been it would certainly not be so spick and span perfect as it is at present. The ditch has not been used for centuries, and now its base is spread with tea-gardens and orchards, of which some of the trees are of quite respectable growth. As we wandered round the wall, dawdling in the hot July sunshine, we often paused to admire the views spread before us, and in especial the great plain covered with towns and villages and bounded with a blue line of hills, like a landscape of Claude Lorraine. From this we always turned with new delight to the city itself, with its myriad quaint old gables and acre-wide red roofs dotted with dormer windows, tier upon tier. A little to our right rose the towers of the Burg, and nearer still, standing grim, the Torture Tower, which was, and is, perhaps, the most interesting place in the city. For centuries the tradition of the Iron Virgin of Nurnberg has been handed down as an instance of the horrors of cruelty of which man is capable; we had long looked forward to seeing it; and here at last was its home.

In one of our pauses we leaned over the wall of the moat and looked down. The garden seemed quite fifty or sixty feet below us, and the sun pouring into it with an intense, moveless heat like that of an oven. Beyond rose the grey, grim wall seemingly of endless height, and losing itself right and left in the angles of bastion and counterscarp. Trees and bushes crowned the wall, and above again towered the lofty houses on whose massive beauty Time has only set the hand of approval. The sun was hot and we were lazy; time was our own, and we lingered, leaning on the wall. Just below us was a pretty sight – a great black cat lying stretched in the sun, whilst round her gambolled prettily a tiny black kitten. The mother would wave her tail for the kitten to play with, or would raise her feet and push away the little one as an encouragement to further play. They were just at the foot of the wall, and Elias P. Hutcheson, in order to help the play, stooped and took from the walk a moderate-sized pebble.

"See!" he said, "I will drop it near the kitten, and they will both wonder where it came from."

"Oh, be careful," said my wife; "you might hit the dear little thing!"

"Not me, ma'am," said Elias P. "Why, I'm as tender as a Maine cherry-tree. Lor, bless ye, I wouldn't hurt the poor pooty little critter more'n I'd scalp a baby. An' you may bet your variegated socks on that! See, I'll drop it fur away on the outside so's not to go near her!" Thus saying, he leaned over and held his arm out at full length and dropped the stone. It may be that there is some attractive force which draws lesser matters to greater; or more probably that the wall was not plumb but sloped to its base – we not noticing the inclination from above; but the stone fell with a sickening thud that came up to us through the hot air, right on the kitten's head, and shattered out its little brains then and there. The black cat cast a swift upward glance, and we saw her eyes like green fire fixed an instant on Elias P. Hutcheson; and then her attention was given to the kitten, which lay still with just a quiver of her tiny limbs, whilst a thin red stream trickled from a gaping wound. With a muffled cry, such as a human being might give, she bent over the kitten, licking its wound and moaning. Suddenly she seemed to realize that it was dead, and again threw her eyes up at us. I shall never forget the sight, for she looked the perfect incarnation of hate. Her green eyes blazed with lurid fire, and the white, sharp teeth seemed to almost shine through the blood which dabbled her mouth and whiskers. She gnashed her teeth, and her claws stood out stark and at full length on every paw. Then she made a wild rush up the wall as if to reach us, but when the momentum ended fell back, and further added to her horrible appearance for she fell on the kitten, and rose with her back fur smeared with its brains and blood. Amelia turned quite faint, and I had to lift her back from the wall. There was a seat close by in shade of a spreading plane-tree, and here I placed her whilst she composed herself. Then I went back to Hutcheson, who stood without moving, looking down on the angry cat below.

As I joined him, he said: "Wall, I guess that air the savagest beast I ever see – 'cept once when an Apache squaw had an edge on a half-breed what they nicknamed 'Splinters' 'cos of the way he fixed up her papoose which he stole on a raid just to show that he appreciated the way they had given his mother the fire torture. She got that kinder look so set on her face that it just seemed to grow there. She followed Splinters more'n three year till at last the braves got him and handed him over to her. They did say that no man, white or Injun, had ever been so long a-dying under the tortures of the Apaches. The only time I ever see her smile was when I wiped her out. I kem on the camp just in time to see Splinters pass in his checks, and he wasn't sorry to go either. He was a hard citizen, and though I never could shake with him after that papoose business – for it was bitter bad, and he should have been a white man, for he looked like one – I see he had got paid out in full. Durn me, but I took a piece of his hide from one of his skinnin' posts an' had it made into a pocket-book. It's here now!" and he slapped the breast pocket of his coat.

Whilst he was speaking the cat was continuing her frantic efforts to get up the wall. She would take a run back and then charge up, sometimes reaching an incredible height. She did not seem to mind the heavy fall which she got each time but started with renewed vigour; and at every tumble her appearance became more horrible. Hutcheson was a kind-hearted man – my wife and I had both noticed little acts of kindness to animals as well as to persons – and he seemed concerned at the state of fury to which the cat had wrought herself.

"Wall now!" he said, "I du declare that that poor critter seems quite desperate. There! there! poor thing, it was all an accident – though that won't bring back your little one to you. Say! I wouldn't have had such a thing happen for a thousand! Just shows what a clumsy fool of a man can do when he tries to play! Seems I'm too darned slipperhanded to even play with a cat. Say, Colonel!" – it was a pleasant way he had to bestow titles freely – "I hope your wife don't hold no grudge against me on account of this unpleasantness? Why, I wouldn't have had it occur on no account."

He came over to Amelia and apologized profusely, and she with her usual kindness of heart hastened to assure him that she quite understood that it was an accident. Then we all went again to the wall and looked over.

The cat, missing Hutcheson's face, had drawn back across the moat, and was sitting on her haunches as though ready to spring. Indeed, the very instant she saw him she did spring, and with a blind unreasoning fury, which would have been grotesque, only that it was so frightfully real. She did not try to run up the wall, but simple launched herself at him as though hate and fury could lend her wings to pass straight through the great distance between them. Amelia, womanlike, got quite concerned, and said to Elias P. in a warning voice: "Oh! you must be very careful. That animal would try to kill you if she were here; her eyes look like positive murder."

He laughed out jovially. "Excuse me, ma'am," he said, "but I can't help laughin'. Fancy a man that has fought grizzlies an' Injuns bein' careful of bein' murdered by a cat!"

When the cat heard him laugh, her whole demeanour seemed to change. She no longer tried to jump or run up the wall, but went quietly over, and sitting again beside the dead kitten began to lick and fondle it as though it were alive.

"See!" said I, "the effect of a really strong man. Even that animal in the midst of her fury recognizes the voice of a master, and bows to him!"

"Like a squaw!" was the only comment of Elias P. Hutcheson, as we moved on our way round the city fosse. Every now and then we looked over the wall and each time saw the cat following us. At first she had kept going back to the dead kitten, and then as the distance grew greater took it in her mouth and so followed. After a while, however, she abandoned this, for we saw her following all alone; she had evidently hidden the body somewhere. Amelia's alarm grew at the cat's persistence, and more than once she repeated her warning; but the American always laughed with amusement, till finally, seeing that she was beginning to be worried, he said: "I say, ma'am, you needn't be skeered over that cat. I go heeled, I du!" Here he slapped his pistol pocket at the back of his lumbar region. "Why, sooner'n have you worried, I'll shoot the critter, right here, an' risk the police interferin' with a citizen of the United States for carryin' arms contrairy to reg'lations!" As he spoke he looked over the wall, but the cat, on seeing him, retreated, with a growl, into a bed of tall flowers, and was hidden. He went on: "Blest if that ar critter ain't got more sense of what's good for her than most Christians. I guess we've seen the last of her! You bet, she'll go back now to that busted kitten and have a private funeral of it, all to herself!"

Amelia did not like to say more, lest he might, in mistaken kindness to her, fulfil his threat of shooting the cat: and so we went on and crossed the little wooden bridge leading to the gateway whence ran the steep paved roadway between the Burg and the pentagonal Torture Tower. As we crossed the bridge we saw the cat again down below us. When she saw us her fury seemed to return, and she made frantic efforts to get up the steep wall. Hutcheson laughed as he looked down at her, and said:

"Goodbye, old girl. Sorry I injured your feelin's, but you'll get over it in time! So long!" And then we passed through the long, dim archway and came to the gate of the Burg.

When we came out again after our survey of this most

beautiful old place which not even the well-intended efforts of the Gothic restorers of forty years ago have been able to spoil – though their restoration was then glaring white – we seemed to have quite forgotten the unpleasant episode of the morning. The old lime tree with its great trunk gnarled with the passing of nearly nine centuries, the deep well cut through the heart of the rock by those captives of old, and the lovely view from the city wall whence we heard, spread over almost a full quarter of an hour, the multitudinous chimes of the city, had all helped to wipe out from our minds the incident of the slain kitten.

We were the only visitors who had entered the Torture Tower that morning – so at least said the old custodian – and as we had the place all to ourselves were able to make a minute and more satisfactory survey than would have otherwise been possible. The custodian, looking to us as the sole source of his gains for the day, was willing to meet our wishes in any way. The Torture Tower is truly a grim place, even now when many thousands of visitors have sent a stream of life, and the joy that follows life, into the place; but at the time I mention it wore its grimmest and most gruesome aspect. The dust of ages seemed to have settled on it, and the darkness and the horror of its memories seemed to have become sentient in a way that would have satisfied the Pantheistic souls of Philo or Spinoza. The lower chamber where we entered was seemingly, in its normal state, filled with incarnate darkness; even the hot sunlight streaming in through the door seemed to be lost in the vast thickness of the walls, and only showed the masonry rough as when the builder's scaffolding had come down, but coated with dust and marked here and there with patches of dark stain which, if walls could speak, could have given their own dread memories of fear and pain. We were glad to pass up the dusty wooden staircase, the custodian leaving the outer door open to light us somewhat on our way; for to our eyes the one long-wick'd, evil-smelling candle stuck in a sconce on the wall gave an inadequate light. When we came up through the open trap in the corner of the chamber overhead, Amelia held on to me so tightly that I could actually feel her heart beat. I must say for my own part that I was not surprised at her fear, for this room was even more gruesome than that below. Here there was certainly more light, but only just sufficient to realize the horrible surroundings of the place. The builders of the tower had evidently intended that only they who should gain the top should have any of the joys of light and prospect. There, as we had noticed from below, were ranges of windows, albeit of medieval smallness, but elsewhere in the tower were only a very few narrow slits such as were habitual in places of medieval defence. A few of these only lit the chamber, and these so high up in the wall that from no part could the sky be seen through the thickness of the walls. In racks, and leaning in disorder against the walls, were a number of headmen's swords, great double-handed weapons with broad blade and keen edge. Hard by were several blocks whereon the necks of the victims had lain, with here and there deep notches where the steel had bitten through the guard of flesh and shored into the wood. Round the chamber, placed in all sorts of irregular ways, were many implements of torture which made one's heart ache to see – chairs full of spikes which gave instant and excruciating pain; chairs and couches with dull knobs whose torture was seemingly less, but which, though slower, were equally efficacious; racks, belts, boots, gloves, collars, all made for compressing at will; steel baskets in which the head could be slowly crushed into a pulp if necessary; watchmen's hooks with long handle and knife that cut at resistance – this a specialty of the old Nurnberg police system; and many, many other devices for man's injury to man. Amelia grew quite pale with the horror of the things, but fortunately did not faint, for being a little overcome she sat down on a torture chair, but jumped up again with a shriek, all tendency to faint gone. We both pretended that it was the injury done to her dress by the dust of the chair, and the rusty spikes which had upset her, and Mr Hutcheson acquiesced in accepting the explanation with a kind-hearted laugh.

But the central object in the whole of this chamber of horrors was the engine known as the Iron Virgin, which stood near the centre of the room. It was a rudely shaped figure of a woman, something of the bell order, or, to make a closer comparison, of the figure of Mrs Noah in the children's Ark, but without that slimness of waist and perfect *rondeur* of hip which marks the aesthetic type of the Noah family. One would hardly have recognized it as intended for a human figure at all had not the founder shaped on the forehead a rude semblance of a woman's face. This machine was coated with rust without, and covered with dust; a rope was fastened to a ring in the front of the figure, about where the waist should have been, and was drawn through a pulley, fastened on the wooden pillar which sustained the flooring above. The custodian pulling this rope showed that a section of the front was hinged like a door at one side; we then saw that the engine was of considerable thickness, leaving just room enough inside for a man to be placed. The door was of equal thickness and of great weight, for it took the custodian all his strength, aided though he was by the contrivance of the pulley, to open it. This weight was partly due to the fact that the door was of manifest purpose hung so as to throw its weight downwards, so that it might shut of its own accord when the strain was released. The inside was honeycombed with rust – nay more, the rust alone that comes through time would hardly have eaten so deep into the iron walls; the rust of the cruel stains was deep indeed! It was only, however, when we came to look at the inside of the door that the diabolical intention was manifest to the full. Here were several long spikes, square and massive, broad at the base and sharp at the points, placed in such a position that when the door should close the upper ones would pierce the eyes of the victim, and the lower ones his heart and vitals. The sight was too much for poor Amelia, and this time she fainted dead off, and I had to carry her down the stairs, and place her on a bench outside till she recovered. That she felt it to the quick was afterwards shown by the fact that my eldest son bears to this day a rude birthmark on his breast, which has, by family consent, been accepted as representing the Nurnberg Virgin.

When we got back to the chamber we found Hutcheson still

opposite the Iron Virgin; he had been evidently philosophizing, and now gave us the benefit of his thought in the shape of a sort of exordium.

"Wall, I guess I've been learnin' somethin' here while madam has been gettin' over her faint. 'Pears to me that we're a long way behind the times on our side of the big drink. We uster think out on the plains that the Injun could give us points in tryin' to make a man oncomfortable; but I guess your old medieval law-and-order party could raise him every time. Splinters was pretty good in his bluff on the squaw, but this here young miss held a straight flush all high on him. The points of them spikes air sharp enough still, though even the edges air eaten out by what uster be on them. It'd be a good thing for our Indian section to get some specimens of this here play-toy to send round to the Reservations jest to knock the stuffin' out of the bucks, and the squaws too, by showing them as how old civilization lays over them at their best. Guess but I'll get in that box a minute jest to see how it feels!"

"Oh no! no!" said Amelia. "It is too terrible!"

"Guess, ma'am, nothin's too terrible to the explorin' mind. I've been in some queer places in my time. Spent a night inside a dead horse while a prairie fire swept over me in Montana Territory – an' another time slept inside a dead buffler when the Comanches was on the war path an' I didn't keer to leave my kyard on them. I've been two days in a caved-in tunnel in the Billy Broncho gold mine in New Mexico, an' was one of the four shut up for three parts of a day in the caisson what slid over on her side when we was settin' the foundations of the Buffalo Bridge. I've not funked an odd experience yet, an' I don't propose to begin now!"

We saw that he was set on the experiment, so I said: "Well, hurry up, old man, and get through it quick?"

"All right, General," said he, "but I calculate we ain't quite ready yet. The gentlemen, my predecessors, what stood in that thar canister, didn't volunteer for the office – not much! And I guess there was some ornamental tyin' up before the big stroke was made. I want to go into this thing fair and square, so I must get fixed up proper first. I dare say this old galoot can rise some string and tie me up accordin' to sample?"

This was said interrogatively to the old custodian, but the latter, who understood the drift of his speech, though perhaps not appreciating to the full the niceties of dialect and imagery, shook his head. His protest was, however, only formal and made to be overcome. The American thrust a gold piece into his hand, saying, "Take it, pard! it's your pot; and don't be skeer'd. This ain't no necktie party that you're asked to assist in!" He produced some thin frayed rope and proceeded to bind our companion, with sufficient strictness for the purpose. When the upper part of his body was bound, Hutcheson said: "Hold on a moment, Judge. Guess I'm too heavy for you to tote into the canister. You jest let me walk in, and then you can wash up regardin' my legs!"

Whilst speaking he had backed himself into the opening which was just enough to hold him. It was a close fit and no mistake. Amelia looked on with fear in her eyes, but she evidently did not like to say anything. Then the custodian completed his task by tying the American's feet together so that he was now absolutely helpless and fixed in his voluntary prison. He seemed to really enjoy it, and the incipient smile which was habitual to his face blossomed into actuality as he said: "Guess this here Eve was made out of the rib of a dwarf! There ain't much room for a full-grown citizen of the United States to hustle. We uster make our coffins more roomier in Idaho territory. Now, Judge, you just begin to let this door down, slow, on to me. I want to feel the same pleasure as the other jays had when those spikes began to move toward their eyes!"

"Oh no! no! no!" broke in Amelia hysterically. "It is too terrible ! I can't bear to see it! — I can't! I can't!"

But the American was obdurate. "Say, Colonel," said he, "why not take Madame for a little promenade? I wouldn't hurt her feelin's for the world; but now that I am here, havin' kem eight thousand miles, wouldn't it be too hard to give up the very experience I've been pinin' an' pantin' fur ? A man can't get to feel like canned goods every time! Me and the Judge here'll fix up this thing in no time, an' then you'll come back, an' we'll all laugh together!"

Once more the resolution that is born of curiosity triumphed, and Amelia stayed holding tight to my arm and shivering whilst the custodian began to slacken slowly inch by inch the rope that held back the iron door. Hutcheson's face was positively radiant as his eyes followed the first movement of the spikes.

"Wall!" he said, "I guess I've not had enjoyment like this since I left Noo York. Bar a scrap with a French sailor at Wapping – an' that warn't much of a picnic neither – I've not had a show fur real pleasure in this dod-rotted Continent, where there ain't no b'ars nor no Injuns, an' wheer nary man goes heeled. Slow there, Judge! Don't you rush this business! I want a show for my money this game – I du!"

The custodian must have had in him some of the blood of his predecessors in that ghastly tower, for he worked the engine with a deliberate and excruciating slowness which after five minutes, in which the outer edge of the door had not moved half as many inches, began to overcome Amelia. I saw her lips whiten, and felt her hold upon my arm relax. I looked around an instant for a place whereon to lay her, and when I looked at her again found that her eye had become fixed on the side of the Virgin. Following its direction I saw the black cat crouching out of sight. Her green eyes shone like danger lamps in the gloom of the place, and their colour was heightened by the blood which still smeared her coat and reddened her mouth. I cried out: "The cat! look out for the cat!" for even then she sprang out before the engine. At this moment she looked like a triumphant demon. Her eyes blazed with ferocity, her hair bristled out till she seemed twice her normal size, and her tail lashed about as does a tiger's when the quarry is before it.

Elias P. Hutcheson when he saw her was amused, and his eyes positively sparkled with fun as he said: "Darned if the squaw hain't got on all her war paint! Jest give her a shove off if she comes any of her tricks on me, for I'm so fixed everlastingly by the boss, that durn my skin if I can keep my eyes from her if she wants them! Easy there, Judge! Don't you slack that ar rope or I'm euchered!"

At this moment Amelia completed her faint, and I had to clutch hold of her round the waist or she would have fallen to the floor. Whilst attending to her I saw the black cat crouching for a spring, and jumped up to turn the creature out.

But at that instant, with a sort of hellish scream, she hurled herself, not as we expected at Hutcheson, but straight at the face of the custodian. Her claws seemed to be tearing wildly as one sees in the Chinese drawings of the dragon rampant, and as I looked I saw one of them light on the poor man's eye, and actually tear through it and down his cheek, leaving a wide band of red where the blood seemed to spurt from every vein.

With a yell of sheer terror which came quicker than even his sense of pain, the man leaped back, dropping as he did so the rope which held back the iron door. I jumped for it, but was too late, for the cord ran like lightning through the pulley-block, and the heavy mass fell forward from its own weight.

As the door closed I caught a glimpse of our poor companion's face. He seemed frozen with terror. His eyes stared with a horrible anguish as if dazed, and no sound came from his lips.

And then the spikes did their work. Happily the end was quick, for when I wrenched open the door they had pierced so deep that they had locked in the bones of the skull through which they had crushed, and actually tore him – it – out of his iron prison till, bound as he was, he fell at full length with a sickly thud upon the floor, the face turning upward as he fell.

I rushed to my wife, lifted her up and carried her out, for I feared for her very reason if she should wake from her faint to such a scene. I laid her on the bench outside and ran back. Leaning against the wooden column was the custodian moaning in pain whilst he held his reddening handkerchief to his eyes. And sitting on the head of the poor American was the cat, purring loudly as she licked the blood which trickled through the gashed sockets of his eyes.

I think no one will call me cruel because I seized one of the old executioner's swords and shore her in two as she sat.

A CLOWDER
OF CATS

"A house without a cat, and a well-fed, well-petted
and properly revered cat, may be a perfect home,
perhaps, but how can it prove its title?"
Mark Twain (1835–1910)

The Young Cats' Club for Poetry-Music

HEINRICH HEINE (1797–1856)

The philharmonic young cats' club
  Upon the roof was collected
Tonight, but not for sensual joys,
  No wrong could there be detected.

No summer night's wedding dream there was dreamt,
  No song of love did they utter
In the winter season, in frost and snow,
  For frozen was every gutter.

A newborn spirit hath recently
  Come over the whole cat-nation,
But chiefly the young, and the young cat feels
  More earnest with inspiration.

The frivolous generation of old
  Is extinct, and a newborn yearning,
A pussy-springtime of poetry
  In art and in life they're learning.

The philharmonic young cats' club
  Is now returning to artless
And primitive music, and naiveté,
  From modern fashions all heartless.

It seeks in music for poetry,
  Roulades with the quavers omitted;
It seeks for poetry, music-void,
  For voice and instrument fitted.

It seeks for genius's sovereign sway,
  Which often bungles truly,

Yet oft in art unconsciously
    Attains the highest stage duly.

It honours the genius which prefers
    Dame Nature to keep at a distance,
And will not show off its learning – in fact
    Its learning not having existence.

This is the programme of our cat club,
    And with these intentions elated,
It holds its first winter concert tonight
    On the roof, as before I have stated.

Yet sad was the execution, alas,
    Of this great idea so splendid;
I'm sorry, my dear friend Berlioz,
    That by thee it wasn't attended.

It was a charivari, as though
    With brandy elated greatly,
Three dozen pipers struck up the tune
    That the poor cow died of lately.

It was an utter medley, as though
    In Noah's ark were beginning
The whole of the beasts in unison
    The Deluge to tell of in singing.

O what a croaking, snarling, and noise!
    O what a mewing and yelling!
And even the chimneys all join'd in,
    The wonderful chorus swelling.

And loudest of all was heard a voice
    Which sounded languid and shrieking
As Sontag's voice became at the last,
    When utterly broken and squeaking.

The whimsical concert! Methinks that they
   A grand Te Deum were chanting,
To honour the triumph o'er reason obtain'd
   By commonest frenzy and canting.

Perchance moreover the young cats' club
   The open grand were essaying
That the greatest pianist of Hungary*
   Composed for Charenton's playing.

It was not till the break of day
   That an end was put to the party;
A cook was in consequence brought to bed,
   Who before had seem'd well and hearty.

The lying-in woman lost her wits,
   Her memory, too, was affected,
And who was the father of her child
   No longer she recollected.

Say, was it Peter? Say, was it Paul?
   Say who is the father, Eliza!
"O Liszt, thou heavenly cat!" she said,
   And simper'd and look'd the wiser.

*Liszt

from *The Poems of Heine* (1861)
translated by E. A. Bowring

The Trinity Cat

ELLIS PETERS (1913–99)

He was sitting on top of one of the rear gate-posts of the churchyard when I walked through on Christmas Eve, grooming in his lordly style, with one back leg wrapped round his neck, and his bitten ear at an angle of forty-five degrees, as usual. I reckon one of the toms he'd tangled with in his nomad days had ripped the starched bit out of that one, the other stood up sharply enough. There was snow on the ground, a thin veiling, just beginning to crackle in promise of frost before evening, but he had at least three warm refuges around the place whenever he felt like holing up, besides his two houses, which he used only for visiting and cadging. He'd been a known character around our village for three years then, ever since he walked in from nowhere and made himself agreeable to the vicar and the verger, and finding the billet comfortable and the pickings good, constituted himself resident cat to Holy Trinity church, and took over all the jobs around the place that humans were too slow to tackle, like rat-catching, and chasing off invading dogs.

Nobody knows how old he is, but I think he could only have been about two when he settled here, a scrawny, chewed-up black bandit as lean as wire. After three years of being fed by Joel Woodward at Trinity Cottage, which was the verger's house by tradition, and flanked the lych-gate on one side, and pampered and petted by Miss Patience Thomson at Church Cottage on the other side, he was double his old size, and sleek as velvet, but still had one lop ear and a kink two inches from the end of his tail. He still looked like a brigand, but a highly prosperous brigand. Nobody ever gave him a name, he wasn't the sort to get called anything fluffy or familiar. Only Miss Patience ever dared coo at him, and he was very gracious about that, she being elderly and innocent and very free with little perks like raw liver, on which he doted. One way and another, he had it made. He lived mostly outdoors, never staying in either house overnight. In winter he had his own little ground-level hatch into the furnace-room of the church, sharing his lodgings matily with a hedgehog that had qualified as assistant vermin-destructor around the churchyard, and preferred sitting out the winter among the coke to hibernating like common hedgehogs. These individualists keep turning up in our valley, for some reason.

All I'd gone to the church for that afternoon was to fix up with the vicar about the Christmas peal, having been roped into the bell-ringing team. Resident police in remote areas like ours get dragged into all sorts of activities, and when the area's changing, and new problems cropping up, if they have any sense they don't need too much dragging, but go willingly. I've put my finger on many an astonished yobbo who thought he'd got clean away with his little breaking-and-entering, just by keeping my ears open during a darts match, or choir practice.

When I came back through the churchyard, around half-past two, Miss Patience was just coming out of her gate, with a shopping-bag on her wrist, and heading towards the street, and we walked along together a bit of the way. She was getting on for seventy, and hardly bigger than a bird, but very independent. Never having married or left the valley, and having looked after a mother who lived to be nearly ninety, she'd never had time to catch up with new ideas in the style of dress suitable for elderly ladies. Everything had always been done mother's way, and fashion, music and morals had stuck at the period when mother was a carefully brought-up girl learning domestic skills, and preparing for a chaste marriage. There's a lot to be said for it! But it had turned Miss Patience into a frail little lady in long-skirted black or grey or navy blue, who still felt undressed without hat and gloves, at an age when Mrs Newcombe, for instance, up at the pub, favoured shocking pink trouser-suits and red-gold hairpieces. A pretty little old lady Miss Patience was, though, very straight and neat. It was a pleasure to watch her walk. Which is more than I could say for Mrs Newcombe in her trouser suit, especially from the back!

"A happy Christmas, Sergeant Moon!" she chirped at me on sight. And I wished her the same, and slowed up to her pace.

"It's going to be slippery by twilight," I said. "You be careful how you go."

"Oh, I'm only going to be an hour or so," she said serenely. "I shall be home long before the frost sets in. I'm only doing the last bit of Christmas shopping. There's a cardigan I have to collect for Mrs Downs." That was her cleaning-lady, who went in three mornings a week. "I ordered it long ago, but deliveries are so slow nowadays. They've promised it for today. And a gramophone record for my little errand-boy." Tommy Fowler that was, one of the church trebles, as pink and wholesome-looking as they usually contrive to be, and just as artful. "And one mustn't forget our dumb friends, either, must one?" said Miss Patience cheerfully. "They're all important, too."

I took this to mean a couple of packets of some new product to lure wild birds to her garden. The Church Cottage thrushes were so fat they could hardly fly, and when it was frosty she put out fresh water three or four times a day.

We came to our brief street of shops, and off she went, with her big jet-and-gold brooch gleaming in her scarf. She had quite a few pieces of Victorian and Edwardian jewellery her mother'd left behind, and almost always wore one piece, being used to the belief that a lady dresses meticulously every day, not just on Sundays. And I went for a brisk walk round to see what was going on, and then went home to Molly and high tea, and took my boots off thankfully.

That was Christmas Eve. Christmas Day little Miss Thomson didn't turn up for eight o'clock Communion, which was unheard-of. The vicar said he'd call in after matins and see that she was all right, and hadn't taken cold trotting about in the snow. But somebody else beat us both to it. Tommy Fowler! He was anxious about that pop record of his. But even he had no chance until after service, for in our village it's the custom for the choir to go and sing the vicar an aubade in the shape of "Christians, Awake!" before the main service, ignoring the fact that he's then been up four hours, and conducted two Communions. And Tommy Fowler had a solo in the anthem, too. It was a quarter past twelve when he got away, and shot up the garden path to the door of Church Cottage.

He shot back even faster a minute later. I was heading for home when he came rocketing out of the gate and ran slam into me, with his eyes sticking out on stalks and his mouth wide open, making a sort of muted keening sound with shock. He clutched hold of me and pointed back towards Miss Thomson's front door, left half-open when he fled, and tried three times before he could croak out: "Miss Patience . . . She's there on the floor – she's bad!"

I went in on the run, thinking she'd had a heart attack all alone there, and was lying helpless. The front door led through a diminutive hall, and through another glazed door into the living-room, and that door was open, too, and there was Miss Patience face-down on the carpet, still in her coat and gloves, and with her shopping-bag lying beside her. An occasional table had been knocked over in her fall, spilling a vase and a book. Her hat was askew over one ear, and caved in like a trodden mushroom, and her neat grey bun of hair had come undone and trailed on her shoulder, and it was no longer grey but soiled, brownish black. She was dead and stiff. The room was so cold, you could tell those doors had been ajar all night.

The kid had followed me in, hanging on to my sleeve, his teeth chattering. "I didn't open the door – it was open! I didn't touch her, or anything. I only came to see if she was all right, and get my record."

It was there, lying unbroken, half out of the shopping-bag by her arm. She'd meant it for him, and I told him he should have it, but not yet, because it might be evidence, and we mustn't move anything. And I got him out of there quick, and gave him to the vicar to cope with, and went back to Miss Patience as soon as I'd telephoned for the outfit. Because we had a murder on our hands.

So that was the end of one gentle, harmless old woman, one of very many these days, battered to death because she walked in on an intruder who panicked. Walked in on him, I judged, not much more than an hour after I left her in the street. Everything about her looked the same as then, the shopping-bag, the coat, the hat, the gloves. The only difference, that she was dead. No, one more thing! No handbag, unless it was under the body, and later, when we were able to move her, I wasn't surprised to see that it wasn't there. Handbags are where old ladies carry their money. The sneak-thief who panicked and lashed out at her had still had greed and presence of mind enough to grab the bag as he fled. Nobody'd have to describe that bag to me, I knew it well, soft black leather with an old-fashioned gilt clasp and a short handle, a small thing, not like the holdalls they carry nowadays.

She was lying facing the opposite door, also open, which led to the stairs. On the writing-desk by that door stood one of a pair of heavy brass candlesticks. Its fellow was on the floor beside Miss Thomson's body, and though the bun of hair and the felt hat had prevented any great spattering of blood, there was blood enough on the square base to label the weapon. Whoever had hit her had been just sneaking down the stairs, ready to leave. She'd come home barely five minutes too soon.

Upstairs, in her bedroom, her bits of jewellery hadn't taken much finding. She'd never thought of herself as having valuables, or of other people as coveting them. Her gold and turquoise and funereal jet and true-lover's-knots in gold and opals, and mother's engagement and wedding rings, and her little Edwardian pendant watch set with seed pearls, had simply lived in the small top drawer of her dressing-table. She belonged to an honest epoch, and it was gone, and now she was gone after it. She didn't even lock her door when she went shopping. There wouldn't have been so much as the warning of a key grating in the lock, just the door opening.

Ten years ago not a soul in this valley behaved differently from Miss Patience. Nobody locked doors, sometimes not even overnight. Some of us went on a fortnight's holiday and left the doors unlocked. Now we can't even put out the milk money until the milkman knocks at the door in person. If this generation likes to pride itself on its progress, let it! As for me, I thought suddenly that maybe the innocent was well out of it.

We did the usual things, photographed the body and the scene of the crime, the doctor examined her and authorized her removal, and confirmed what I'd supposed about the approximate time of her death. And the forensic boys lifted a lot of smudgy latents that weren't going to be of any use to anybody, because they weren't going to be on record, barring a million to one chance. The whole thing stank of the amateur. There wouldn't be any easy matching up of prints, even if they got beauties. One more thing we did for Miss Patience. We tolled the dead-bell for her on Christmas night, six heavy, muffled strokes. She was a virgin. Nobody had to vouch for it, we all knew. And let me point out, it is a title of honour, to be respected accordingly.

We'd hardly got the poor soul out of the house when the Trinity cat strolled in, taking advantage of the minute or two while the door was open. He got as far as the place on the carpet where she'd lain, and his fur and whiskers stood on end, and even his lop ear jerked up straight. He put his nose down to the pile of the Wilton, about where her shopping-bag and handbag must have lain, and started going round in interested circles, snuffing the floor and making little throaty noises that might have been distress, but sounded like pleasure. Excitement, anyhow. The chaps from the CID were still busy, and didn't want him under their feet, so I picked him up and took him with me when I went across to Trinity Cottage to talk to the verger. The cat never liked being picked up; after a minute he started clawing and cursing, and I put him down. He stalked away again at once, past the corner where people shot their dead flowers, out at the lych-gate, and straight back to sit on Miss Thomson's doorstep. Well, after all, he used to get fed there, he might well be uneasy at all these queer comings and goings. And they don't say "as curious as a cat" for nothing, either.

I didn't need telling that Joel Woodward had had no hand in what had happened, he'd been nearest neighbour and good friend to Miss Patience for years, but he might have seen or heard something out of the ordinary. He was a little, wiry fellow, gnarled like a tree-root, the kind that goes on spry and active into his nineties, and then decides that's enough, and leaves overnight. His wife was dead long ago, and his daughter had come back to keep house for him after her husband deserted her, until she died, too, in a bus accident. There was just old Joel now, and the grandson she'd left with him, young Joel Barnett, nineteen, and a bit of a tearaway by his grandad's standards, but so far pretty innocuous by mine. He was a sulky, graceless sort, but he did work, and he stuck with the old man when many another would have lit out elsewhere.

"A bad business," said old Joel, shaking his head. "I only wish I could help you lay hands on whoever did it. But I only saw her yesterday morning about ten, when she took in the milk. I was round at the church hall all afternoon, getting things ready for the youth social they had last night, it was dark before I got back. I never saw or heard anything out of place. You can't see her living-room light from here, so there was no call to wonder. But the lad was here all afternoon. They only work till one, Christmas Eve. Then they all went boozing together for an hour or so, I expect, so I don't know exactly what time he got in, but he was here and had the tea on when I came home. Drop round in an hour or so and he should be here, he's gone round to collect this girl he's mashing. There's a party somewhere tonight."

I dropped round accordingly, and young Joel was there, sure enough, shoulder-length hair, frilled shirt, outsize lapels and all, got up to kill, all for the benefit of the girl his grandad had mentioned. And it turned out to be Connie Dymond, from the comparatively respectable branch of the family, along the canal-side. There were three sets of Dymond cousins, boys, no great harm in 'em but worth watching, but only this one girl in Connie's family. A good-looker, or at least most of the lads seemed to think so, she had a dozen or so on her string before she took up with young Joel. Big girl, too, with a lot of mauve eye-shadow and a mother-of-pearl mouth, in huge platform shoes and the fashionable drab granny-coat. But she was acting very prim and proper with old Joel around.

"Half past two when I got home," said young Joel. "Grandad was round at the hall, and I'd have gone round to help him, only I'd had a pint or two, and after I'd had me dinner I went to sleep, so it wasn't worth it by the time I woke up. Around four, that'd be. From then on I was here watching the telly, and I never saw nor heard a thing. But there was nobody else here, so

I could be spinning you the yarn, if you want to look at it that way."

He had a way of going looking for trouble before anybody else suggested it, there was nothing new about that. Still, there it was. One young fellow on the spot, and minus any alibi. There'd be plenty of others in the same case.

In the evening he'd been at the church social. Miss Patience wouldn't be expected there, it was mainly for the young, and anyhow, she very seldom went out in the evenings.

"I was there with Joel," said Connie Dymond. "He called for me at seven, I was with him all the evening. We went home to our place after the social finished, and he didn't leave till nearly midnight."

Very firm about it she was, doing her best for him. She could hardly know that his movements in the evening didn't interest us, since Miss Patience had then been dead for some hours.

When I opened the door to leave, the Trinity cat walked in, stalking past me with a purposeful stride. He had a look round us all, and then made for the girl, reached up his front paws to her knees, and was on her lap before she could fend him off, though she didn't look as if she welcomed his attentions. Very civil he was, purring and rubbing himself against her coat sleeve, and poking his whiskery face into hers. Unusual for him to be effusive, but when he did decide on it, it was always with someone who couldn't stand cats. You'll have noticed it's a way they have.

"Shove him off," said young Joel, seeing she didn't at all care for being singled out. "He only does it to annoy people."

And she did, but he only jumped on again, I noticed as I closed the door on them and left. It was a Dymond party they were going to, the senior lot, up at the filling station. Not much point in trying to check up on all her cousins and swains when they were gathered for a booze-up. Coming out of a hangover, tomorrow, they might be easy meat. Not that I had any special reason to look their way, they were an extrovert lot, more given to grievous bodily harm in street punch-ups than anything secretive. But it was wide open.

Well, we summed up. None of the lifted prints was on record, all we could do in that line was exclude all those that were Miss Thomson's. This kind of sordid little opportunist break-in had come into local experience only fairly recently, and though it was no novelty now, it had never before led to a death. No motive but the impulse of greed, so no traces leading up to the act, and none leading away. Everyone connected with the church, and most of the village besides, knew about the bits of jewellery she had, but never before had anyone considered them as desirable loot. Victoriana now carry inflated values, and are in demand, but this still didn't look calculated, just wanton. A kid's crime, a teenager's crime. Or the crime of a permanent teenager. They start at twelve years old now, but there are also the shiftless louts who never get beyond twelve years old, even in their forties.

We checked all the obvious people, her part-time gardener – but he was demonstrably elsewhere at the time – and his drifter of a son, whose alibi was non-existent but voluble, the window-cleaner, a sidelong soul who played up his ailments and did rather well out of her, all the delivery men. Several there who were clear, one or two who could have been around, but had no particular reason to be. Then we went after all the youngsters who, on their records, were possibles. There were three with breaking-and-entering convictions, but if they'd been there they'd been gloved. Several others with petty theft against them were also without alibis. By the end of a pretty exhaustive survey the field was wide, and none of the runners seemed to be ahead of the rest, and we were still looking. None of the stolen property had so far showed up.

Not, that is, until the Saturday. I was coming from Church Cottage through the graveyard again, and as I came near the corner where the dead flowers were shot, I noticed a glaring black patch making an irregular hole in the veil of frozen snow that still covered the ground. You couldn't miss it, it showed up like a black eye. And part of it was the soil and rotting leaves showing through, and part, the blackest part, was the Trinity cat, head down and back arched, digging industriously like a terrier after a rat. The bent end of his tail lashed steadily, while the remaining eight inches stood erect. If he knew I was standing watching him, he didn't care. Nothing was going to deflect him from what he was doing. And in a minute or two he heaved his prize clear, and clawed out to the light a little black leather handbag with a gilt clasp. No mistaking it, all stuck over as it was with dirt and rotting leaves. And he loved it, he was patting it and playing with it and rubbing his head against it, and purring like a steam-engine. He cursed, though, when I took it off him, and walked round and round me, pawing and swearing, telling me and the world he'd found it, and it was his.

It hadn't been there long. I'd been along that path often enough to know that the snow hadn't been disturbed the day before. Also, the mess of humus fell off it pretty quick and clean, and left it hardly stained at all. I held it in my hand kerchief and snapped the catch, and the inside was clean and empty, the lining slightly frayed from long use. The Trinity cat stood upright on his hind legs and protested loudly, and he had a voice that could outshout a Siamese.

Somebody behind me said curiously: "Whatever've you got there?" And there was young Joel standing open-mouthed, staring, with Connie Dymond hanging on to his arm and gaping at the cat's find in horrified recognition.

"Oh, no! My Gawd, that's Miss Thomson's bag, isn't it? I've seen her carrying it hundreds of times."

"Did *he* dig it up?" said Joel, incredulous. "You reckon the chap who – you know, *him!* – he buried it there? It could be anybody, everybody uses this way through."

"My Gawd!" said Connie, shrinking in fascinated horror against his side. "Look at that cat! You'd think he *knows* . . . He gives me the shivers! What's got into him?"

What, indeed? After I'd got rid of them and taken the bag away with me I was still wondering. I walked away with his prize and he followed me as far as the road, howling and swearing, and once I put the bag down, open, to see what he'd do, and he pounced on it and started his fun and games again until I took it from him. For the life of me I couldn't see what there was about it to delight him, but he was in no doubt. I was beginning to feel right superstitious about this avenging detective cat, and to wonder what he was going to unearth next.

I know I ought to have delivered the bag to the forensic lab, but somehow I hung on to it overnight. There was something fermenting at the back of my mind that I couldn't yet grasp.

Next morning we had two more at morning service besides the regulars. Young Joel hardly ever went to church, and I doubt if anybody'd ever seen Connie Dymond there before, but there they both were, large as life and solemn as death, in a middle pew, the boy sulky and scowling as if he'd been press-ganged into it, as he certainly had, Connie very subdued and big-eyed, with almost no make-up and an unusually grave and thoughtful face. Sudden death brings people up against daunting possibilities, and creates penitents. Young Joel felt silly there, but he was daft about her, plainly enough, she could get him to do what she wanted, and she'd wanted to make this gesture. She went through all the movements of devotion, he just sat, stood and kneeled awkwardly as required, and went on scowling.

There was a bitter east wind when we came out. On the steps of the porch everybody dug out gloves and turned up collars against it, and so did young Joel, and as he hauled his gloves out of his coat pocket, out with them came a little bright thing that rolled down the steps in front of us all and came to rest in a crack between the flagstones of the path. A gleam of pale blue and gold. A dozen people must have recognized it. Mrs Downs gave tongue in a shriek that informed even those who hadn't.

"That's Miss Thomson's! It's one of her turquoise ear-rings! *How did you get hold of that, Joel Barnett?*"

How, indeed? Everybody stood staring at the tiny thing, and then at young Joel, and he was gazing at the flagstones, struck white and dumb. And all in a moment Connie Dymond had pulled her arm free of his and recoiled from him until her back was against the wall, and was edging away from him like somebody trying to get out of range of flood or fire, and her face a sight to be seen, blind and stiff with horror.

"You!" she said in a whisper. "It was you! Oh, my God, *you* did it – you killed her! And me keeping company – how could I? How could *you!*"

She let out a screech and burst into sobs, and before anybody could stop her she turned and took to her heels, running for home like a mad thing.

I let her go. She'd keep. And I got young Joel and that single ear-ring away from the Sunday congregation and into Trinity Cottage before half the people there knew what was happening, and shut the world out, all but old Joel who came panting and shaking after us a few minutes later.

The boy was a long time getting his voice back, and when he did he had nothing to say but, hopelessly, over and over: "I didn't! I never touched her, I wouldn't. I don't know how that thing got into my pocket. I didn't do it. I never . . ."

Human beings are not all that inventive. Given a similar set of circumstances they tend to come out with the same formula. And in any case, "deny everything and say nothing else" is a very good rule when cornered.

They thought I'd gone round the bend when I said: "Where's the cat? See if you can get him in."

Old Joel was past wondering. He went out and rattled a saucer on the steps, and pretty soon the Trinity cat strolled in. Not at all excited, not wanting anything, fed and lazy, just curious enough to come and see why he was wanted. I turned him loose on young Joel's overcoat, and he couldn't have cared less. The pocket that had held the ear-ring held very little interest for him. He didn't care about any of the clothes in the wardrobe, or on the pegs in the little hall. As far as he was concerned, this new find was a non-event.

I sent for a constable and a car, and took young Joel in with me to the station, and all the village, you may be sure, either saw us pass or heard about it very shortly after. But I didn't stop to take any statement from him, just left him there, and took the car up to Mary Melton's place, where she breeds Siamese, and borrowed a cat-basket from her, the sort she uses to carry her queens to the vet. She asked what on earth I wanted it for, and I said to take the Trinity cat for a ride. She laughed her head off.

"Well, *he's* no queen," she said, "and no king, either. Not even a jack! And you'll never get that wild thing into a basket."

"Oh, yes, I will," I said. "And if he isn't any of the other picture cards, he's probably going to turn out to be the joker."

A very neat basket it was, not too obviously meant for a cat. And it was no trick getting the Trinity cat into it, all I did was drop in Miss Thomson's handbag, and he was in after it in a moment. He growled when he found himself shut in, but it was too late to complain then.

At the house by the canal Connie Dymond's mother let me in, but was none too happy about letting me see Connie, until I explained that I needed a statement from her before I could fit together young Joel's movements all through those Christmas days. Naturally I understood that the girl was terribly upset, but she'd had a lucky escape, and the sooner everything was cleared up, the better for her. And it wouldn't take long.

It didn't take long. Connie came down the stairs readily enough when her mother called her. She was all stained and pale and tearful, but had perked up somewhat with a sort of shivering pride in her own prominence. I've seen them like that before, getting the juice out of being the centre of attention even while they wish they were elsewhere. You could even say she hurried down, and she left the door of her bedroom open behind her, by the light coming through at the head of the stairs.

"Oh, Sergeant Moon!" she quavered at me from three steps up. "Isn't it *awful*? I still can't believe it! *Can* there be some mistake? Is there any chance it *wasn't* . . .?"

I said soothingly, yes, there was always a chance. And I slipped the latch of the cat-basket with one hand, so that the flap fell open, and the Trinity cat was out of there and up those stairs like a black flash, startling her so much she nearly fell down the last step, and steadied herself against the wall with a small shriek. And I blurted apologies for accidentally loosing him, and went up the stairs three at a time ahead of her, before she could recover her balance.

He was up on his hind legs in her dolly little room, full of pop posters and frills and garish colours, pawing at the second drawer of her dressing-table, and singing a loud, joyous, impatient song. When I came plunging in, he even looked over his shoulder at me and stood down, as though he knew I'd open the drawer for him. And I did, and he was up among her fancy undies like a shot, and digging with his front paws.

He found what he wanted just as she came in at the door. He yanked it out from among her bras and slips, and tossed it into the air, and in seconds he was on the floor with it, rolling and wrestling it, juggling it on his four paws like a circus turn, and purring fit to kill, a cat in ecstasy. A comic little thing it was, a muslin mouse with a plaited green nylon string for a tail, yellow beads for eyes, and nylon threads for whiskers, that rustled and sent out wafts of strong scent as he batted it around and sang to it. A catmint mouse, old Miss Thomson's last-minute purchase from the pet shop for her dumb friend. If you could ever call the Trinity cat dumb! The only thing she bought that day small enough to be slipped into her handbag instead of the shopping bag.

Connie let out a screech, and was across that room so fast I only just beat her to the open drawer. They were all there, the little pendant watch, the locket, the brooches, the true-lover's-knot, the purse, even the other ear-ring. A mistake, she should have ditched both while she was about it, but she was too greedy. They were for pierced ears, anyhow, no good to Connie.

I held them out in the palm of my hand – such a large haul they made – and let her see what she'd robbed and killed for.

If she'd kept her head she might have made a fight of it even then, claimed he'd made her hide them for him, and she'd been afraid to tell on him directly, and could only think of staging that public act at church, to get him safely in custody before she came clean. But she went wild. She did the one deadly thing, turned and kicked out in a screaming fury at the Trinity cat. He was spinning like a humming-top, and all she touched was the kink in his tail. He whipped round and clawed a red streak down her leg through the nylon. And then she screamed again, and began to babble through hysterical sobs that she never meant to hurt the poor old sod, that it wasn't her fault! Ever since she'd been going with young Joel she'd been seeing that little old bag going in and out, draped with her bits of gold. What in hell did an old witch like her want with jewellery? She had no *right!* At her age!

"But I never meant to hurt her! She came in too soon," lamented Connie, still and for ever the aggrieved. "What was I supposed to do? I had to get away, didn't I? *She was between me and the door!*"

She was half her size, too, and nearly four times her age! Ah well! What the courts would do with Connie, thank God, was none of my business. I just took her in and charged her, and got her statement. Once we had her dabs it was all over, because she'd left a bunch of them sweaty and clear on that brass candlestick. But if it hadn't been for the Trinity cat and his single-minded pursuit, scaring her into that ill-judged attempt to hand us young Joel as a scapegoat, she might, she just might, have got clean away with it. At least the boy could go home now, and count his blessings.

Not that she was very bright, of course. Who but a stupid harpy, soaked in cheap perfume and gimcrack dreams, would have hung on even to the catmint mouse, mistaking it for a herbal sachet to put among her smalls?

I saw the Trinity cat only this morning, sitting grooming in the church porch. He's getting very self-important, as if he knows he's a celebrity, though throughout he was only looking after the interests of Number One, like all cats. He's lost interest in his mouse already, now most of the scent's gone.

The Parson and the Cat

WILLIAM COWPER JUNIOR (1784–1872)

Let Cowper's ease and merry vein,
  In every verse appear,
And soon shall Nimrod's cassock'd train
  To Gilpin tune the ear.

'Twas at a time when scent was keen,
  What dog his nose could blame?
A Vicar paced the sylvan scene,
  In hot pursuit of game.

Only more strong the burning scent,
  When livings were in view;
The fleece possess'd – he lived content,
  Though vacant every pew.

More fragrant far such scent inhaled,
  Than incense upward borne,
No psalmody his ears assailed,
  Like clang of huntsman's horn.

Dearer to him the pack's full cry,
  Than Sabbath-bell's deep tone;
Not half so sweet the sinner's sigh,
  As Reynard's dying groan.

He saw a swain as forth he hied,
  Advancing to a brook,
Whose cat beneath his arm was tied,
  With wildness in her look.

"And whither," asked the buckskin priest,
  "Say, whither dost thou go?
If silent here, relate at least,
  Why bind Miss Pussey so?"

"Why," said John, "may't please your honour,
    I go this cat to drown."
"Why not set the dogs upon her?
    They soon will hunt her down."

To please his heavenly minded guide,
    Of tenderness composed,
He took poor pussey from his side,
    By hungry dogs enclosed.

And soon he snapp'd her hempen fetters,
    For sport prepared the way –
Sport, so fitting men of letters,
    Returned to childhood's day.

Full joyous was the priest as pack,
    When John threw down the cat,
The tide of early life roll'd back,
    In spite of wig and hat.

Tho' paid for preaching, 'twas his choice
    To whisper out the truth:
But now he stretch'd his stentor voice,
    More loud than any youth.

The dogs who knew their patron's shout,
    Nor did his flock so well,
Fired with parsonic zeal throughout,
    Made echo every dell.

Poor puss, in fright, for mercy begs,
    Nor tree nor mercy near,
She fastens on the horse's legs,
    And mounts him by the rear.

The steed unused to such a guest,
    Still less to spurs behind,

Snorted, and kicked, and onward press'd,
  A resting place to find.

Nor were her fangs the less employed,
  Her safety to complete,
'Twas through their grasp she still enjoyed,
  Her elevated seat.

The angry pack in dread array,
  With widened jaws and throats,
Leaped round and round the prancing bay,
  Howling their hideous notes.

Through raising fear and lengthened pain,
  The horse still raged the more,
And now, to sit, and guide the rein,
  The rider deemed were o'er.

Off went the parson with his mate,
  The hounds in full pursuit;
Transferr'd to him was her dread fate,
  He now, alas! was mute.

A change of scene effected thus;
  The priest appeared the game;
The triumph seemed to rest with puss,
  Till near the trackers came.

At length the ardour of the steed,
  Was checked by strength of arm;
The dog closed in which took the lead,
  And puss was all alarm.

Afraid lest some rude hound should reach,
  And drag her through the pack,
She left the horse's goaded breech,
  And scaled the parson's back.

Around his neck, in apish mood,
　　Her foremost limbs she twined,
And from each cheek she drew the blood,
　　As erst from steed behind.

Thus author-like, fair EXTRACTS made,
　　Not ELEGANT, 'tis true,
But cutting as the sharpest blade,
　　And flowing to the view.

Such Extracts from a work so rare –
　　A Sportsman and Divine,
Must surely make the reader stare,
　　Be doomed for aye to shine.

Himself he could not disengage,
　　From pussey's fond embrace;
'Twas toil enough to calm the rage,
　　And check the horse's pace.

The howling dogs now thickened round
　　All thirsting for the cat;
The hunter made a sudden bound,
　　And off flew wig and hat.

Away went priest – away went he,
　　Like Gilpin fam'd of yore
The villagers came out to see,
　　The dogs kept up the roar.

Both old and young their voices raised,
　　"Our Parson!" was the cry;
To see such game they stood amazed,
　　And rent with shouts the sky.

Not long before they saw him borne,
　　Full stately to the sight,

But little dreamt so swift return,
   And in such piteous plight.

His cheeks were like the damask rose,
   But not with morning air;
Miss Pussey, with the tint that glows,
   Had placed her pencil there.

All mingled in the merry chase,
   The greatest and the least,
The village cur e'en shewed his face,
   To kennel up the priest.

As forth, the hound and human pack,
   Poured like a stream along
Some joined, like minor rills, their track,
   And sang the jocund song.

Again the rider checked his horse,
   And hoped for parish aid,
But noisy crowds made matters worse,
   The steed was more afraid.

Away went priest – away went he,
   Like Gilpin famed of yore;
'Twas laughable Miss Puss to see,
   As high as heretofore.

The seat of learning she had gained,
   Which spoke superior sense,
And though unroofed, she still maintained
   It should not drive her thence.

The time was once – but then had fled,
   When easy had it been,
To deck, with frizzled roof, her head,
   Enlivening thus the scene.

For, in her fear, she might have placed,
    Her head beneath the wig,
And, forcing upward, might in haste,
    Have run another rig.

One sudden spring, when on the rise,
    Had borne it off complete;
With hat and wig – how wondrous wise!
    So near to learning's seat.

Ah, luckless wight, he should have been,
    Within his study walls,
Where seldom such as he are seen,
    Though loud the church's calls.

He brought from college his degree,
    But studious habits left;
The scholar's shadow you might see,
    Of substance he was reft.

Preferment's goal he long had gained,
    And fattened on the spoil;
The present goal unseen remained –
    For this he still must toil.

Miss Pussey like the parson rode,
    And like him kept her hold,
And while she o'er his Reverence strode,
    Each twitch she gave him told.

Her form between his shoulders lay,
    Her head behind his own,
Her foremost limbs were free to play,
    And straight before her thrown.

Her limbs – the rein, her claws – the bit,
    Like tenter hooks to view,

And while she held as seemed her fit,
  His cheeks she backward drew.

The more she drew as moved by fear;
  If fancy speak the truth,
She nearly stretched from ear to ear,
  His Reverence's mouth.

The neighbouring swains who met him straight,
  Would deem him catching flies,
But soon he passed – they saw his fate,
  When pussey caught their eyes.

Ah! luckless wight, had he but been,
  Intent upon his call
He had not now beheld this scene,
  Nor thus been jeered by all.

But still though greatly out of place,
  For safety he must strive,
Once more he checked his horse's pace,
  To every fear alive.

The roar of dogs and swains was heard,
  And nearer as they came,
More desperate still the steed appeared,
  Nor skill his rage could tame.

Away went priest – away went he,
  Like Gilpin famed of yore,
The fence-crushed farmer said with glee,
  "We ne'er shall see him more."

Others, anon as loudly cried,
  "No fear of him today;
Far better he is skill'd to ride,
  Than skill'd to preach and pray."

Let him, some wags might next have said,
    Nor limb nor cranium break,
The goal by him must soon be made,
    Or puss will tithe his cheek.

And why not pay like those around,
    For pleasures thus received?
It matters not how harsh the sound,
    The tithed are always grieved;

And grieved the more, as tithes are given,
    To those, whom all declare,
Nor either seek the road to heaven,
    Nor point their hearers there.

These are the Church's greatest foes,
    And not the different sects;
From these she feels the heaviest blows,
    On these the muse reflects.

And yet, than drunkards, and the gay,
    Dancers, and stage offenders;
Few talk of "DANGER" more than they,
    Or plume themselves defenders.

Not on the good, in heaven's pursuit,
    Who toil with all their power;
But grubs who only eat the fruit,
    Would satire's vengeance shower.

In virtue's cause – whate'er the name,
    The muse would e'er assume,
The two-edged sword – a sword of flame,
    Her enemies to consume.

But stay, while wandering from my tale,
    Wide as the priest from sport,

The painted claws his cheeks assail,
His features still distort.

The pars'nage-house at length was gained,
Without a broken limb,
But ne'er was he so tightly reined,
Nor caught in such a trim.

The house-dog heard the horse's feet,
And hastened to the door,
His master's reverend eye to meet,
And greet him as before.

How much surprised to see his lord,
With mouth so widely stretched!
Though grinning – not an angry word,
No hand to him was reach'd.

The mastiff knew – for wise was he,
That he had done no harm,
Nor sooner did Miss Pussey see,
Than he began to warm.

Forward he dashed in bristled mood,
The horse again took fright,
But ere he drew a drop of blood,
The pack was full in sight.

And who his gruffness could gainsay,
Though with the hounds he fought?
He wished a snack as well as they,
For this he sternly sought.

Tremendous was the fray indeed,
And madly did they strive;
The priest, in poor Miss Pussey's stead,
Was next to flayed alive.

Fancy would sketch another scene,
    For farming priests abound,
And shew the stack-yard, and the green,
    In motion all around.

The chuckling hens and cackling geese,
    United with the dogs,
Cows, calves and sheep, who sought their peace,
    Fled with the grunting hogs.

Fear, ire, and mirth, prevailed throughout,
    Though slight indeed the cause,
For all were moved or put to rout,
    By touch of pussey's claws.

With Hogarth's genius brought to bear,
    On villagers and beasts,
On poultry flying through the air,
    On chief of hunting priests;

Soon would a new creation rise,
    With cat and scampering crowd,
The clerk, to lead, with leering eyes,
    The choristers so loud.

The parson, more than satisfied,
    With leave, we now dismount,
And place both mirth and wounded pride,
    To pussey's just account.

But what can inmates say or do,
    Returning in such haste?
He carries game − Miss Puss, 'tis true −
    But not to suit the taste.

Enough of her to stay his fast,
    For one fair morning's meal;

He gladly hoped 'twould be the last,
    His appetite should feel.

'Tis but to guess how pussey fared,
    Though guiltless more than he;
For cruel intent, he was not spared,
    His friends must e'en agree.

But all may know how he was heard,
    And heard with what applause,
When in the rostrum, he appeared,
    With scars in such a cause.

What merriment would Paul inspire,
    Religion how much slur,
Clothed with huntsman's red attire,
    In boots, and cap, and spur!

How strange to Christian ears the sound,
    To come from Peter's lip,
"Hark, hark to cover," to the hound,
    And see him crack his whip!

In other language than to bless,
    It were outrageous quite;
In other than the priestly dress,
    Unseemly to the sight.

As strange it were to see a pig,
    Come bolting from the stye,
With three-cocked hat, and powdered wig,
    Laced coat, and buskins high.

Oh! worse than swine, more useless far,
    And still more out of place,
No more in Christ's right hand, a star,
    A blot on Zion's face —

Yes, worse – whose fate we here rehearse,
  And may he stand alone!
May priests no longer shine in verse,
  Where knaves and fools are shown.

Repent, reform, and imitate
  Those clergymen of fame –
True pillars of the Church and State,
  Of EVANGELIC name;

Those men, whose piety and zeal,
  Put sportsmen to the blush,
Who only toil for Zion's weal,
  And scorn to beat the bush.

This, for the tuneful organ calls,
  To draw the thoughtless crowd,
And *that*, to warm the church's walls,
  For blazing fires is loud.

Thus wide the good man never roves;
  For these ne'er opes his mouth;
He warms his church with living stoves,
  He draws by force of TRUTH.

Let every pulpit once be fill'd,
  With EVANGELIC men,
Soon shall the voice of foes be still'd,
  And useless be their pen.

May glorious days the church await!
  Such glories meet our eyes!
When every pile shall prove too straight,
  And new ones towering rise.

And now we sign God save the King,
  And Church from selfish ends;

Pray for ever, Lord deliver,
From Nimrod's cassock'd friends!

The Widow's Cat

ANNE BRONTË (1820–49)

I took the opportunity of repairing to the widow's cottage, where I found her in some anxiety about her cat, which had been absent all day. I comforted her with as many anecdotes of that animal's roving propensities as I could recollect. "I'm feared o' th' gamekeepers," said she, "that's all 'at I think on. If th' young gentlemen had been at home, I should a' thought they'd been setting their dogs at her, an' worried her, poor thing, as they did *many* a poor thing's cat; but I haven't that to be feared on now." Nancy's eyes were better, but still far from well: she had been trying to make a Sunday shirt for her son, but told me she could only bear to do a little bit at it now and then, so that it progressed but slowly, though the poor lad wanted it sadly. So I proposed to help her a little, after I had read to her, for I had plenty of time that evening, and need not return till dusk. She thankfully accepted the offer.

"An' you'll be a bit o' company for me too, miss," said she; "I like as I feel lonesome without my cat." But when I had finished reading, and done the half of a seam, with Nancy's capacious brass thimble fitted on to my finger by means of a roll of paper, I was disturbed by the entrance of Mr Weston, with the identical cat in his arms. I now saw that he could smile, and very pleasantly too.

"I've done you a piece of good service, Nancy," he began: then seeing me, he acknowledged my presence by a slight bow. I should have been invisible to Hatfield, or any other gentleman of those parts. "I've delivered your cat," he continued, "from the hands, or rather the gun, of Mr Murray's gamekeeper."

"God bless you, sir!" cried the grateful old woman, ready to weep for joy as she received her favourite from his arms.

447

"Take care of it," said he, "and don't let it go near the rabbit warren, for the gamekeeper swears he'll shoot it if he sees it there again: he would have done so today, if I had not been in time to stop him. I believe it is raining, Miss Grey," added he, more quietly, observing that I had put aside my work, and was preparing to depart. "Don't let me disturb you — I shan't stay two minutes."

"You'll *both* stay while this shower gets owered," said Nancy, as she stirred the fire, and placed another chair beside it; "what! there's room for all."

"I can see better here, thank you, Nancy," replied I, taking my work to the window, where she had the goodness to suffer me to remain unmolested, while she got a brush to remove the cat's hairs from Mr Weston's coat, carefully wiped the rain from his hat, and gave the cat its supper, busily talking all the time: now thanking her clerical friend for what he had done; now wondering how the cat had found out the warren; and now lamenting the probable consequences of such a discovery. He listened with a quiet, good-natured smile, and at length took a seat in compliance with her pressing invitations, but repeated that he did not mean to stay.

"I have another place to go to," said he, "and I see" (glancing at the book on the table) "someone else has been reading to you."

"Yes, sir; Miss Grey has been as kind as read me a chapter; an' now she's helping me with a shirt for our Bill — but I'm feared she'll be cold there. Won't you come to th' fire, miss?"

"No, thank you, Nancy, I'm quite warm. I must go as soon as this shower is over."

"Oh, miss! You said you could stop while dusk!" cried the provoking old woman, and Mr Weston seized his hat.

"Nay, sir," exclaimed she, "pray don't go now, while it rains so fast."

"But it strikes me I'm keeping your visitor away from the fire."

"No, you're not, Mr Weston," replied I, hoping there was no harm in a falsehood of that description.

"No, sure!" cried Nancy. "What, there's lots o' room!"

"Miss Grey," said he, half-jestingly, as if he felt it necessary to change the present subject, whether he had anything particular to say or not, "I wish you would make my peace with the squire when you see him. He was by when I rescued Nancy's cat, and did not quite approve of the deed. I told him I thought he might better spare all his rabbits than she her cat, for which audacious assertion he treated me to some rather ungentlemanly language; and I fear I retorted a trifle too warmly."

"Oh, lawful sir! I hope you didn't fall out wi' th' maister for sake o' my cat! he cannot bide answering again – can th' maister."

"Oh! it's no matter, Nancy: I don't care about it, really; I said nothing *very* uncivil; and I suppose Mr Murray is accustomed to use rather strong language when he's heated."

from *Agnes Grey* (1847)

The Cat

GEOFFREY CHAUCER (c. 1343–1400)

The cat, if you but singe her tabby skin,
The chimney keeps, and sits content within:
But once grown sleek, will from her corner run,
Sport with her tail and wanton in the sun:
She licks her fair round face, and frisks abroad
To show her fur, and to be catterwaw'd.

from the Prologue to "The Wife of Bath's Tale"
in *Canterbury Tales* (c. 1387)

Flaviso

FREDERICK ROLFE (1860–1913)

He rose and went to the window. The yellow cat deliberately stretched himself, yawned, and followed; and proceeded to

449

carry out a wonderful scheme of feints and ambuscades in regard to a ping-pong ball which was kept for his proper diversion. The man looked on almost lovingly. Flavio at length captured the ball, took it between his forepaws, and posed with all the majesty of a lion of Trafalgar Square. Anon he uttered a little low gurgle of endearment, fixing the great eloquent mystery of amber and black and velvet eyes, tardy, grave, upon his human friend. No notice was vouchsafed. Flavio got up; and gently rubbed his head against the nearest hand.

"My boy!" the man murmured; and he lifted the little cat on to his shoulder.

From *Hadrian the Seventh* (1904)

Hodge

JAMES BOSWELL (1740–95)

Nor would it be just under this head, to omit the fondness which he shewed for animals which he had taken under his protection. I never shall forget the indulgence with which he treated Hodge, his cat; for whom he himself used to go out and buy oysters, lest the servants, having that trouble, should take a dislike to the poor creature. I am, unluckily, one of those who have an antipathy to a cat, so that I am uneasy when in the room with one; and I own, I frequently suffered a good deal from the presence of this same Hodge. I recollect him one day scrambling up Dr Johnson's breast, apparently with much satisfaction, while my friend smiling and half-whistling, rubbed down his back, and pulled him by the tail; and when I observed he was a fine cat, saying "why, yes, Sir, but I have had cats whom I liked better than this"; and then as if perceiving Hodge to be out of countenance, adding, "but he is a very fine cat, a very fine cat indeed."

This reminds me of the ludicrous account which he gave Mr Langton, of the despicable state of a young gentleman of good family. "Sir, when I heard of him last, he was running about town shooting cats." And then in a sort of kindly reverie, he bethought himself of his own favourite cat, and said, "But Hodge shan't be shot: no, no, Hodge shall not be shot."

from *The Life of Dr Johnson* (1783)

Cats

ALEXANDRE DUMAS (1802–70)

[A cat is] the emblem of restlessness and impatience at the same moment. A restless cat no more remains in the same place than a silk thread does which is wafted idly to and fro with every breath of air. A cat on the watch is as motionless as death stationed at its place of observation, and neither hunger nor thirst can possibly draw it away from its meditation.

from *The Three Musketeers* (1844)

The Miracle of St Simon's

MARIAN EVANS (b. 1953)

On Cornwall's rugged coastline bare,
A steeple scythed into the air
Above a fishing village scene
That time had frozen, like a dream;
The cobbled streets, the hedgerow flowers,
St Simon's chimes that marked the hours.
Inside a cat slept on a pew,
In stained-glass sunlight, red and blue.

And when the fleet brought in its catch
At dawn old puss would sit and watch
As on the quay the herring writhed
Beneath the fishwives' flashing knives.
Yet never once, the sailors learned,
Did the cat steal what he'd not earned.

He only ate, inside God's house,
The vicar's scraps or heathen mouse.

The seasons passed, the years went by,
But still the cat went to the quay.
Then one fine day the village folk
Decided all their fish to smoke,
And so beside the church they raised
A smokehouse, which the vicar praised.
But as the building reached its height
None noticed how it blocked the light.

Outside the church the smokehouse grew
Until the stained glass, red and blue,
No longer shed its saintly glow
Upon the cat asleep below.
One day at dusk a builder's pole
Fell on the glass and made a hole,
At this the cat took great affright
And disappeared into the night.

It wasn't till a week had passed
That the church cat returned at last:
Bedraggled now he turned away
All proffered food, and scorned the quay.
The vicar tried his best to cheer
But all now knew his end was near.
Only a miracle, they said,
Could prevent him soon from being dead.

In penance for their carelessness
The workmen tidied up the mess
And on the sill installed a mat
Of softest velvet for the cat
So that through the clear-glass plate
He could see out and meditate
On life's short span and Heaven's throne
Which countless souls like his have known.

Another sight which caught his eye
Were seagulls by the smokery,
But ever at the close of day
The squealing birds all flew away.
Intrigued, one day the cat crept down
And weakly crossed the hallowed ground
Until he reached the herring shed
And gingerly stuck round his head . . .

High above on wires of steel
Hung row on row of fishy meal.
Temptation racked him like a fever,
But the cat knew he could never
Take what belonged to other men
And so he turned away, but then
A kipper fell right at his feet
And, startled, he began to eat.

When he had finished half the flesh
A dozen fish fell with a crash.
The cat then rushed out of the door
As snapped wires tossed down dozens more.
His strength returned, he then raced,
Back through the churchyard to the place
By the window whence he came
Just as the smoke-house burst in flame.

The vicar, working late that night,
Was filled with joy at the glad sight
Of his cat running down the aisle
And stroked the tabby with a smile.
The cat, slipping his fingers through,
Leapt to the window, red and blue.
The priest then saw all was not well
Through the clear pane and rang the bell.

The villagers rushed up the hill,
Leaving their boats and evening meal,

But though the firemen crowded round
The smokehouse burnt down to the ground.
A miracle, declared the people,
Had saved their church and its steeple
Which, the guidebooks were all agreed,
Was a holy treasure indeed.

As the fisherfolk knelt to pray
To thank their God for this good day,
The vicar blessed the old church cat
And praised the Lord in Heaven that
His pious fast had brought no harm
For without the cat the alarm
Would not have rung in loud, long notes
And brought them quickly from their boats.

The inquest found after some days
What had caused the smokehouse blaze:
The kippers falling from their wire
Upset a lamp and caused a fire.
When the insurance was all paid
A brand new smokehouse then was made,
Far away in a sheltered pass
And excess funds bought new stained glass.

So now our tale is almost done
Of a brave cat and honour won.
Above that rugged coastline bare
A steeple scythes yet in the air;
St Simon's chimes still mark the hours
O'er cobbled streets and hedgerow flowers;
A cat once more sleeps on a pew
In stained-glass sunlight, red and blue.

The Diminutive Lyon

WILLIAM SALMON (1644–1713)

I. It is called in Hebrew, בְּטוּל, סחנר, *Catul, Schanar;* in Chaldean, חתול, *pl.* חתולין, *Chatul, pl. Chatulin;* in Greek, Κατλης, αιλουρος; in Latin, *Catus, felis;* in English, *the Cat,* but the wild Cat is supposed to be called in Hebrew, אײם, *Jim. Isa.* 13, 22, and 34, 14. for so *Arius Montanus* translates it; as for *Kat* or *Cat,* it is the most usual name that almost all Nations call it by.

II. It is bred and is an Inhabitant of almost all Countries in the World, all *Cats* were at first wild, but were at length tamed by the industry of Mankind; it is a Beast of prey, even the tame one, more especially the wild, it being in the opinion of many nothing but a diminutive Lyon.

III. It is now said to be of three kinds, 1. *The tame Cat.* 2. *The wild wood Cat.* 3. *The Cat of Mountain,* all which are of one nature, and agree much in one Shape, save as to their magnitude, the *wild Cat* being larger much than the *tame,* and the *Cat of Mountain* much larger than the *wild Cat.*

IV. It has a broad Face almost like a Lyon, short Ears, large Whiskers, shining Eyes, short smooth Hair, long Tail, rough Tongue, and armed on its Feet with Claws, being a crafty, subtle watchful Creature, very loving and familiar with Mankind, the mortal enemy to the Rat, Mouse, and all sorts of Birds, which it seizes on as its prey. As to its Eyes, Authors say that they shine in the Night, and see better at the full, and more dimly at the change of the Moon; as also that the Cat doth vary his Eyes with the Sun, the Apple of its Eye being long at Sunrise, round towards Noon, and not to be seen at all at night, but the whole Eye shining in the night. These appearances of the Cats Eyes I am sure are true, but whether they answer to the times of the day, I never observed.

V. It is a neat and cleanly creature, often licking itself, to keep it fair and clean, and washing its Face with its forefeet; the best are such as are of a fair and large kind, and of an exquisite Tabby colour, called *Cyprus* Cats. They usually generate in the winter Season, making a great noise, go 56 Days or 8 weeks with young, and bring forth 2, 3, 4, 5, 6, or more at a time, they cover their excrements, and love to keep their old habitations.

VI. *Its Flesh* is not usually eaten, yet in some Countries it is accounted an excellent Dish, but the Brain is said to be poisonous, causing madness, stupidity, and loss of memory, which is cured only by vomiting, and taking musk in Wine.

From *The Compleat English Physician* (1693)

The Cat and the Cornfield

BRYAN MACMAHON

In Ireland, all you need to make a story is two men with completed characters – say, a parish priest and his sexton. There at once you have conflict. When, as a foil for the sexton, you throw in a mature tinker girl, wild and lissom, love interest is added to conflict. And when, finally, you supply a snow-white cat, a cornfield, and a shrewish woman who asks three questions, the parts, if properly put together, should at least provide a moderate tale.

The scene is laid in a village asleep on a summer hill: the hour of the day is mid-morning. The village is made up of a church that lacks a steeple, a pair of pubs – one thatched and the other slated – with maybe a dozen higgledy-piggledy houses divided equally as between thatch and slate. The gaps between the houses yield glimpses of well-foliaged trees beyond which the countryside falls away into loamy fields.

On the morning of our story, the sexton, a small grumpy fellow of middle age with irregular red features, by name Denny Furey, had just finished sweeping out the brown flagstones of the church porch. He then took up the wire mat at the door and tried irritably but vainly to shake three pebbles out of it.

At the sound of the rattling pebbles, the sexton's white cat which was sitting on the sunny wall of the church beside his master's cabin, looked up and mewed soundlessly. Denny glanced sourly at the cat. "Pangur Bán," he said, "if you didn't sleep in my breeches and so have 'em warm before my shanks on frosty mornings, I'd have you drowned long 'go!" The cat – he had pale green eyes and a blotch on his nose – silently mewed his misunderstanding.

Suddenly there came a sound of harness bells. A tinker's spring-cart, painted bright green and blue, with a shaggy piebald cob between the shafts, drew slowly past the church gate. Sitting on the near wing of the cart was a tinker girl wearing a tartan dress and a bright shoulder-shawl. Eighteen, perhaps; more likely, nineteen. She had wild fair hair and a nut-brown complexion. Spying the sexton struggling with the mat, her eyes gleamed with puckish pleasure.

Meeting her gaze, Denny grimaced ill-temperedly and then half-turned his back on her. As on a thought he swung around to scowl her a reminder of her duty. Slowly the girl cut the sign of the Cross on herself.

Just beyond the church gateway, the cob's lazy motion came to a halt. The girl continued to stare at the sexton. Angrily Denny dropped the mat. Swiftly he raised his right hand as if he had been taken with a desire to shout: "Shoo! Be off with yourself at once!" The words refused to come.

Pangur Bán raised himself on shuddering legs, arched his back and sent a gracious but soundless mew of welcome in the girl's direction.

"That you may be lucky, master!" the tinker girl said. Then: "Your wife – have she e'er an old pair of shoes?"

"Wife! Wife! I've no wife!" Denny turned sharply away and snatched up his brush.

The girl watched as the sexton's movements of sweeping became indefinably jaunty. Then her smiling eyes roved and rested for a moment on the thatched cabin at the left of the church gate.

Without turning round, Denny shouted: "Nothing for you today!"

The girl was slow in replying. Her eyes still fast on the cabin, she said: "I know you've nothin' for me, master!" She did not draw upon the reins.

Denny stopped brushing. His stance indicated that again he was struggling to say: "Be off!" Instead of speaking, he set his brush against the church wall, turned his head without moving his shoulders and looked fully at the girl. She answered his eyes with frankness. They kept looking at one another for a long time. At last, his altering gaze still locked in hers, Denny turned his body around.

As if caught in drowse Denny set aside his brush. He donned his hat, then walked slowly towards the church gate. Lost rosaries clinked as the white-painted iron yielded to his fingers. Denny looked to left and to right. Up to this their eyes had been bound fast to one another.

The sunlit village was asleep. Pangur Bán lay curled and still on the warm wall.

A strange tenderness glossed Denny's voice. "Where are you headin' for?" he asked. The gate latched shut behind him.

"Wherever the cob carries me!"

Again the girl's gaze swivelled to the cabin. "Is that your house?" she asked, and then, as she glanced again at the wall: "Is that your cat?"

"Ay! . . . Ay!"

For a long while the girl kept looking at the little house with its small deeply recessed windows. She noted well the dark-green half-door above which shone a latch of polished brass.

"Do you never tire of the road?" Denny asked.

"Do you never tire of being fettered?" the girl flashed. She had turned to look at him directly.

Both sighed fully and deeply. Under the black hat Denny's eyes had begun to smoulder.

Secretly the girl dragged on the rein. As the cob shifted from one leg to another, she uttered a small exclamation of annoyance. Her red and green skirt made a wheel as she leaped from the vehicle and advanced to make an obscure adjustment to the harness. This done she prepared to lead her animal away.

Denny glanced desperately around. Uproad stood a hissing gander with his flock of geese serried behind him.

"I'll convey you apass the gander!" he blurted.

The tinker girl glanced at the gander; her mouth-corners twitched in a smile. She made a great to-do about gathering up the reins and adjusting her shawl. As she led the animal away, Denny moved to the far side of the road and kept pace with her as she went. Walking thus, apart yet together, they left the village and stepped downhill. Once the sexton glanced fearfully over his shoulder; the village was not so much asleep as stone-dead.

As the white road twisted, the village on the hillock was unseen. The cob – a hairy, bony animal – moved swiftly on the declivity so that Denny had to hurry to keep up with the girl and her animal.

The splendour of the summer accompanied them. The gauds of the harness were winking in the bright light. The countryside was a silver shield inclining to gold. Their footfalls were muted in the limestone road dust. Muted also were the noise of the horse's unshod hooves and the ringing of the harness bells. At last they came to the foot of the hillock. Here the road ran between level fields. Denny looked over his shoulder and saw Pangur Bán fifty yards behind him walking stealthily on the road margin.

"Be off!" the sexton shouted.

Pangur Bán paused to utter his soundless mew.

The girl smiled. They walked on for a space. Again Denny turned. "Be off, you Judas!" he shouted. He snatched up a stone and flung it at the cat.

The instant the stone left the sexton's hand, Pangur judged that it was going to miss him. He remained utterly without movement. When the stone had gone singing away into stillness, the cat went over and smelled at a piece of road metal

the bounding stone had disturbed. Pangur mewed his mysti-
fication into the sky; then spurted faithfully on.

The road again twisted. Now it was commanded by the
entrance to the village on the hillock.

Here in a cornfield at the left-hand side of the road, the
ripening corn was on the swing from green to gold. The field
was a house of brightness open to the southern sky. Directly
beside their boots a gap offered descent to the sown ground.
The cob stopped dead and began to crop the roadside grass.

"Let us sit in the sun," the sexton ventured. He indicated the
remote corner of the cornfield.

The girl smiled in dreamy agreement. With slow movements
she tied her cob to the butt of a whitethorn bush. The pair
walked along by the edge of the corn and sat down on the
grassy edge of the farthest headland. Here the corn screened
them from the view of a person passing on the road. The
fierceness and lushness of growth in this sun-trap had made the
hedge behind them impenetrable. Denny set his hat back on his
poll. Then he took the girl's hand in his and began to fondle it.
Points of sweat appeared on his agitated face.

Twice already, from the top of the grassy fence, Pangur Bán
had stretched out a paw in an attempt to descend into the
cornfield. On each occasion thistles and thorns tipping his pads
had dissuaded him from leaping. Through slim upended ovals
of dark pupil the cat ruefully eyed the cropping horse, then
turned to mew his upbraidings in the direction of his master.
Tiring of this, he settled himself patiently to wait.

Pangur Bán sat with his tail curled around his front paws. His
eyes were reluctant to open in the sunlight. His ears began to
sift the natural sounds of the day.

Reading his Office, the huge old priest walked the village.
Glancing up from his breviary, he noticed the brush idle against
the church wall: he also spied the wire mat that lay almost
concealed on the lawn grass. The impudence of the gander the
priest punished with a wave of his blackthorn stick. Standing on
the road in front of the sexton's cabin, he sang out: "Denny!
Denny Furey!" There was no reply.

The priest shuffled to the church door and in a lowered voice again called for his sexton. At last, with an angry shrug of his shoulders, he again turned his attention to his breviary. Still reading, he sauntered downhill and out into the open country. After a while he raised his eyes. First he saw the brown-and-white pony, then he spied the flame that was the cat burning white beside the olive cornfield.

The old man's face crinkled. He grunted. Imprisoning his stick in his left armpit, he began to slouch in the direction of Pangur Bán. From time to time his eyes strayed over the gilt edging and the coloured markers of his book.

Denny glanced up from his sober love-making.

"Divine God!" he exclaimed.

The girl was leaning back on the grass: her posture tautened a swath of green hay to silver. She was smiling up at the sky as she spaced her clean teeth along a grass stem.

Reaching the cat, the priest halted. "Pangur Bán," he wheedled in a low voice. His eyes were roving over the cornfield. The cat tilted his back against the lower may leaves, set his four paws together and drooped as if for a bout of languid gaiety.

For a moment or two the priest tricked with the cat. Then he threw back his shoulders. "To think that I don't see you, Denny Furey!" he clarioned.

Denny and the girl were silent and without movement. About them the minute living world asserted itself in the snip of grasshoppers.

Again the priest thundered: "Nice example for a sexton!"

The sweat beaded above Denny's eyebrows. His thighs began to shiver in the breeches his cat slept in. The girl peered at the priest through the altering lattice of the corn-heads. Her expression was quizzical as she glanced at Denny.

From the roadway came again the dreaded voice: "If it's the last thing I do, Denny Furey, I'll strip you of your black coat!"

At this moment a shrewish woman, wearing a black and green shawl, thrust around the bend of the road. She was resolutely headed for the village.

Seeing the woman approach, the priest quickly turned his face away from the cornfield and resumed his pacing along the road. His lips grew busy with the Latin psalms.

Peeping out and recognizing the newcomer, Denny Furey at first swore softly, then he began to moan. "The parish will be ringin' with the news before dark!" he sniffled.

The woman blessed the priest so as to break him from his Office: then in a tone of voice that expressed thin concern: "Did I hear your voice raised, Father?"

The priest lowered his shaggy eyebrows. "Sermons don't sprout on bushes, my good woman!"

"Ah! Practisin' you were!"

Her crafty eyes alighted on the white cat. "Would it be bird-chasin' the sexton's cat is?"

"It could be, now that you mention it!"

There was a pause. The conversation of the wheat spars was only one step above silence. Flicking the cornfield and the cart with a single glance, the woman said, in a half whisper: "People say that tinker girls'd pick the eye out of your head!"

"Did you never hear tell of the virtue of charity, woman?" the priest growled.

The woman made her grumbled excuses. It suited the priest not to accept them. Hurriedly she walked away. Resentment was implicit in the puffs of road-dust that spouted from beneath her toe-caps. Before the village swallowed her up, she looked over her shoulder. The priest was standing in mid-road waiting to parry this backward glance.

Again the priest turned his attention to the cornfield. With a sound half-grunt, half-chuckle, he untied the cob, and leading it by the head, turned away in the direction of the village.

The instant the harness bells began to ring, the tinker girl sprang to her feet and raced wildly but surefootedly along the edge of the cornfield. "Father!" she cried out. "Father!"

The priest came to a halt. Well out of the range of his stick, the girl stopped. "So I've drawn you, my vixen!" the priest said.

Breathlessly, the girl bobbed a half-curtsey.

"What're you goin' to do with my animal, Father?"

"Impounding him I am – unless you get that sexton o' mine out of the cornfield at once."

The girl leaped on to the low fence: "Come out o' the cornfield," she shouted, "I want to recover my cob!"

There was a pause. Then Denny shuffled to his feet. The cat stood up and mewed loyal greetings to his lord.

The priest stood at the horse's head. The angry girl was on the fence; her arms akimbo. Shambling dismally, Denny drew nearer. When he had reached the roadway, the tinker girl cried out: "I was goin' my road, Father, when he coaxed me into the cornfield!"

Denny opened his mouth, but no words came. He began to blink his moist eyes. His mouth closed fast. He kept his distance from the priest's stick. As Pangur Bán began rubbing himself against the end of the beloved breeches, the sexton gave the cat the side of his long boot and sent him careening into the bushes.

"*A chait*, ou'r that!" he said.

"Aha, you scoundrel!" the priest reproved, "Can you do no better than abuse a dumb animal?"

Turning to the girl: "Take your cob! And if I catch you in this village again, by the Holy Man, I'll give you the length and breadth of my blackthorn!"

"He said he'd convey me apass the gander, Father!"

Three times she lunged forward. Three times her buttocks winced away. At last she mustered courage enough to grasp the winkers. Clutching the ring of the mouthpiece, she swung the pony downroad. When she had gained a few yards she leaped lightly on to the broad board on the side of the cart and slashed at the cob's rump with the free dangle of the reins. The animal leaped forward.

The priest, the sexton, the cat. The sunlit, rustling cornfield.

"Come on, me bucko!" the priest said grimly.

He began to lead the way home. The sexton trailed a miserable yard or two behind. Glory was gone out of his life. The wonderful day seemed to mock him. The future was a known road stretching before his leaden legs. What he had thought would prove a pleasant bauble had turned to a crown of thorns. In the past, whenever he had chafed against the drab nature of his existence, he had consoled himself thus: "One day, perhaps today, I'll run and buy me a hoop of bright colours."

Denny began to compare his soul to a pebble trapped in a wire mat of despair.

Gradually the priest became infected with Denny's moroseness. Side by side, the priest and his sexton continued to move homewards. In the faraway, the sound of the harness bells was a recessional song of adventure.

Behind the pair and at a discreet distance, Pangur Bán travelled quietly. Now and again he paused to mew his loyalty into the sunny world.

from *The Red Petticoat and Other Stories*

Verses on a Cat

PERCY BYSSHE SHELLEY (1792–1822)

A cat in distress,
Nothing more, nor less;
Good folks, I must faithfully tell ye,
As I am a sinner,
It waits for some dinner
To stuff out its own little belly.

You would not easily guess
All the modes of distress
Which torture the tenants of earth;
And the various evils,
Which like so many devils,
Attend the poor souls from their birth.

Some a living require,
And others desire

An old fellow out of the way:
And which is the best
I leave to be guessed,
For I cannot pretend to say.

One wants society,
Another variety,
Others a tranquil life;
Some want food,
Others, as good,
Only want a wife.

But this poor little cat
Only wanted a rat,
To stuff out its own little maw;
And it were as good
Some people had such food,
To make them *hold their jaw*!

The Gentleman Farmer and his Eleven Cats

w.h. hùdson (1841–1922)

One of my old shepherd's stories about strange or eccentric persons he had known during his long life was of a gentleman farmer, an old bachelor, in the parish of Winterbourne Bishop, who had (for a man) an excessive fondness for cats and who always kept eleven of these animals as pets. For some mysterious reason that number was religiously adhered to. The farmer was fond of riding on the downs, and was invariably attended by a groom in livery – a crusty old fellow; and one of this man's duties was to attend to his master's eleven cats. They had to be fed at their proper time, in their own dining-room, eating their meals from a row of eleven plates on a long, low table made expressly for them. They were taught to go each one to his own place and plate, and not to get on to the table, but to eat "like Christians", without quarrelling or interfering with their neighbours on either side. And, as a rule, they all behaved properly, except one big tom-cat, who developed so greedy, spiteful, and tyrannical a disposition that there was never a meal but he upset the harmony and brought it to a disorderly end, with spittings, snarlings, and scratchings. Day after day the old groom went to his master with a long, dolorous plaint of this cat's intolerable behaviour, but the farmer would not consent to its removal, or to any strong measures being taken; kindness combined with patience and firmness, he maintained, would at last win even this troublesome animal to a better mind. But in the end he, too, grew tired of this incorrigible cat, who was now making the others spiteful and quarrelsome by his example; and one day, hearing a worse account than usual, he got into a passion, and taking a loaded gun handed it to the groom with orders to shoot the cat on the spot on the very next occasion of its misbehaving, so that not only would they be rid of it but its death in that way would serve as a warning to the others. At the very next meal the bad cat got up the usual row, and by and by they were all fighting and tearing each other on the table, and the groom, seizing the gun, sent a charge of shot into the thickest of the fight, shooting three of the cats dead. But the author of all the mischief escaped without so much as a pellet! The farmer was in a great rage at this disastrous blundering, and gave notice to his groom on the spot; but the man was an old and valued servant, and by and by he forgave him, and the quarrelsome animal having been got rid of, and four fresh cats obtained to fill up the gaps, peace was restored.

from *A Shepherd's Life* (1910)

The Monkey and the Cat

JEAN DE LA FONTAINE (1621–95)

Sly Bertrand and Ratto in company sat,
(The one was a monkey, the other a cat)
Co-servants and lodgers:

More mischievous codgers
Ne'er mess'd from a platter, since platters were flat.
Was anything wrong in the house or about it,
The neighbours were blameless – no mortal could doubt it;
For Bertrand was thievish, and Ratto so nice,
More attentive to cheese than he was to the mice.
One day the two plunderers sat by the fire,
Where chestnuts were roasting, with looks of desire.
To steal them would be a right noble affair.
A double inducement our heroes drew there –
'Twould benefit them, could they swallow their fill,
And then 'twould occasion to somebody ill.
Said Bertrand to Ratto, "My brother, today
Exhibit your powers in a masterly way,
And take me these chestnuts, I pray.
Which were I but otherwise fitted
(As I am ingeniously witted)
For pulling things out of the flame,
Would stand but a pitiful game."
" 'Tis done," replied Ratto, all prompt to obey;
And thrust out his paw in a delicate way.
First giving the ashes a scratch,
He open'd the coveted batch;
Then lightly and quickly impinging,
He drew out, in spite of the singeing,
One after another, the chestnuts at last –
While Bertrand contrived to devour them as fast.
A servant girl enters. Adieu to the fun.
Our Ratto was hardly contented, says one.

No more are the princes, by flattery paid
For furnishing help in a different trade,
And burning their fingers to bring
More power to some mightier king.

from *The Fables* (1842) translated by Elizur Wright

The Hen and the Cat

AESOP (6th century BC)

All the barnyard knew that the hen was indisposed. So one day the cat decided to pay her a visit of condolence. Creeping up to her nest the cat in his most sympathetic voice said: "How are you, my dear friend? I was so sorry to hear of your illness. Isn't there something that I can bring you to cheer you up and to help you feel like yourself again?"

"Thank you," said the hen. "Please be good enough to leave me in peace, and I have no fear but I shall soon be well."

MORAL:

Uninvited guests are often most welcome when they are gone.

from *Fables*

Tybert the Cat

ANONYMOUS

Then the King said: "Sir Tybert, ye shall now go to Reynard, and say to him this second time that he come to Court unto the plea for to answer; for, though he be fell to other beasts, he trusteth you well and will do by your counsel. And tell [him], if he come not, he shall have the third warning and be summoned, and, if he then come not, we shall proceed by law against him and all his lineage without mercy."

Tybert spake: "My Lord the King, they that this counselled you were not my friends. What shall I do there? He will not for me neither come ne abide. I beseech you, dear King, send some other to him. I am little and feeble. Bruin the Bear, which was so great and strong, could not bring him: how should I then take it on hand?"

"Nay," said the King, "Sir Tybert, ye are wise and well learned. Though ye be not great, there lieth not much in that. Many do more with skill and knowledge than with might and strength."

Then said the Cat: "Sith it must needs be done, I must then take it upon me. God give grace that I may well achieve it, for my heart is heavy, and evil-willed thereto."

Tybert made him soon ready toward Maleperduys. And he saw from far come flying one of Saint Martin's birds; then cried he [a]loud and said: "All hail, gentle bird, turn thy wings hitherward, and fly on my right side." The bird flew forth upon a tree which stood on the left side of the Cat. Then was Tybert woe; for he thought it was a sinister token and a sign of harm. For, if the bird had flown on his right side, he had been merry and glad; but now he was anxious lest his journey should turn to misfortune. Nevertheless, he did as many do, and gave to himself better hope than his heart said. He went and ran toward Maleperduys, and there he found the Fox alone standing before his house.

Tybert said: "The rich God give you good even, Reynard! The King hath menaced you for to take your life from you if ye come not now with me to the Court."

The Fox then spake and said: "Tybert, my dear cousin, ye be right welcome! I would well truly that ye had much good luck." What hurted [it] the Fox to speak fair? Though he said well, his heart thought it not; and that shall be seen ere they depart.

Reynard said: "Shall we this night be together? I will make you good cheer, and tomorrow early in the dawning we will together go to the Court. Good nephew, let us so do: I have none of my kin that I trust so much to as to you. Here was Bruin the Bear – the traitor! He looked so knavishly on me, and methought he was so strong, that I would not for a thousand mark have gone with him; but, cousin, I will tomorrow early go with you."

Tybert said: "It is best that we now go, for the moon shineth all so light as it were day: I never saw fairer weather."

469

"Nay, dear cousin, such might meet us by daytime that would make us good cheer and by night peradventure might do us harm. It is suspicious to walk by night. Therefore abide this night here by me."

Tybert said· "What should we eat if we abode here?"

Reynard said: "Here is but little to eat. Ye may well have an honeycomb, good and sweet. What say ye, Tybert, will ye any thereof?"

Tybert answered: "I set naught thereby. Have ye nothing else? If ye gave me a good fat mouse, I should be better pleased."

"A fat mouse!" said Reynard. "Dear cousin, what say ye? Hereby dwelleth a Priest and hath a barn by his house; therein are so many mice that a man could not lead them away upon a wain. I have heard the Priest many times complain that they did him much harm."

"Oh, dear Reynard, lead me thither for all that I may do for you!"

"Yea, Tybert, say ye me truth? Love ye well mice?"

"If I love them well?" said the Cat. "I love mice better than anything that men give me! Know ye not that mice savour better than game – yea, than pancakes or pasties? Will ye well do, so lead me thither where the mice are, and then shall ye win my love, yea, although ye had slain my father, mother, and all my kin."

Reynard said: "Ye mock and jest therewith!"

The Cat said: "So help me God, I do not!"

"Tybert," said the Fox, "wist I that verily, I would yet this night make that ye should be full of mice."

"Reynard!" quoth he, "Full? That were many."

"Tybert, ye jest!"

"Reynard," quoth he, "in truth I do not. If I had a fat mouse, I would not give it for a golden noble."

"Let us go, then, Tybert," quoth the Fox; "I will bring you to the place ere I go from you."

"Reynard," quoth the Cat, "upon your safe-conduct I would well go with you to Montpellier."

"Let us then go," said the Fox; "we tarry all too long."

Thus went they forth, without hindrance to the place where they would be, to the Priest's barn, which was fast walled about with a mud wall. And the night before the Fox had broken in, and had stolen from the Priest a good fat hen; and the Priest, all angry, had set a snare before the hole to avenge him; for he would fain have taken the Fox. This knew well the fell thief, the Fox, and said: "Sir Tybert, cousin, creep into this hole, and ye shall not long tarry but that ye shall catch mice by great heaps. Hark how they pipe! When ye be full, come again; I will tarry here after you before this hole. We will tomorrow go together to the Court. Tybert, why tarry ye thus long? Come off, and so may we return soon to my wife which waiteth for us, and shall make us good cheer."

Tybert said: "Reynard, cousin, is it then your counsel that I go into this hole? These Priests are so wily and shrewish I dread to take harm."

"Oh, ho, Tybert!" said the Fox, "I saw you never so sore afraid! What aileth you?"

The Cat was ashamed, and sprang into the hole. And anon he was caught in the snare by the neck, ere he wist. Thus deceived Reynard his guest and cousin.

As Tybert was ware of the snare, he was afraid and sprang forth – the snare went to. Then he began to shout, for he was almost strangled. He called, he cried, and made a villainous noise.

Reynard stood before the hole and heard all, and was well satisfied, and said: "Tybert, love ye well mice? Be they fat and good? Knew the Priest hereof, or Mertynet, they be so gentle that they would bring you sauce. Tybert, ye sing and eat – is that the custom of the Court? Lord God, if Isegrim were there by you, in such rest as ye now be, then should I be glad; for oft he hath done me damage and harm."

Tybert could not go away; but he mewed and cried out so loud, that Mertynet sprang up, and cried [a]loud: "God be thanked, my snare hath taken the thief that hath stolen our hens. Arise up; we will reward him!"

With these words arose the Priest in an evil time; and waked all them that were in the house, and cried with a loud voice: "The Fox is taken!"

There leapt and ran all that there was. The Priest himself ran, all mother-naked. Mertynet was the first that came to Tybert. The Priest took to Julocke his wife an offering candle, and bade her light it at the fire; and he smote Tybert with a great staff. There received Tybert many a great stroke over all his body. Mertynet was so angry that he smote the Cat an eye out. The naked Priest lifted up and should have given a great stroke to Tybert, but Tybert, that saw that he must die, sprang between the Priest's legs with his claws and with his teeth that he tore out his right colyon or balock-stone. That leap became ill to the Priest, and to his great shame.

This thing fell down upon the floor. When Dame Julocke knew that, she sware by her father's soul, that she would [rather] it had cost her all the offering of a whole year [than] that the Priest should have had that harm, hurt, and shame and that it had not happened; and said: "In the Devil's name was the snare there set! See Mertynet, dear son, this is thy father's harness. This is a great shame and to me a great hurt, for, though he be healed thereof, he is but a lost man to me, and also shall never be able to do that sweet play and game." The Fox stood without, before the hole, and heard all these words, and laughed so sore that he scarcely could stand. He spake thus all softly: "Dame Julocke, be all still, and your great sorrow sink. Although hath the Priest lost one of his stones, it shall not hinder him: he shall do with you well enough. There is in the world many a chapel in which is rung but one bell." Thus scorned and mocked the Fox the Priest's wife, Dame Julocke, that was full of sorrow.

The Priest fell down a-swoon. They took him up, and brought him again to bed. Then went the Fox again in towards his burrow and left Tybert the Cat in great dread and jeopardy, for the Fox wist none other but that the Cat was nigh dead. But, when Tybert the Cat saw them all busy about the Priest, then began he to bite and gnaw the snare in the middle asunder, and sprang out of the hole, and went rolling and rolling towards the King's Court. Ere he came thither it was fair day, and the sun began to rise. And he came to the Court as a poor wight. He had caught harm at the Priest's house by the help and counsel of the Fox. His body was all beaten to pieces, and blind on the one eye. When the King wist this, that Tybert was thus arrayed, he was sore angry, and menaced Reynard the thief sore; and anon gathered his Council to know what they would advise him how he might bring the Fox to the law, and how he should be fetched.

Then spake Sir Grymbart, which was the Fox's sister's son, and said: "Ye Lords, though my uncle were twice so bad and knavish, yet is there remedy enough. Let him be done to as to a free man. When he shall be judged, he must be warned the third time for all; and, if he come not then, he is then guilty in all the trespasses that are laid against him and his, or complained on."

"Grymbart, who would ye that should go and summon him to come? Who will adventure for him his ears, his eye, or his life – which is so fell a beast? I trow there is none here so much a fool."

Grymbart spake: "So help me God, *I* am so much a fool that I will do this message myself to Reynard, if ye will command me."

from *History of Reynard the Fox* (1481)

Breakfast and Puss

ANONYMOUS

Here's my baby's bread and milk,
For her lips as soft as silk;
Here's the basin clean and neat,
Here's the spoon of silver sweet,
Here's the stool, and here's the chair,
For my little lady fair.

No, you must not spill it out,
And drop the bread and milk about;
But let it stand before you flat,
And pray remember pussy-cat:
Poor old pussy-cat that purrs
All so patiently for hers.

True, she runs about the house,
Catching now and then a mouse;
But, though she thinks it very nice,
That only makes a tiny slice:
So don't forget that you should stop
And leave poor puss a little drop.

from *Rhymes for the Nursery* (new edition, 1839)

Borodin's Cats

N.A. RIMSKY-KORSAKOV (1844–1908)

Their whole home life was one unending disorder. Dinner-time and other meal-times were most indefinite. Once I came to their house at eleven in the evening and found them at dinner. Leaving out of account the girls, their protégées, of whom their house had never any lack, their apartment was often used as shelter or a night's lodging by various poor (or "visiting") relations, who picked that place to fall ill or even lose their minds. Borodin had his hands full of them, doctored them, took them to hospitals, and then visited them there. In the four rooms of his apartment there often slept several strange persons of this sort; sofas and floors were turned into beds. Frequently it proved impossible to play the piano, because someone lay asleep in the adjoining room. At dinner and at tea, too, great disorder prevailed. Several tom-cats that found a home in Borodin's apartment paraded across the dinner-table, sticking their noses into plates, unceremoniously leaping to the diners' backs. These tom-cats basked in Yekatyerina Sergeyevna's protection; various details of their biography were related. One tabby was called *Rybolov* ("Fisherman"), because, in the winter, he contrived to catch small fish with his paw through the ice-holes; the other was called *Dlinyenki* ("Longy") and he was in the habit of fetching homeless kittens by the neck to Borodin's apartment; these the Borodins would harbour, later finding homes for them. Then there were other, and less remarkable specimens of the genus *Felis*. You might sit at their tea-table – and behold! Tommy marches along the board and makes for your plate; you shoo him off, but Yekatyerina Sergeyevna invariably takes his part and tells some incident from his biography. Meantime, zip! another cat has bounded at Alyeksandr Porfiryevich's neck and, twining himself about it, has fallen to warming that neck without pity. "Listen, dear Sir, this is too much of a good thing!" says Borodin, but without stirring; and the cat lolls blissfully on.

from *My Musical Life* (1924)

Monsignore Capelecatro and His Cat

WALTER SAVAGE LANDOR (1775–1864)

Taranto now has lost her guide,
A prelate without prelate's pride.
On that Parthenopean coast,
Incredulous of fog or frost.
His Persian puss he smiles to see
Leap boldly on a stranger's knee,
And stretch out flat and lick his fur,
And switch his tail, and gape and purr.
Oh my two friends! may, many a day,
Both think of me when far away.

Cat Quotations

VARIOUS

Cat: A soft indestructible automaton provided by nature to be kicked when things go wrong in the domestic circle.

Ambrose Bierce

Everything that moves seems to interest and amuse a cat.

Paradis de Moncrif

If you want to be a psychological novelist and write about human beings, the best thing you can do is to keep a pair of cats.

Aldous Huxley

By associating with the cat, one only risks becoming richer.

Colette

Refined and delicate natures understand the cat. Women, poets and artists hold it in great esteem, for they recognize the exquisite delicacy of its nervous system; indeed, only coarse natures fail to discern the natural distinction of the animal.

Champfleury

Of all God's creatures there is only one that cannot be made the slave of the lash. That one is the cat. If man could be crossed with the cat it would improve man, but it would deteriorate the cat.

Mark Twain

Cats, by the way, rarely suffer from excess of adulation. A cat possesses a very fair sense of the ridiculous, and will put her paw down kindly but firmly upon any nonsense of this kind.

Jerome K. Jerome

Far in the stillness a cat languishes loudly.

W.E. Henley

The Case of the Rolls-Royce and the Flying Cat

CHRISTOPHER PARK (b. 1953)

Bleary-eyed after an uncomfortable night, I drew back the curtains and watched a heron, like some grey pterodactyl, circle and land beside the pond. From my upstairs room in the West Wing I could see that his earlier attention to the fish in the lozenge with the fountains beneath my window had allowed the algae to grow back apace. Now, it seemed, as he stalked among the rhododendrons at its edge, he was intent on picking clean the duck-pond as well when an extraordinary thing happened. A large, cat-like animal suddenly swooped from the branch of an overhanging tree and grabbed hold of a mouthful of the heron's feathers. The bird reacted instantly and took flight into the orchard. For a few brief seconds the cat held on, but then, seeing that the heron was too strong, released its grip and plummeted some twenty feet through the air at great speed. The cat's bravery − or foolishness if you are, like me, not an avid ailurophile − was rewarded when it landed in a pear-tree (Conference, by the look of them). But what was more extraordinary still than this dramatic stunt at eight o'clock on a July morning in Surrey was the fact that, silhouetted against the Downs behind Aunt Effie's estate as the black cat squirmed and twirled its tail in its downward spiral through the void − rub my eyes as much as I could − I distinctly recollected the impression that on its back flapped a pair of wings!

We'd arrived the previous night in the mistaken assumption that the 3rd of July was American Independence Day. To be fair, dear old Bunty had insisted all along that it was the 4th, but as there was due to be a rail strike on the Wednesday and the roads would be packed with irate commuters arriving two hours late for work, the uncertainty about the date, combined with this prospect, won the day, and within a comparatively short while after leaving Beauchamp Magna I piloted my royal

blue Lagonda, Hermione, across the gravel and parked her –
with a certain panache, I thought – at an angle in front of Aunt
Effie's enormous mock-Tudor pile in the deepest fringes of
Reigate.

We'd come to the mid-point of our visits to my wife's
relations. In the idyllic months since my marriage last No-
vember to the Hon. Bunty Scroope, the only interruptions to
our bliss had been these four-weekly sojourns to the various
bizarre members of her mother's family dotted about the British
Isles. I say "bliss" in the broadest sense of the word, of course, as
due to a series of remarkable coincidences I had yet to
experience the highest pleasures expected by a vigorous 40-
year-old recently hitched to a gazelle-like beauty half my age.
Her devoted service to the wildlife, especially the inhabitants of
the stable-block, on that small part of the Memburys' Sussex
estate I had inherited from my father, always seemed to result in
some fiendish symptom – colds, headache, strained muscles,
straw allergy, etc. – that militated against the matrimonial act.
But good old Bunty seemed to take it all in good heart and was
ever in high spirits. Why, even the uncertainty of the date of
our visit didn't seem to throw her, and when I insisted we go
on the 3rd she rushed off to look at the horses and didn't return
until I'd got Hermione all packed up and idling in the drive.
When Hickey, the young estate manager she had appointed,
waved us farewell as he led a large bay gelding into the yard, it
struck me as odd that he never suffered from the same country
fevers as Bunty did. But then again, he was of open-air rural
stock whereas the Scroopes had the weaknesses of gentility.

Another weakness, which as a member of the hound-loving
Membury clan I find difficulty in appreciating, was their
apparently irrational devotion to cats. Almost without exception, every member of the Scroope family was an ailurophile of
the *n*th order, where *n* is cuckoo plus bananas rolled into one
with a generous helping of moonshine and saccharin ladled
over the lot. However, the exception – the delightful exception as I had learnt from my brief encounter with him at the
Spaniel & Ferret on my stag night half a year earlier – was Uncle

Jasper. Unfortunately, though, this refreshing innovation in the Scroope genes was held in check by his wife Effie Mackintosh of That Ilk. Not only was she the image of Jean Brodie with all the best and worst of an upbringing in the genteel but austere Morningside district of Edinburgh, but she was also a signed-up activist for the Society for the Preservation of the Scottish Wildcat. Luckily, her husband rarely gave her occasion to return to her native Scotland to exercise her passion for rabidly sensationalist demonstrations – a litter-bin filled with sheep's intestines which had exploded as the Scottish Secretary passed the pavement plaque to the reviled Heart of Midlothian prison, covering him in offal, had borne traces of her involvement. However, she was very much the (tartan) trouser-wearer of the couple, and Plimpton Hall was very much Effie's domain.

This was brought home to us the moment we entered the building at eight the previous evening when a surprised maid ushered us into the lobby area and we were confronted by an enormous set of Mackintosh armorial bearings subscribed with the motto "Touch not the cat but with a glove" next to a striking grisaille portrait of Jasper's father, Bunty's great-uncle Granville, by Sir William Orpen. Sir Granville Scroope, my wife explained, had manufactured and patented a form of variegated grey cement that, like Coade stone, could be moulded, but had the added property of being indistinguishable from marble. The painting obviously reflected this remarkable material which was the basis of the family fortune, and many examples of it could be seen in the hallway, the most immediate being the floor upon which we were then standing.

When I seemed confused that her uncle's father was not Bunty's grandfather, my dear wife pointed out that, strictly speaking, Uncle Jasper was not her uncle at all but rather her first cousin once removed, as Sir Granville was her grandfather's younger – and poorer – brother. However, as Jasper had been largely "farmed out" in his childhood on the wealthy peer with his huge brood and sizeable household, prior to Granville's achieving his own not inconsiderable success in "trade", he had always been treated as an honorary sibling by his cousins german and thus was introduced as an "uncle" to Bunty and her brother and sister and addressed as such.

Having handed over our coats and hats and given the key to the boot of the Lagonda to the maid's helper, we learnt, both by the expression on her face and the words which followed, that not only were we definitely wrong about the date but we were alone in the house, as Jasper and Effie had motored over to the house of their American neighbours to help with the preparations for the 4th of July celebrations. The head servant made a telephone call to our hosts to clarify how best to proceed in the circumstances and it was decreed that, as it was late and as dining and accommodation arrangements had already been made with the American friends, who lived in the next valley, Bunty and I should shift for ourselves as best we could – with the implication, it seemed to me, that it was our fault for arriving too early.

Accordingly, a scratch meal of cold meats later appeared and, whilst Bunty settled into the master bedroom in the East Wing, I prepared myself for a pleasant stroll around the grounds. Apart from the pleasure of meeting Uncle Jasper again – we had an additional mutual interest in that he ran a prestigious literary puzzle magazine, a hobby in which I found great delight – I had always wanted to visit the scene of that excellent tale "The Case of the Reigate Squires" by the Blessed Conan. I had taken up the study of the writings of Sir Arthur Conan Doyle on our honeymoon and, like an athlete in training, had increasing confidence in my powers of deduction as a result. To be in such a place, with the editor of *The Literary Enigma*, was the next best thing to nuptial bliss imaginable.

Deep in remembrance of Doyle's story, I passed out through the double entry doors and round the West Wing of the house, and began to fantasize if this indeed might have been a model for the house of Watson's old friend, Colonel Hayter, to which the good doctor had brought an exhausted Holmes to recuperate after his sickness in the Hotel Dulong in Lyons. Or indeed might it even have been the house of the Cunninghams in which poor Kiwarn was to lose his life? But then my idle reverie was broken – of course not, the story was set in the late 1880s and Doyle himself died in 1930, the very year Uncle Jasper's pile was built.

But there were other associations. Rumour had it that Rudolf Hess had been incarcerated here during the war and still stalked the corridors late at night. But such stories are as fanciful and as legion, I am sure, as those regarding the sleeping-places of Elizabeth I. With such thoughts as these my mind entertained itself as I picked my way down the lawn to the hedge bounding the orchard, when I saw in the gathering dusk two figures walking smartly off down the path and out the back gate. Evidently the staff didn't live in and had gone home for the night. The thought suddenly excited a dormant instinct in me and I looked back at the house where a light indicated the room in the East Wing where Bunty was, even now, preparing for bed. With the place to ourselves, perhaps tonight we might . . .

I retraced my steps with some alacrity and reached the front door once more to find it inexplicably locked. The staff had obviously thought we were both inside the house and had made it secure for the night. I looked around for a bell but there was none to be found – the letterbox and all communication with the outside world being attached to the inner door. *Nil desperandum whatsit*, as Suetonius might have put it, I thought. There's always a way. However, after finding access to the East Wing blocked by an outbuilding, the only solution after ten minutes' hard searching in the dark only revealed a small bathroom window open on the second floor of the West Wing. Thus, with the help of a large cast-iron sundial trundled heavily across from the lawn, I managed to get a leg up on to the ivy covering the wall beneath, and by degrees worked my way up to the aperture. To cut a long story short, I eventually reached my object and with minor damage – a cracked washbasin that collapsed under my weight and a torn shower curtain grabbed as I tumbled to the floor – found myself inside once more.

I then proceeded in an easterly direction along the corridor but found to my further consternation that the whole wing had been partitioned off by locked glass panels, beyond which were two extremely solid-looking firedoors, also evidently locked. By now exhausted and out of earshot of Bunty, I decided to make the best of my situation and cast about for a place to rest my head for the night, and hence found myself in the end room of the West Wing, facing the garden as mentioned before.

The immediate occasion of my rude awakening on the morning of 4th July was a loud crashing made by the bedder as she threw back the firedoors and hastily searched the rooms, followed by Bunty in some agitation. It appeared that the dear old thing had dropped off to sleep waiting for me and had only returned to the land of the living when the staff arrived that morning. Thinking some terrible accident had occurred – a shriek at the sight of the destruction in the bathroom confirmed their suspicions – she and the bedder, the nearest domestic she could find, burst into my room and turned on all the lights. After a short explanation and a rather longer apology, my wife and her helpmeet departed to leave me to my toilet and a first peek at the dawning day.

Downstairs at around nine thirty, Bunty and I mopped the last globules of grapefruit flesh from our lips and swilled Earl Grey to chase down the remains of a remarkable Finnan Haddie. I then pressed the foot-button beneath the carpet in the breakfast room to summon the staff to clear away, and held the door for my wife to withdraw into the adjoining library for a cursory look at the day's papers.

No sooner had we ensconced ourselves there than a crunch of gravel announced the arrival of our hosts' family saloon. Intrigued to see what kind of conveyance Jasper kept in the country (he and Effie had arrived by train when we'd met them before), I gave Bunty a prod to get her on her toes and we sloped out to greet them.

As it turned out, the only occupant of the limo that had lined up alongside Hermione and was now reversing into the garage was Jasper himself, and the machine he was driving was a forlorn sight. A quick glance to my expert eye revealed that it was a 1925 Rolls-Royce Phantom I, originally painted in deep maroon but showing great signs of decrepitude due to lack of attention. Twelve feet long and with a bonnet as high as a vaulting-horse, it was still every inch a prince, but one fallen on extremely hard times. Jasper climbed out and, dwarfed by the car, took off his gloves as he came towards us. His George V beard twitched a little in the moustache area and his left eyebrow appeared somewhat quizzical as he noticed the torn ivy at the side of the house.

"So, Toby and Bunty," he began, shaking hands as we came forward. I winced a little at the shortening of my name but let it go – we had, after all, arrived too early and he had yet to see the damage to the bathroom inside. After exchanging the usual civilities about our trip down, he wafted Bunty inside with the promise that Effie would be joining us shortly as she was proceeding by bicycle. Inclining his head to receive a discreet whispered explanation regarding the ivy and trellis from the maid, he then took my arm and steered me back to Hermione, who I felt held her own rather well against her big brother. Though only a 2½-litre and a good two feet shorter than his 7.6-litre monster, the Lagonda none the less still emphasized the diminutive stature of Bunty's uncle, and I remarked on the fact to him.

"Yes, our side of the family are short whilst Bunty's are tall. My father was the same. I am afraid I have to sit on cushions to reach the controls, and the pedals have been specially extended so that my feet can reach. But for the joy of riding such a beast it is a small sacrifice."

We were wandering back to the Phantom to inspect these additional fittings when I was rather struck by the radiator statuette. Instead of the usual Silver Lady mascot diving forward with angelic draperies spread behind, there was a singular design that, unless I was mistaken, was of a cat with wings.

Noticing my interest, Jasper explained.

"Ah, I see you've spotted our little friend," he began, and leaned on the spare wheel strapped on the right wing, one foot supported on the running-board. "You see, the truth of it is that this is really Effie's car, an heirloom from her father, who bought it back in '25 and which we inherited when he died last year. At the time we already had a modern Rover, which was a lot easier for me to get in and out of, but one sight of this and I was smitten. However, on second sight I nearly wept, for it was in terrible condition outside, and inside the leatherwork had been torn to shreds by generations of Mackintosh cats – their motto certainly holds true of their household pets.

"Since the loss of the family's wealth in the market crash a few decades back, and the effect this had on Effie's father – he went completely loco (and between you and me I am beginning to wonder if my darling wife isn't beginning to inherit this tendency) – since then it hadn't been driven and had been stored in a shed on their farm in Scotland. Effie hadn't seen it for years and was equally disappointed by the damage.

"However, nothing daunted, I said I would sell the Rover and spend as much as I could on restoring the Phantom to its former glory, but on one condition only: that no cats would be allowed inside it. Which is why Effie isn't with us yet – she is following behind with the cat in her basket. However, as you can see, shelling out thousands has only resulted so far in getting it past its MOT. But I suppose that is at least a start."

Seeing that he seemed to have slowed up in his discourse, I remarked on the Pegasus-like wings of the mascot. He explained that one of the marks of pride on the escutcheon of this particular branch of the noble Mackintosh family was that they had once captured a legendary Scottish wildcat called "Tamdhiu", which had terrorized the Highlands and seemed to be able to glide out of trees on to rabbits and even small sheep, supported by what appeared to be wings sprouted from its sides. "The legend also held that the wildcat brought them good luck and thus there has always been a descendant of the original cat in the family, though none of the photos I've seen have shown any evidence of wings. Effie remembers the last of the breed as a girl some forty-odd years ago and swears that its death had something to do the rapid decline in the family's fortunes, which will only be restored if a wildcat can be kept in the house once more – hence her vociferous defence of the creatures back in Edinburgh."

At this point in his narrative I stopped him short and explained that I had seen what I thought was a flying cat that very morning, and it had nearly received its come-uppance from a fishing heron.

Jasper laughed sympathetically.

"No, no, impossible, old man," he continued. "Tam-dhiu existed in the seventeenth century and, well, legends being what they are . . ."

"But I saw a cat with wings this morning – I'm positive of it," I persisted.

"I think not," returned Jasper. "But to put your mind at rest I can reveal that what you probably saw was Beezer, though . . ."

At that very moment a bell could be heard and an odd sight met our eyes. Smoking a pipe and gingerly steering an old Raleigh bicycle over the gravel came an old woman dressed in a Mackintosh plaid outfit surmounted by a bowler hat. A strange black animal sat in the basket on the handlebars and bared its teeth at me as it passed.

The door to the house swung open and Bunty, evidently alerted by the sound of the bell, rushed out to greet her Aunt Effie. No sooner had the machine drawn to a halt than the animal in the basket lunged forward, touched the drive for a moment, and then shot up the trellis and into an overhanging tree.

I stood dumbstruck, not only by the sight of this curiously dressed old woman now tapping out the dottle from her briar against the wicker bicycle pannier, but also by the creature eyeing me maliciously from the nearby tree. It had, without a question of doubt I could now see, rudimentary wings of sorts twitching at forty-five degrees from each side of its body.

Jasper followed my gaze, and as Bunty embraced her aunt he continued the explanation broken by her arrival.

". . . as I was about to say, Beezer, the cat before you,

continues the tradition but can't really fly. We called him Beezer because of his beezer smile, which he grins down on the world from branches of trees. In fact, it's probably not really a smile either," he continued, as the cat persisted in twitching its lips widely at me, "but more likely some sort of hypnotic device like snakes use to confuse their prey. Wasn't it said of Davy Crockett that he used to kill bears by first grinning at them? Anyway, if you look closely, you'll see that his wings aren't real but are part of a little jacket Effie's stitched up for him." He lowered his voice. "I let her indulge these fantasies for the sake of peace and quiet. Hence also the pipe and bowler – her father used to wear one, and it's his old briar . . . But to return to the cat – it would undoubtedly have been Beezer that you saw this morning."

At this point, however, a nagging feeling persisted in my mind and I interrupted him. "I still think you're wrong there, Jasper, as I'm sure that the one I saw this morning was much smaller and browner than Beezer and, having crashed into one of your pear-trees from a considerable height, might even limp a little."

"Really?" Jasper responded, and quizzed Effie about Beezer's movements. When it was ascertained that he'd not left Effie's side all morning, I suddenly became somewhat of a celebrity in my wife's aunt's eyes, and the news of my earlier catastrophe with the bathroom fittings and the trellis-work quickly faded as she wanted to hear more of what she hoped might be a new generation of this remarkable breed.

After lunch it was decided that we should go over to their American friends' house in the adjacent valley for tea, prior to the large gathering in the evening for the 4th of July celebrations – the idea being that we would help out with setting up the barbecue, organizing the fireworks and music, etc. We duly all clambered into the monstrous four-door phantom and chugged off, Jasper driving and wearing a chauffeur's hat in the open-top front section with me beside him, while the ladies settled in the back under the ragged hood. I was surprised to find there were still cat hairs on the passenger seat after all this time, especially after what Jasper had said about not allowing Beezer in, but perhaps it was just some of the stuffing that had worked loose. Anyway, off we set. We also gave the new maid a lift as she would be off for the rest of the day and we were going her way.

As we drove sedately along, hardly a whisper coming from the enormous nose of the Rolls, Jasper filled me in on his neighbours. As it turned out, they too had fallen on hard times of late. The husband's family – the Plimptons of Savannah, Georgia – had been the original occupants of Plimpton Hall before the Scroope clan took it over, enlarged it and added their grey concrete decor in the late 1930s. It also turned out that old man Plimpton – their friend Joshua's father – had died recently and his will revealed that he had put aside a substantial fortune to guard against insolvency during the Great Depression half a century earlier. However, instead of investing it in the National Bank of Georgia, or some such, he had reputedly turned it into gold bars and buried it somewhere in the grounds of the Hall. Needless to say, this was deeply aggravating not only to Joshua, now eking out a meagre living as a publisher's proofreader – including doing the odd bit of work for Jasper's riddle magazine – but perhaps equally so to Jasper and Effie who had inherited the title to the land, as well as the Hall, following Sir Granville Scroope's death, and long before the document revealing the existence of the hidden Plimpton treasure had been discovered.

The invitation to the 4th of July celebrations were thus a double delight, as Jasper and Joshua had recently signed a joint declaration that in the event of the Plimpton Inheritance ever being found it would be split fifty-fifty between the two parties. To prevent a manic hunt which would destroy the entire estate and bring in ruthless prospectors who would stop at nothing short of murder (the haul was rumoured to be many millions), the two men had kept the affair very close to their chests and had even – Jasper dropped his voice still further – kept it from their wives. I nodded sagely as the womenfolk chatted animatedly in the back seats.

I was about to inquire further about the clues in the document left by Plimpton Senior, and how far they had got in their search, when we swerved and pulled up suddenly to avoid a small, rather misshapen-looking brown cat that darted out under the wheels. The maid shrieked and leapt out of the car after it, followed by Bunty and Effie, and for a few lunatic minutes Jasper and I were left to ourselves as they scoured the bushes at the side of the road for the creature.

Within a short while they returned, the maid Lizzie carrying the cat – which had one back leg missing and couldn't move very fast – under her chin, kissing it repeatedly. It transpired, as the ladies cooed over the silly creature, that this was one of a recent litter of five, all of whom had been born with some genetic fault. Dandy – the one at present in our midst – wasn't actually legless, as it were, but more "pedally challenged" in that he had a somewhat curtailed thalidomide-like mini-leg with a normal-sized paw at the end. The other four, Lizzie explained, had similar omissions or additions, but the one whose description caught the attention of all was Korky, who apparently had little growths like chicken wings sprouting from his back.

Being a recent addition to the Scroope ménage, Lizzie hadn't yet heard of the Mackintosh family tradition and this, combined with my earlier sightings of such a creature, suddenly created great interest. Eager inquiries were made as to the whereabouts of this extraodinary beast, but it appeared that Korky had turned feral and disappeared some months ago. Postcards placed in the local shop-windows had yet to produce any results in tracing his whereabouts. Somewhat disillusioned, but with the assurance of a large reward should the cat be found, and an even larger sum for its purchase, we dropped Lizzie off and drove on to the Plimpton household in high spirits.

Joshua and Adelie Plimpton, it transpired, were an extremely agreeable couple, though of considerable personal mass. Each stood at well over six foot, though they must both have been pushing 70, and both had an uncanny resemblance to the film director, John Huston, being long-jowled and heavy-lidded. We were welcomed into a modestly furnished but high-ceilinged house like Lilliputians entering the home of the Gullivers. The noticeable orangey-yellow pallor of their faces and the commendable clarity of their skin was explained after compliments to this effect by my wife at tea. They put it down to their latest wave of food faddism: "This last two months we've been on a heavy citrus diet, dear," Adelie expanded. "Four oranges a day if we can get them – if not, it's the same weight in tangerines and satsumas."

She went on to say that they only drank lemon with their tea but that, if it was Earl Grey (as it was today), they always picked out the pieces of bergamot because, though they liked the flavouring, they were sure that a waxy preservative had been used on the fruit skins before they were dried. The conversation went on in this way until the question of children inevitably reared its ugly head, as Bunty and I were in the early blossoming of our marriage still. Finding it a struggle to put my lack of success in the bonking department down to any real or justifiable cause, I let Bunty do the talking. This quickly seemed to transpose into a secret argot understandable solely by the fairer sex, with a number of winks and nudges in the direction of the menfolk and their lack of stamina or otherwise, according to whether they regularly took garlic capsules, arnica homoeopathic treatment or ample doses of zinc.

Thankfully, Joshua made excuses for Jasper and myself to adjourn upstairs to his study for an inspection of his pool trophies, with a passing reference to "talk about diapers and the Lord knows what else". I picked him up on this, surprised a little at his preservation of the American word, though he had referred to "chips" in the English manner during our discussion of diet earlier.

"Well, you see, it's probably because it's actually a rather more accurate word for the article of clothing in question – your native English 'nappy' being, after all, only short for 'napkin', which really covers a host of textiles; 'diaper', by contrast," he added, "is the technical term for a particular kind of cloth used specifically in the area of babies' butts."

He made a deliberate wry emphasis on the final word, then went on: "In large part, after living here for most of my life, I speak the local lingo – my father, by contrast, being only stationed here during the pre-war years as a cryptanalyst, spoke broad Yankee till the end of his days."

I found his candour and wit refreshing, and began to warm to the man. On reaching the study I was fascinated to find, as I hoped I would, that the conversation quickly turned to the subject of the buried loot. Joshua, it emerged, had been, like his father, a cryptanalyst and so, together with Jasper the enigma magazine editor, ought to be more than a match for Plimpton Senior's puzzling last testament – for a riddle it certainly was.

As Joshua laid out the handwritten sheet with the clues on, I could only gasp with amazement that they had made any progress at all. I remarked on the fact that even the close study of the works of the Blessed Conan could not have prepared me for this. By a complicated acrostic in which each line of verse spelt out, with the help of other clues, the word "Occident" they had figured out a direction: west. And the following enigma produced the solution 13 by 8:

> Four things there are, all of a height,
> One of them crooked, the rest upright.
> Take three away, and you will find
> Exactly ten remain behind.
> But if you cut the four in twain,
> You'll find one-half doth eight retain.

This was complete gobbledegook to me until Jasper took me through it: the four things were the roman numerals comprising XIII which, if divided horizontally, leaves VIII. So thus far they had got west 13 feet (or inches or metres) out by 8 feet (etc.) down – or vice versa.

But the thing that had got them stumped was the most critical clue of them all, the one that gave them the identity of the object that the treasure was to the west of. This was the following jumble of letters: QSLFCIJ. I scratched my head and suggested that it might be some kind of mnemonic, the initials standing for "Quite Slow, Left Front", etc., but they quickly dismissed that as it wasn't particularly memorable and anyway the other bits in the clue suggested it was a Caesar cipher and that the key word should be "Tap".

At this I was completely dumbfounded. Jasper explained.

"A Caesar cipher is one of a kind used in ancient Rome by people like Julius Caesar when they wanted to write secret messages in code. It's quite simple really; you just write the third letter in the alphabet after the one you want to encode and, bingo, it's disguised. Thus DOG would be GRJ, CAT would FDW and so forth. Where it gets really complicated, though, is where you use two alphabets, one above the other, with the coded or decoded Caesar cipher as keyword, and then miss out every letter that has already been used in the keyword. Thus for CAT:

ABCDEFGHIJKLMNOPQRSTUVWXYZ
CATBDEFGHIJKLMNOPQRSUVWXYZ

"Our cat's name, BEEZER, reading the top line against the bottom, would be ADDZDQ. So we tried TAP, and its Caesar cipher WDS, against the coded answer given in old Mr Plimpton's will – QSLFCIJ – but all we got was nonsense and no matter how we reversed it, put it at the end of the line and all kinds of variations, we're still no further forward. We even tried HIT, PAT and all manner of synonyms for TAP in the thesaurus, but to no avail. So any suggestions you can make will be greatly appreciated – Joshua and myself are completely stumped."

At this point, my mind was frankly spinning and, feeling the effects of bergamot tea start to build up in my bladder, I politely begged leave of absence to visit the bathroom, and left the study with what I hoped was a quizzical, but intelligent, look on my face.

After finishing my business and washing my hands, I was struck by the curious old-fashioned shower arrangement in the massive bath, which had a hinged glass panel at the side for easy access. Seeing the shower head was leaking, I tried to tighten the control to turn it off – such is my irritation with such devices in our house at Beauchamp Magna – but somehow only managed to spray my head with ice-cold water. I towelled it dry and combed over the result as best I could, but on my reappearance in the study the change was still noticeable. I explained about the leak and made a light allusion to my earlier encounter with the sink in Plimpton Hall.

"I shouldn't worry about that," said Joshua encouragingly. "That faucet's been leaking ever since we moved in here."

I smiled and commented on another Americanism that seemed to linger in his vocabulary, and wondered if it too was a more accurate description for what we humble Brits would call a common or garden tap.

Joshua began to say something about stop-cocks and water-valves when suddenly – it seemed almost simultaneously – Jasper and Joshua clasped each other's hands in wonderment.

"That's it!" cried Joshua. "Of course. It's not that kind of tap at all. As a home-grown American, Dad would naturally have called all *plumbers'* taps faucets."

They rushed back to their tables and, working backwards against the cipher, came up with the combination IDXFHW as a Caesar cipher for the keyword FAUCET. To me this looked no further forward in the quagmire than before until Jasper slowly and deliberately laid out the two alphabets, thus:

ABCDEFGHIJKLMNOPQRSTUVWXYZ
IDXFHWABCEGJKLMNOPQRSTUVYZ

Then, substituting the letters of the code QSLFCIJ backwards, from bottom to top, he spelt out the following word: SUN-DIAL!

At this point the two men's excitement was interrupted when it was announced that the first guests for the 4th of July party had arrived – and I too experienced the irritation of people turning up long before they were expected. As a result, we were called downstairs again, and after the usual introductory civilities were dragooned into preparing food for the barbecue and other such chores. The final leg of the treasure-hunt would have to wait till the next day. Old Plimpton's secret had, after all, remained hidden for sixty years – a few hours more could hardly make much difference.

Accordingly, then, we set to, with Jasper and myself taking on the additional task of wiring up the fireworks under the supervision of Joshua, who it appeared was also something of a pyrotechnics expert and had managed to get hold of some marine distress flares as well as some military Thunderflash bangers used on ranges to imitate hand-grenades – this promised to be an impressive display.

The evening wore on, and by degrees the rest of the guests arrived, many with strong American accents – friends from the Trade Delegation and holiday visitors – and, aware of the Plimptons' somewhat straitened circumstances, many had brought contributory dishes for the buffet, additional fireworks and bottles of Californian wine or American beer.

When the moon came out it was like some giant sleepy beast lying on its side with one yellow eye gazing in our direction, and on the stroke of nine the festivities began.

First off was an unfurling of the Stars and Stripes from a flagpole in the courtyard, spotlit by the security lamps at the front of the house as the American national anthem blared out of the sound system. Then we all trooped round the side to the back garden where, in the centre of the pond, a large group of multicoloured balloons shivered – red, white and blue – all held in place by a single cord. Adelie had the honour of releasing these, which, spotlit from underneath, slowly lifted away from the water to the strains of *Also Sprach Zarathustra*.

Meanwhile, Joshua sent up the marine flare, which opened out at the height of about 200 feet and produced an amazing umbrella of light that made everyone gasp. As the guests' attention alternated between the flare and the balloons, the latter were rippled by a cross-wind and one or two began to stray towards the trees. One in particular drifted into a lime at the edge of the pond and was suddenly pounced upon by an animal from an overhanging branch.

Effie heard the pop as the creature's claws burst the rubber and its flailing body plummeted earthwards. Silhouetted by the dazzling light of the flare, she could clearly make out the white tip to its tail and two mobile growths on its back.

"It's him, it's Korky," she cried, grabbing her husband's hands and racing across the lawn. "Come on, Jasper, we've got to catch him."

The cat, however, had other thoughts on its mind. Already scared half out its wits by the shock of the bursting balloon and making tremendous efforts to survive a fall of some twenty-odd feet, he hit the ground running. Or rather, he would have done had he not landed in the pond. The added shock of the cold water, combined with the sight of a bowler-hatted madwoman tearing towards him, hastened his paddle through the water-lilies to the side. And after briefly contemplating whether to sit down and clean himself, the final insult was the release of six Thunderflash firecrackers in quick succession, which saw him disappear into the undergrowth in the direction of the front of the house at a speed faster than sprinters from a starting-pistol.

Effie's disappointment was intense, but the excitement of actually seeing the winged cat in the flesh was an enormous boost to her flagging sanity and she declared that the following day we had to instigate a full-scale search of the area. Her husband, Joshua and myself countered equally vehemently that we would have some extremely serious business of our own to pursue in the morning, but Effie was adamant and we reluctantly agreed.

The rest of the evening was a tremendous success. The sky was a mass of multicoloured pyrotechnic delight, the food delicious in its variety, and such was the effect of the alcohol and the music that many of the guests – including, I may say, dear B. and myself – were drawn to dancing in the moonlight.

The witching-hour came and went, and with it many of the

guests who'd come from far afield departed as well. Bunty and I, together with the Scroopes, stayed on to help with the clearing up and, that done, settled down in the early hours of the morning for a final drink. The farewell tot became another and yet another until, our mainbraces well and truly spliced, it was felt that we would be unwise to drive home. We thus all collapsed – by now pretty insensible – on cushions in the conservatory. My animal passions had been briefly aroused by the stimulus of this sustained intake of alcohol, but brewer's droop quickly set in after Bunty pushed me away from her in the greenhouse and remonstrated against such behaviour in the presence of four other people.

Friday morning was not a pleasant experience. Everyone was deeply hung over, and after brief cups of coffee all round – no one could face a proper breakfast – we headed out towards the car in the driveway, the menfolk unshaven and the women scarcely recognizable as they hadn't "put their faces on". Limply, we walked over to the Phantom and I remarked to Jasper on the fact that he had left the hood off the front seats and it was lucky it hadn't rained in the night. He agreed and, seeing that it was a bright sunny day, asked me to reach up and help him pull back the covering from the rear seats as well, as it would be stuffy inside and he was too short to do so without standing on the spare wheel.

I said I would be glad to and had just reached the passenger door whilst Jasper clambered on to the running-board opposite, when I happened to glance down inside and suddenly held my breath. There, on the passenger seat, curled up fast asleep, was the elusive Korky the Flying Cat, contented as could be in the musty warmth of the interior. My eyes met Jasper's, and quick as a flash we both pulled the hood over the whole car. Awoken by the noise, the cat yawned and stretched but seemed otherwise unconcerned, so I carefully released the door-handle, slipped in beside him and wrapped him in my arms. By the time the ladies reached the Rolls, Korky was purring like a sewing-machine on my lap, his little stunted chicken wings vibrating back and forth with every breath.

Jasper indicated to Effie and Bunty what had taken place and put his finger to his lips while they got in the back doors and he took up his position in the driver's seat. Then, with a look of triumph and glee, we waved our farewells to the Plimptons.

The final chapter of the saga then began to unfold. Korky, terrified by his fall, the bursting balloon, his soaking in the pond and the noise and chaos of the party and its fireworks, had obviously torn round the front of the house where, to his delight, he had discovered the familiar smell of cats on old leather in the Rolls-Royce parked outside. As it had afforded some degree of comfort and a refuge from the horrors outside and as – judging by the hairs that I had spotted on the passenger seat earlier – he may well have been hiding out in it for months after he escaped from the maid Lizzie's cottage, it had obviously seemed a good place to spend the night. Thus, Korky having been captured, Jasper thereby felt released from the promise to search for him that day and rang Joshua the moment we reached the Hall, inviting him over to finish our own investigations. Within the hour Joshua duly arrived and we recommenced our search for the missing millions while Bunty and Effie were left to coo over their newly acquired pet in the living-room.

So, armed with steel tape-measure, spade and compass, we set off towards the sundial. Unfortunately, of course, it still remained where I had placed it in my attempts to gain entry to the upstairs loo window. But this, fortuitously, was all to the good, because what the great puzzle-solvers had failed to notice was that one of the many clues to the whereabouts of the treasure had been in plain English.

When we traced the original position of the sundial – which wasn't difficult, as a circular patch of earth had been exposed where it had stood in the middle of the upper lawn on the west side of the house – we found to our amazement a rusty Chubblock key! Thus not only was the old sundial the key to the cipher, but it was also where the key to the vault lay.

Using our compass and tape-measure, we had a number of

stabs at digging up the lawn, but all to no avail, and we sat down exhausted. Looking around, I was intrigued by a stone sculpture of three figures back-to-back on the lower lawn, which was reached by some steps below us. I asked Jasper what it was.

"Oh, it's just some creation or other. I don't really know what it is, in fact. It was here when my father moved in and was too heavy to shift. And anyway, it looked attractive enough so we left it. I think it was designed by the same chap who built the sundial. There's some kind of signature on both of them."

I wandered down to it and found the artist's mark. Then, in that odd way we all have of wanting to see if things really do match, I went back to the sundial to check the similarity. It was the same: "K. Simons, 1932". Looking at the sundial set me thinking about time-keeping in the days when clocks were less common than now, and I checked the hour against my Rolex.

"Hello," I said jokingly in the general direction of the others, still lying on the grass in the hot noonday sun. "Looks like someone's set this sundial wrong."

"You've probably not taken account of British Summer Time," suggested Jasper.

I looked again, but it was obviously way out of synch, and I said so.

The others came across and were intrigued, and then Joshua remarked that we must have put it back in the wrong position, so excited had we been by the discovery of the key underneath. With careful adjustment we realigned it correctly – a spur stuck out one side so it was a simple matter of straightening it up against the equivalent mark in the ground.

At this point, however, Jasper noticed that all the figures around the dial were in Latin numerals, and something clicked. Pointing this out to us, we traced around to the figure VIII and found ourselves staring away to the strange statue on the lower lawn. Jasper rushed back to where he and Joshua had been sitting and picked up the tape-measure. Laying it out, it transpired that the statue was exactly 13 feet away from the sundial in the direction of the numeral VIII. We had been entirely misled into thinking that one of the dimensions was of depth and that west meant west of the sundial, when in fact it just meant west of the house!

We ran over to the statue and, after some searching, found a loose piece of stonework in the base, which revealed a keyhole. Our rusted key, with a little application, fitted perfectly and, using the spade as a lever, a whole section of the base swung outwards to reveal an outdoor strong-box. Confused slightly that this didn't seem capable of holding a sufficient number of gold bars, and now confronted by one of those infuriating tumbler-dial combination locks, we tidied up the garden as best we could, closed up the stone cladding on the plinth and went in to Jasper's study. Here we looked again at the clues and felt that somehow the verse enigma held the final solution.

At this point, Bunty arrived with some coffee and wondered what on earth "we boys" were up to here so secretly, and why we had been digging up the garden. I began to explain, but the looks on the faces of Joshua and Jasper soon quietened me. Shooed away with some excuse about a puzzle for Jasper's magazine, she glanced over at our calculations and commented that it was rather us than her as she'd never been very good at numbers games. As she left the room she turned once more.

"What was that funny verse about 'I sigh for you and you sigh for a cipher . . .'?"

Jasper remembered it well and politely explained.

"It was a rather complicated four-line riddle by the philosopher William Whewell in which letters stood for words -- the first line read UOAOOIOU, meaning 'You sigh for a cipher, oh I sigh for you'. Complicated stuff, but logical enough."

"Well, that's about as much as I remember, anyway. I'll leave you to it. Good luck."

We looked again at the verse enigma and something sparked in Joshua's mind. "Hey, you don't think we're being too clever here after all, and that's the trick?"

"How do you mean?" I asked.

"Well, how about if we just wrote down all the numbers in the verse as they stand – not the implied numbers but the actual ones: 4, 1, 3, 10, 4, 8?"

Despairing of ever cracking the code, we agreed to give it a try and proceeded out into the garden again. To our amazement the combination worked and the door swung open to reveal . . . yet another key! This time, though, the brainwork involved was less complicated, as a note had been left with it. Or, rather, a copper fob was attached to the key, on which was engraved a note of congratulation from old man Plimpton to his son saying that, as a just reward for this cryptanalytical rite of passage, he would find something of interest to him in . . . and here followed the details of an offshore bank and strong-box number.

The rest of my story is simple enough. Joshua, accompanied by Jasper, caught a flight from Gatwick the following day. I stayed behind with the womenfolk whilst they were away, with strict instructions not to say a word until they came back.

Shortly thereafter they returned with beaming faces. When they unlocked the strong-box a fortune in gold coins and ingots had been revealed, which on presentation to the bank were happily converted into cash in the form of international money orders payable to a British bank. This information was disclosed with great relish to their wives by the two friends, while Bunty and I looked on with wonderment and, on my part, some satisfaction.

Joshua then turned to me.

"And it's all thanks to you, Tobias. If you hadn't arrived early and got yourself locked out . . . if you hadn't moved the sundial to climb inside, thereby exposing the key which we wouldn't have known was beneath it . . . if you hadn't smashed the sink and made us think of the word 'faucet' – if, in short, you hadn't been such a wonderful clumsy dunderhead, we wouldn't now be rich beyond our wildest dreams!"

Not quite sure how to react to such a mixture of compliment and insult, I took this all in good heart and grinned nervously. However, Bunty's beam of approval quickly strengthened my confidence and I began to feel that perhaps, at last, the world was starting to become a better place.

At this point Effie, still bowler-hatted and sitting in an

armchair with her new cat on her lap – Beezer having stormed out in a huff – added: "But aren't you all forgetting something? The real reason for our good luck? It's the legend, of course – and it's all come true. Now that the Flying Cat has been returned to the Mackintoshes our fortunes are restored!"

At that she stroked the cat more vigorously and caught her hand in his stubbly wings. Not surprisingly, Korky objected to this rough treatment and indicated his displeasure by twisting his head round and nipping her.

"Ah," I said, quick as a flash and pleased with my observation. "But don't forget your motto: 'Touch not the cat but with a glove!' "

And we all roared with laughter.

Of Jeoffry, His Cat

CHRISTOPHER SMART (1722–71)

For I will consider my Cat Jeoffry.

For he is the servant of the Living God, duly and daily
serving him.

For at the first glance of the glory of God in the East
he worships in his way.

For is this done by wreathing his body seven times
round with elegant quickness.

For then he leaps up to catch the musk, which is the
blessing of God upon his prayer.

For he rolls upon prank to work it in.

For having done duty and received blessing he begins
to consider himself.

For this he performs in ten degrees.

For first he looks upon his forepaws to see if they are
clean.

For secondly he kicks up behind to clear away there.

For thirdly he works it upon stretch with the forepaws
extended.

For fourthly he sharpens his paws by wood.

For fifthly he washes himself.

For sixthly he rolls upon wash.

For Seventhly he fleas himself, that he may not be interrupted upon the beat.

For Eighthly he rubs himself against a post.

For Ninthly he looks up for his instructions.

For Tenthly he goes in quest of food.

For having consider'd God and himself he will consider his neighbour.

For if he meets another cat he will kiss her in kindness.

For when he takes his prey he plays with it to give it chance.

For one mouse in seven escapes by his dallying.

For when his day's work is done his business more properly begins.

For [he] keeps the Lord's watch in the night against the adversary.

For he counteracts the powers of darkness by his electrical skin and glaring eyes.

For he counteracts the Devil, who is death, by brisking about the life.

For in his morning orisons he loves the sun and the sun loves him.

For he is of the tribe of Tiger.

For the Cherub Cat is a term of the Angel Tiger.

For he has the subtlety and hissing of a serpent, which in goodness he suppresses.

For he will not do destruction, if he is well-fed, neither will he spit without provocation.

For he purrs in thankfulness, when God tells him he's a good Cat.

For he is an instrument for the children to learn benevolence upon.

For every house is incompleat without him and a blessing is lacking in the spirit.

For the Lord commanded Moses concerning the cats at the departure of the Children of Israel from Egypt.

For every family had one cat at least in the bag.

For the English Cats are the best in Europe.

For he is the cleanest in the use of his forepaws of any quadrupede.

For the dexterity of his defence is an instance of the love of God to him exceedingly.

For he is the quickest to his mark of any creature.

For he is tenacious of his point.

For he is a mixture of gravity and waggery.

For he knows that God is his Saviour.

For there is nothing sweeter than his peace when at rest.

For there is nothing brisker than his life when in motion.

For he is of the Lord's poor and so indeed is he called by benevolence perpetually – Poor Jeoffry! poor Jeoffry! the rat has bit thy throat.

For I bless the name of the Lord Jesus that Jeoffry is better.

For the divine spirit comes about his body to sustain it in compleat cat.

For his tongue is exceeding pure so that it has in purity what it wants in musick.

For he is docile and can learn certain things.

For he can set up with gravity which is patience upon approbation.

For he can fetch and carry, which is patience in employment.

For he can jump over a stick which is patience upon proof positive.

For he can spraggle upon waggle at the word of command.

For he can jump from an eminence into his master's bosom.

For he can catch the cork and toss it again.

For he is hated by the hypocrite and miser.
For the former is afraid of detection.
For the latter refuses the charge.
For he camels his back to bear the first notion of
business.
For he is good to think on; if a man would express
himself neatly.
For he made a great figure in Egypt for his signal
services.
For he killed the Ichneumon-rat very pernicious by
land.
For his ears are so acute that they sting again.
For from this proceeds the passing quickness of his
attention.
For by stroking of him I have found out electricity.
For I perceived God's light about him both wax and ·
fire.
For the Electrical fire is the spiritual substance, which
God sends from heaven to sustain the bodies both of
man and beast.
For God has blessed him in the variety of his
movements.
For, tho he cannot fly, he is an excellent clamberer.
For his motions upon the face of the earth are more
than any other quadrupede.
For he can tread to all the measures upon the musick.
For he can swim for life.
For he can creep.

from *Jubilate Agno*

Enjolras and Gavroche

THÉOPHILE GAUTIER (1811–72)

Just at that time Victor Hugo's *Misérables* was in great vogue,
and the names of the characters in the novel were on everyone's

lips. I called the two male kittens Enjolras and Gavroche, while the little female received the name of Eponine.

They were perfectly charming in their youth. I trained them like dogs to fetch and carry a bit of paper crumpled into a ball, which I threw for them. In time they learnt to fetch it from the tops of cupboards, from behind chests or from the bottom of tall vases, out of which they would pull it very cleverly with their paws. When they grew up they disdained such frivolous games, and acquired that calm philosophic temperament which is the true nature of cats.

To people landing in America in a slave colony all negroes are negroes, and indistinguishable from one another. In the same way, to careless eyes, three black cats are three black cats; but attentive observers make no such mistake. Animal physiognomy varies as much as that of men, and I could distinguish perfectly between those faces, all three as black as Harlequin's mask, and illuminated by emerald discs shot with gold.

Enjolras was by far the handsomest of the three. He was remarkable for his great leonine head and big ruff, his powerful shoulders, long back and splendid feathery tail. There was something theatrical about him, and he seemed to be always posing like a popular actor who knows he is being admired. His movements were slow, undulating and majestic. He put each foot down with as much circumspection as if he were walking on a table covered with Chinese bric-à-brac or Venetian glass. As to his character, he was by no means a stoic, and he showed a love of eating which that virtuous and sober young man, his namesake, would certainly have disapproved. Enjolras would undoubtedly have said to him, like the angel to Swedenborg: "You eat too much."

I humoured this gluttony, which was as amusing as a gastronomic monkey's, and Enjolras attained a size and weight seldom reached by the domestic cat. It occurred to me to have him shaved poodle-fashion, so as to give the finishing touch to his resemblance to a lion.

We left him his mane and a big tuft at the end of his tail, and I would not swear that we did not give him mutton-chop whiskers on his haunches like those Munito wore. Thus tricked out, it must be confessed he was much more like a Japanese monster than an African lion. Never was a more fantastic whim carved out of a living animal. His shaven skin took odd blue tints, which contrasted strangely with his black mane.

Gavroche, as though desirous of calling to mind his name-sake in the novel, was a cat with an arch and crafty expression of countenance. He was smaller than Enjolras, and his movements were comically quick and brusque. In him absurd capers and ludicrous postures took the place of the banter and slang of the Parisian gamin. It must be confessed that Gavroche had vulgar tastes. He seized every possible occasion to leave the drawing-room in order to go and make up parties in the back yard, or even in the street, with stray cats, *"De naissance quelconque et de sang peu prouvé"*, in which doubtful company he completely forgot his dignity as cat of Havana, son of Don Pierrot de Navarre, grandee of Spain of the first order, and of the aristocratic and haughty Doña Seraphita.

Sometimes in his truant wanderings he picked up emaciated comrades, lean with hunger, and brought them to his plate of food to give them a treat in his good-natured, lordly way. The poor creatures, with ears laid back and watchful side-glances, in fear of being interrupted in their free meal by the broom of the housemaid, swallowed double, triple, and quadruple mouth-fuls, and, like the famous dog Siete-Aguas (seven waters) of Spanish *posadas* (inns), they licked the plate as clean as if it had been washed and polished by one of Gerard Dow's or Mieris's Dutch housewives.

Seeing Gavroche's friends reminded me of a phrase which illustrates one of Gavarni's drawings, *"Ils sont jolis les amis dont vous êtes susceptible d'aller avec!"* ("Pretty kind of friends you like to associate with!")

But that only proved what a good heart Gavroche had, for he could easily have eaten all the food himself.

from "The White and Black Dynasties"
in *La Ménagerie Intime* translated by Lady Chance

A Cat's Appearance

ANONYMOUS

Some pussies' coats are yellow; some amber streaked with dark;
No member of the feline race but has a special mark.
This one has feet with hoarfrost tipped; that one has tail that curls;
Another's inky hide is striped; another's decked with pearls.

The Grinning Cat

LEWIS CARROLL (1832–98)

The door led right into a large kitchen, which was full of smoke from one end to the other: the Duchess was sitting on a three-legged stool in the middle, nursing a baby; the cook was leaning over the fire, stirring a large cauldron which seemed to be full of soup.

"There's certainly too much pepper in that soup!" Alice said to herself, as well as she could for sneezing.

There was certainly too much of it in the *air*. Even the Duchess sneezed occasionally; and as for the baby, it was sneezing and howling alternately without a moment's pause. The only two creatures in the kitchen that did *not* sneeze were the cook, and a large cat which was lying on the hearth and grinning from ear to ear.

"Please would you tell me," said Alice a little timidly, for she was not quite sure whether it was good manners for her to speak first, "why your cat grins like that?"

"It's a Cheshire cat," said the Duchess, "and that's why. Pig!"

She said the last word with such sudden violence that Alice quite jumped; but she saw in another moment that it was addressed to the baby, and not to her, so she took courage, and went on again: "I didn't know that Cheshire cats always grinned; in fact, I didn't know that cats *could* grin."

"They all can," said the Duchess; "and most of 'em do."

"I don't know of any that do," Alice said very politely, feeling quite pleased to have got into conversation.

"You don't know much," said the Duchess; "and that's a fact."

from Alice's Adventures in Wonderland (1865)

All Kinds of Cats

ANONYMOUS

Calumnious cats, who circulate faux pas,
And reputations maul with murderous claws;
Shrill cats, whom fierce domestic brawls delight,
Cross cats, who nothing want but teeth to bite,
Starch cats of puritanic aspect sad,
And learned cats who talk their husbands mad;
Uncleanly cats who never pare their nails,
Cat-gossips, full of Canterbury tales;
Cat-grandams, vex'd with asthmas and catarrhs,
And superstitious cats, who curse their stars.

Dick Baker's Cat

MARK TWAIN (1835–1910)

One of my comrades there – another of those victims of eighteen years of unrequited toil and blighted hopes – was one of the gentlest spirits that ever bore its patient cross in a weary exile; grave and simple Dick Baker, pocket miner of Dead-Horse Gulch. He was forty-six, grey as a rat, earnest, thoughtful, slenderly educated, slouchily dressed, and clay-soiled, but his heart was finer metal than any gold his shovel ever brought to light – than any, indeed, that ever was mined or minted.

Whenever he was out of luck and a little downhearted, he would fall to mourning over the loss of a wonderful cat he used to own (for where women and children are not, men of kindly impulses take up with pets, for they must love something). And he always spoke of the strange sagacity of that cat with the air of a man who believed in his secret heart that there was something human about it – maybe even supernatural.

I heard him talking about this animal once. He said: "Gentlemen, I used to have a cat here, by the name of Tom Quartz, which you'd 'a' took an interest in, I reckon – most anybody would. I had him here eight year – and he was the remarkablest cat *I* ever see. He was a large grey one of the Tom specie, an' he had more hard, natchral sense than any man in this camp – 'n' a *power* of dignity – he wouldn't let the Gov'ner of Californy be familiar with him. He never ketched a rat in his life – 'peared to be above it. He never cared for nothing but mining. He knowed more about mining, that cat did, than any man *I* ever, ever see. You couldn't tell *him* noth'n' 'bout placer-diggin's – 'n' as for pocket mining, why he was just born for it. He would dig out after me an' Jim when we went over the hills prospect'n', and he would trot along behind us for as much as five mile, if we went so fur. An' he had the best judgment about mining ground – why, you never see anything like it. When we went to work, he'd scatter a glance round, 'n' if he didn't think much of the indications, he would give a look as much as to say, 'Well, I'll have to get you to excuse me' – 'n' without another word he'd hyste his nose in the air 'n' shove for home. But if the ground suited him, he would lay low 'n' keep dark till the first pan was washed, 'n' then he would sidle up 'n' take a look, an' if there was about six or seven grains of gold *he* was satisfied – he didn't want no better prospect 'n' that – 'n' then he would lay down on our coats and snore like a steamboat till we'd struck the pocket, an' then get up 'n' superintend. He was nearly lightnin' on superintending.

"Well, by an' by, up comes this yer quartz excitement. Everybody was into it – everybody was pick'n' 'n' blast'n' instead of shovellin' dirt on the hillside – everybody was putt'n' down a shaft instead of scrapin' the surface. Noth'n' would do Jim, but *we* must tackle the ledges, too, 'n' so we did. We commenced putt'n' down a shaft, 'n' Tom Quartz he begin to wonder what in the dickens it was all about. He hadn't ever seen any mining like that before, 'n' he was all upset, as you may say – he couldn't come to a right understanding of it no way – it was too many for *him*. He was down on it too, you bet you – he was down on it powerful – 'n' always appeared to consider it the cussedest foolishness out. But that cat, you know, was *always* agin' newfangled arrangements – somehow he never could abide 'em. *You* know how it is with old habits. But by and by Tom Quartz begin to git sort of reconciled a little though he never *could* altogether understand that eternal sinkin' of a shaft an' never pannin' out anything. At last he got to comin' down in the shaft, hisself, to try to cipher it out. An' when he'd git the blues, 'n' feel kind o' scruffy, 'n' aggravated 'n' disgusted – knowin' as he did, that the bills was runnin' up all the time an' we warn't makin' a cent – he would curl up on a gunnysack in the corner an' go to sleep. Well, one day when the shaft was down about eight foot, the rock got so hard that we had to put in a blast – the first blast'n' we'd ever done since Tom Quartz was born. An' then we lit the fuse 'n' clumb out 'n' got off 'bout fifty yards – 'n' forgot 'n' left Tom Quartz sound asleep on the gunnysack. In 'bout a minute we seen a puff of smoke bust up out of the hole, 'n' then everything let go with an awful crash 'n' about four million ton of rocks 'n' dirt 'n' smoke 'n' splinters shot up 'bout a mile an' a half into the air, an' by George, right in the dead centre of it was old Tom Quartz a-goin' end over end, an' a-snortin' an' a-sneezin', an' a-clawin' an' a-reach'n' for things like all possessed. But it warn't no use, you know, it warn't no use. An' that was the last we see of *him* for about two minutes 'n' a half, an' then all of a sudden it begin to rain rocks and rubbage an' directly he come down ker-whoop about ten foot off f'm where we stood. Well, I reckon he was p'r'aps the orneriest-lookin' beast you ever see. One ear was sot back on his neck, 'n' his tail was stove up, 'n' his eye-winkers was singed off, 'n' he was all blacked up with powder an' smoke, an' all sloppy with mud 'n' slush f'm one end to the other. Well, sir, it warn't no use to try to apologize – we couldn't say a word. He took a sort of disgusted look at himself, 'n' then he looked at us – an' it was just exactly the same as if he had said – 'Gents, maybe *you* think it's smart to take advantage of a cat that ain't had no experience of quartz minin', but *I* think different' – an' then he turned on his heel 'n' marched off home without ever saying another word.

"That was jest his style. An' maybe you won't believe it, but after that you never see a cat so prejudiced agin' quartz mining as what he was. An' by an' by when he *did* get to goin' down in the shaft agin', you'd 'a' been astonished at his sagacity. The minute we'd tetch off a blast 'n' the fuse'd begin to sizzle, he'd give a look as much as to say, 'Well, I'll have to git you to excuse *me*,' an' it was surpris'n' the way he'd shin out of that hole 'n' go f'r a tree. Sagacity? It ain't no name for it. 'Twas inspiration!"

I said, "Well, Mr Baker, his prejudice against quartz mining *was* remarkable, considering how he came by it. Couldn't you ever cure him of it?"

"*Cure him!* No! When Tom Quartz was sot once, he was *always* sot – and you might 'a' blowed him up as much as three million times 'n' you'd never 'a' broken him of his cussed prejudice agin' quartz mining."

The Great Cat

ANONYMOUS (c. 1700BC)

Praise be to thee, O Ra, exalted Lion-god, thou art the Great Cat, the Avenger of the Gods and the Judge of Words, the President of the Sovereign Chiefs and the Governor of the Holy Circle; thou art indeed the bodies of the Great Cat.

from *The Seventy-five Praises of Ra* (c. 1700BC)

Arsinoë's Cats

GRAHAM TOMSON (1863–1911)

Arsinoë the fair, the amber-tressed,
    Is mine no more;
Cold as the unsunned snows are, is her breast,
    And closed her door.
No more her ivory feet and tresses braided
    Make glad mine eyes;
Snapt are my viol strings, my flowers are faded;
    My love-lamp dies.

Yet, once for dewy myrtle-buds and roses,
    All summer long,
We searched the twilight-haunted garden closes
    With jest and song.
Ay, all is over now – my heart hath changèd
    Its heaven for hell;
And that ill chance which all our love estrangèd
    In this wise fell:

A little lion, small and dainty sweet
    (For such there be!),
With sea-grey eyes and softly stepping feet,
    She prayed of me.
For this through lands Egyptian far away
    She bade me pass;
But, in an evil hour, I said her nay –
    And now, alas!
Far-travelled Nicias hath wooed and won
    Arsinoë,
With gifts of furry creatures white and dun
    From over-sea.

On Cats

EDWARD TOPSELL

Cats are of divers colours, but for the most part gryseld, like to congealed yse, which cometh from the condition of her meate: her head is like unto the head of a Lyon, except in her sharpe eares: her flesh is soft and smooth: her eyes glitter above measure especially when a man cometh to see a Cat on the sudden, and in the night, they can hardly be endured, for their flaming aspect. Wherefor Democritus describing the Persian smaradge saith that it is not transparent but filleth the eye with pleasant brightnesse, such as in the eyes of Panthers and Cats, for they cast forth beames in the shadow and darkness, but in the sunshine they have no such clearness and therefore Alexander Aphrodise giveth this reason, both for the sight of Cattes and Battes, that they have by nature a most sharp spirit of seeing.

Albertus compareth their eyesight to carbuncles in dark places, because in the night, they can see perfectly to kill Rattes and Myce: the roote of the herbe Valerian (commonly called Phu) is very like to the eye of a Cat, and wherefore it groweth if cats come thereunto, they instantly dig it up, for the love thereof, as I myself have seene in mine owne Garden, and not once onely, but often, even then when I had caused it to be hedged or compassed round about with thornes, for it smelleth marveilous like to a cat.

The Egyptians hath observed in the eyes of a Cat, the encrease of the Moonlight, for with the Moone, they shine more fully at the ful, and more dimly in the change and wain, and the male Cat doth also vary his eyes with the sunne; for when the sunne ariseth, the apple of his eye is long; towards noone it is round, and at the evening it cannot be seene at all, but the whole eye sheweth alike.

The tongue of a Cat is very attractive, and forcible like a file, attenuating by licking the flesh of a man, for which cause, when she is come neere to the blood, so that her own spittle be mingled there with, she falleth mad. Her teeth are like a saw, and if the long haires growing about her mouth (which some call Granons) be cut away, she looseth her courage. Her nailes sheathed like the nailes of a Lyon, striking with her fore-feete, both Dogs and other things, as a man doth with his hand.

The beast is wonderful nimble, setting upon her prey like the Lyon, by leaping: and therefore she hunteth both Rats, all kinds of Myce, and Birds, eating not only them, but also Fish, wherewith all she is best pleased. It is a neat and cleanely creature, oftentimes licking her own body to keepe it smoothe and faire, having naturally a flexible backe for this purpose, and washing her face with her fore-feete, but some observe that if she put her feete beyond the crowne of her head, that it is a presage of raine, and if the backe of a Cat be thinne, the beast is of no courage or value.

It is needlesse to spend any time about her loving nature to man, how she flattereth by rubbing her skinne against one's Legges, how she whurleth with her voyce, having as many tunes as turnes, for she hath one voyce to beg and complain, another to testify her delight and pleasure, another among her own kind by flattering, by hissing, by puffing, by spitting, insomuch as some have thought that they have a peculiar intelligible language among themselves. Therefore how she beggeth, playeth, leapeth, looketh, catcheth, tosseth with her foote, riseth up to strings held over her head, sometimes creeping, sometimes lying on the back, playing with one foot, sometimes on the bely, snatching, now with the mouth, and anon with foot, apprehending greedily anything save the hand of a man with divers such gestical actions, it is needlesse to stand upon; insomuch as Cœlus was wont to say, that being free from his Studies and more urgent weighty affairs, he was not ashamed to play and sport himself with his Cat, and verily it might well be called an idle man's pastime . . .

from *The Historie of Foure-Footed Beastes*

Old Tom-cat into Damsel Gay

PAUL SCARRON (1610–60)

In strictest secrecy I've heard
And promised not to say a word
About a certain Lady's age,
Her name and face and parentage;
This Lady had a Cat whom she
Adored quite immoderately;
For his amusement once, her whim
Invented a disguise for him.
With tresses cleverly attached,
And precious earrings nicely matched,
The Cat's head she adorned, then she
Regarded him admiringly:
About his neck she hung fine pearls
Larger than the eyes of Merles;
A fine, white, laundered, linen shirt,
A little jacket and a skirt,
A collar and a neckerchief
Made, with the help of her belief,
Old Tom-cat into Damsel gay.
Not quite a beauty,
But adequate, at least, to stir
The Dame who'd decorated her.
Then up before a looking-glass
The Lady held this darling lass:
This Cat who showed no evidence
Of being surprised, or of pretence
At joy for being by fool caressed,
Or seeing himself an Idol dressed.
Whatever happened then took place
Because she failed to embrace
Her Cat as closely as she might.
Without considering wrong or right,
The good Cat gained the stair,

And then the attic, and from there
Out upon the tiles he strayed;
Loudly crying, the Lady prayed
Her servants instantly to be
Out after him assiduously:

But in the country of the tiles
Wary Tom-cats show their wiles.
They searched for him until they tired,
And the next day they inquired
Of the neighbours; some averred
They couldn't credit what they heard,
Others their belief asserted;
All were very much diverted;
And all the while the Cat uncaged
Never returned; the Lady raged
Less for the necklace's expense
Than for her Tom-cat vanished thence.

Cured by a Cat

REV. JAMES WOODFORDE (1740–1803)

The Stiony on my right Eye-lid still swelled and inflamed very much. As it is commonly said that the Eye-lid being rubbed by the tail of a black Cat would do it much good if not entirely cure it, and having a black Cat, a little before dinner I made a trial of it, and very soon after dinner I found my Eye-lid much abated of the swelling and almost free from Pain. I cannot therefore but conclude it to be of the greatest service to a Stiony of the Eye-lid. Any other Cat's Tail may have the above effect in all probability – but I did my Eye-lid with my own black Tom Cat's Tail.

from *The Diary of a County Parson*, 11 March 1791

A Cat

ROBERT HERRICK (1591–1674)

A Cat
I keep, that plays about my House,
Grown fat
With eating many a miching Mouse.

Micetto, the Pope's Cat

VICOMTE DE CHATEAUBRIAND (1768–1848)

I find myself at the same time in a Monastery, a farm, an orchard and a park. I have as a companion a fat red-grey cat with black cross stripes, born at the Vatican in the Raphael Gallery: Leo XII brought it up in the skirt of his robe, where I used to watch it with envy, when the Pontiff gave me my audience as Ambassador. On the death of the successor of St Peter, I inherited the cat without a master, as I have told you in writing of my Roman Embassy. They called it Micetto, surnamed the Pope's Cat. In this capacity it enjoys an extreme consideration among pious souls. I strive to make it forget exile, the Sistine Chapel and the sun of Michael Angelo's dome, on which it used to take its walks far removed from earth.

Mrs Bond's Cats

JAMES HERRIOT (b. 1916)

"I work for cats."

That was how Mrs Bond introduced herself on my first visit, gripping my hand firmly and thrusting out her jaw defiantly as though challenging me to make something of it. She was a big woman with a strong, high-cheekboned face and a commanding presence and I wouldn't have argued with her anyway, so I nodded gravely as though I fully understood and agreed, and allowed her to lead me into the house.

I saw at once what she meant. The big kitchen/living-room had been completely given over to cats. There were cats on the sofas and chairs and spilling in cascades on to the floor, cats sitting in rows along the window sills and, right in the middle of it all, little Mr Bond, pallid, wispy-moustached, in his shirt sleeves reading a newspaper.

It was a scene which was going to become very familiar. A lot of the cats were obviously uncastrated toms because the atmosphere was vibrant with their distinctive smell – a fierce pungency which overwhelmed even the sickly wisps from the big saucepans of nameless cat food bubbling on the stove. And Mr Bond was always there, always in his shirt sleeves and reading his paper, a lonely little island in a sea of cats.

I had heard of the Bonds, of course. They were Londoners who for some obscure reason had picked on North Yorkshire for their retirement. People said they had a "bit o' brass" and they had bought an old house on the outskirts of Darrowby where they kept themselves to themselves – and the cats. I had heard that Mrs Bond was in the habit of taking in strays and feeding them and giving them a home if they wanted it and this had predisposed me in her favour, because in my experience the unfortunate feline species seemed to be fair game for every kind of cruelty and neglect. They shot cats, threw things at them, starved them and set their dogs on them for fun. It was good to see somebody taking their side.

My patient on this first visit was no more than a big kitten, a terrified little blob of black and white crouching in a corner.

"He's one of the outside cats," Mrs Bond boomed.

"Outside cats?"

"Yes. All these you see here are the inside cats. The others are the really wild ones who simply refuse to enter the house. I feed them of course but the only time they come indoors is when they are ill."

"I see."

"I've had frightful trouble catching this one. I'm worried about his eyes – there seemed to be a skin growing over them, and I do hope you can do something for him. His name, by the way, is Alfred."

"Alfred? Ah yes, quite." I advanced cautiously on the little half-grown animal and was greeted by a waving set of claws and a series of open-mouthed spittings. He was trapped in his corner or he would have been off with the speed of light.

Examining him was going to be a problem. I turned to Mrs Bond. "Could you let me have a sheet of some kind? An old ironing sheet would do. I'm going to have to wrap him up."

"Wrap him up?" Mrs Bond looked very doubtful but she disappeared into another room and returned with a tattered sheet of cotton which looked just right.

I cleared the table of an amazing variety of cat feeding dishes, cat books, cat medicines and spread out the sheet, then I approached my patient again. You can't be in a hurry in a situation like this and it took me perhaps five minutes of wheedling and "Puss-pussing" while I brought my hand nearer and nearer. When I got as far as being able to stroke his cheek I made a quick grab at the scruff of his neck and finally bore Alfred, protesting bitterly and lashing out in all directions, over to the table. There, still holding tightly to his scruff, I laid him on the sheet and started the wrapping operation.

This is something which has to be done quite often with obstreperous felines and, although I say it, I am rather good at it. The idea is to make a neat, tight roll, leaving the relevant piece of cat exposed; it may be an injured paw, perhaps the tail, and in this case of course the head. I think it was the beginning of Mrs Bond's unquestioning faith in me when she saw me quickly enveloping that cat till all you could see of him was a small black-and-white head protruding from an immovable cocoon of cloth. He and I were now facing each other, more or less eyeball to eyeball, and Alfred couldn't do a thing about it.

As I say, I rather pride myself on this little expertise and even today my veterinary colleagues have been known to remark:

"Old Herriot may be limited in many respects but by God he can wrap a cat."

As it turned out, there wasn't a skin growing over Alfred's eyes. There never is.

"He's got a paralysis of the third eyelid, Mrs Bond. Animals have this membrane which flicks across the eye to protect it. In this case it hasn't gone back, probably because the cat is in low condition – maybe had a touch of cat flu or something else which has weakened him. I'll give him an injection of vitamins and leave you some powder to put in his food if you could keep him in for a few days. I think he'll be all right in a week or two."

The injection presented no problems with Alfred furious but helpless inside his sheet and I had come to the end of my first visit to Mrs Bond's.

It was the first of many. The lady and I established an immediate rapport which was strengthened by the fact that I was always prepared to spend time over her assorted charges; crawling on my stomach under piles of logs in the outhouses to reach the outside cats, coaxing them down from trees, stalking them endlessly through the shrubbery. But from my point of view it was rewarding in many ways.

For instance there was the diversity of names she had for her cats. True to her London upbringing she had named many of the toms after the great Arsenal team of those days. There was Eddie Hapgood, Cliff Bastin, Ted Drake, Wilf Copping, but she did slip up in one case because Alex James had kittens three times a year with unfailing regularity.

Then there was her way of calling them home. The first time I saw her at this was on a still summer evening. The two cats she wanted me to see were out in the garden somewhere and I walked with her to the back door where she halted, clasped her hands across her bosom, closed her eyes and gave tongue in a mellifluous contralto.

"Bates, Bates, Bates, Ba-hates." She actually sang out the words in a reverent monotone except for a delightful little lilt on the "Ba-hates". Then once more she inflated her ample rib

cage like an operatic prima donna and out it came again,
delivered with the utmost feeling.

"Bates, Bates, Bates, Ba-hates."

Anyway it worked, because Bates the cat came trotting from
behind a clump of laurel. There remained the other patient and
I watched Mrs Bond with interest.

She took up the same stance, breathed in, closed her eyes,
composed her features into a sweet half-smile and started again.

"Seven-times-three, Seven-times-three, Seven-times-three-
hee." It was set to the same melody as Bates with the same
dulcet rise and fall at the end. She didn't get the quick response
this time, though, and had to go through the performance again
and again, and as the notes lingered on the still evening air the
effect was startlingly like a muezzin calling the faithful to
prayer.

At length she was successful and a fat tortoiseshell slunk
apologetically along the wall-side into the house.

"By the way, Mrs Bond," I asked, making my voice casual.
"I didn't quite catch the name of that last cat."

"Oh, Seven-times-three?" She smiled reminiscently. "Yes,
she is a dear. She's had three kittens seven times running, you
see, so I thought it rather a good name for her, don't you?"

"Yes, yes, I do indeed. Splendid name, splendid."

Another thing which warmed me towards Mrs Bond was her
concern for my safety. I appreciated this because it is a rare trait
among animal owners. I can think of the trainer after one of his
racehorses had kicked me clean out of a loose box examining
the animal anxiously to see if it had damaged its foot; the little
old lady dwarfed by the bristling, teeth-bared Alsatian saying:
"You'll be gentle with him won't you and I hope you won't
hurt him – he's very nervous"; the farmer, after an exhausting
calving which I feel certain has knocked about two years off my
life expectancy, grunting morosely: "I doubt you've tired that
cow out, young man."

Mrs Bond was different. She used to meet me at the door
with an enormous pair of gauntlets to protect my hands against
scratches and it was an inexpressible relief to find that somebody

cared. It became part of the pattern of my life; walking up the garden path among the innumerable slinking, wild-eyed little creatures which were the outside cats, the ceremonial acceptance of the gloves at the door, then the entry into the charged atmosphere of the kitchen with little Mr Bond and his newspaper just visible among the milling furry bodies of the inside cats. I was never able to ascertain Mr Bond's attitude to cats – come to think of it he hardly ever said anything – but I had the impression he could take them or leave them.

The gauntlets were a big help and at times they were a veritable godsend. As in the case of Boris. Boris was an enormous blue-black member of the outside cats and my *bête noire* in more senses than one. I always cherished a private conviction that he had escaped from a zoo; I had never seen a domestic cat with such sleek, writhing muscles, such dedicated ferocity. I'm sure there was a bit of puma in Boris somewhere.

It had been a sad day for the cat colony when he turned up. I have always found it difficult to dislike any animal; most of the ones which try to do us a mischief are activated by fear, but Boris was different; he was a malevolent bully and after his arrival the frequency of my visits increased because of his habit of regularly beating up his colleagues. I was forever stitching up tattered ears, dressing gnawed limbs.

We had one trial of strength fairly early. Mrs Bond wanted me to give him a worm dose and I had the little tablet all ready held in forceps. How I ever got hold of him I don't quite know, but I hustled him on to the table and did my wrapping act at lightning speed, swathing him in roll upon roll of stout material. Just for a few seconds I thought I had him as he stared up at me, his great brilliant eyes full of hate. But as I pushed my loaded forceps into his mouth he clamped his teeth viciously down on them and I could feel claws of amazing power tearing inside the sheet. It was all over in moments. A long leg shot out and ripped its way down my wrist, I let go my tight hold of the neck and in a flash Boris sank his teeth through the gauntlet into the ball of my thumb and was away. I was left standing there stupidly, holding the fragmented worm tablet in a bleeding hand and looking at the bunch of ribbons which had once been my wrapping sheet. From then on Boris loathed the very sight of me and the feeling was mutual.

But this was one of the few clouds in a serene sky. I continued to enjoy my visits there and life proceeded on a tranquil course except, perhaps, for some legpulling from my colleagues. They could never understand my willingness to spend so much time over a lot of cats. And of course this fitted in with the general attitude because Siegfried didn't believe in people keeping pets of any kind. He just couldn't understand their mentality and propounded his views to anybody who cared to listen. He himself, of course, kept five dogs and two cats. The dogs, all of them, travelled everywhere with him in the car and he fed dogs and cats every day with his own hands – wouldn't allow anybody else to do the job. In the evening all seven animals would pile themselves round his feet as he sat in his chair by the fire. To this day he is still as vehemently anti-pet as ever, though another generation of waving dogs' tails almost obscures him as he drives around and he also has several cats, a few tanks of tropical fish and a couple of snakes.

Tristan saw me in action at Mrs Bond's on only one occasion. I was collecting some long forceps from the instrument cupboard when he came into the room.

"Anything interesting, Jim?" he asked.

"No, not really. I'm just off to see one of the Bond cats. It's got a bone stuck between its teeth."

The young man eyed me ruminatively for a moment. "Think I'll come with you. I haven't seen much small animal stuff lately."

As we went down the garden at the cat establishment I felt a twinge of embarrassment. One of the things which had built up my happy relationship with Mrs Bond was my tender concern for her charges. Even with the wildest and the fiercest I exhibited only gentleness, patience and solicitude; it wasn't really an act, it came quite naturally to me. However, I couldn't help wondering what Tristan would think of my cat bedside manner.

Mrs Bond in the doorway had summed up the situation in a flash and had two pairs of gauntlets waiting. Tristan looked a little surprised as he received his pair but thanked the lady with typical charm. He looked still more surprised when he entered the kitchen, sniffed the rich atmosphere and surveyed the masses of furry creatures occupying almost every available inch of space.

"Mr Herriot, I'm afraid it's Boris who has the bone in his teeth," Mrs Bond said.

"Boris!" My stomach lurched. "How on earth are we going to catch him?"

"Oh I've been rather clever," she replied. "I've managed to entice him with some of his favourite food into a cat basket."

Tristan put his hand on a big wicker cage on the table. "In here, is he?" he asked casually. He slipped back the catch and opened the lid. For something like a third of a second the coiled creature within and Tristan regarded each other tensely, then a sleek black body exploded silently from the basket past the young man's left ear on to the top of a tall cupboard.

"Christ!" said Tristan. "What the hell was that?"

"That," I said, "was Boris, and now we've got to get hold of him again." I climbed on to a chair, reached slowly on to the cupboard top and started "Puss-puss-pussing" in my most beguiling tone.

After about a minute Tristan appeared to think he had a better idea; he made a sudden leap and grabbed Boris's tail. But only briefly, because the big cat freed himself in an instant and set off on a whirlwind circuit of the room; along the tops of cupboards and dressers, across the curtains, careering round and round like a wall-of-death rider.

Tristan stationed himself at a strategic point and as Boris shot past he swiped at him with one of the gauntlets.

"Missed the bloody thing!" he shouted in chagrin. "But here he comes again . . . take that, you black sod! Damn it, I can't nail him!"

The docile little inside cats, startled by the scattering of plates and tins and pans and by Tristan's cries and arm wavings, began to run around in their turn, knocking over whatever Boris had missed. The noise and confusion even got through to Mr Bond because just for a moment he raised his head and looked around him in mild surprise at the hurtling bodies before returning to his newspaper.

Tristan, flushed with the excitement of the chase, had really begun to enjoy himself. I cringed inwardly as he shouted over to me happily.

"Send him on, Jim, I'll get the bugger next time round!"

We never did catch Boris. We just had to leave the piece of bone to work its own way out, so it wasn't a successful veterinary visit. But Tristan as we got back into the car smiled contentedly.

"That was great, Jim. I didn't realize you had such fun with your pussies."

Mrs Bond on the other hand, when I next saw her, was rather tight-lipped over the whole thing.

"Mr Herriot," she said, "I hope you aren't going to bring that young man with you again."

The Cat and the Trumpet

J.V. VON SCHEFFEL (1826–86)

Timidly the maiden entered,
Timid, lifted up the trumpet.
To her rosy lips she pressed it.
But 'twas almost terror thrilled her,
For, within its golden chalice,
Lo! her sweet breath was transmuted
To a peal, loud, harsh, and shrilling,
Which the breezes carried onward;
Onward, ay! but who knows whither?
Now she cannot cease from blowing,
And unlicensed shrieks of horror,
Hideous discords, rough and piercing,

Desecrate the morning stillness,
Till the worthy Hiddigeigei
Felt his coat of long Angora
Bristle like a hedgehog's prickles,
And his ear he softly covered
With his paw, and spake as follows:
"Suffer, gallant heart within me
Which already much hath suffered;
Suffer, eke, this maiden's blaring!
We, we know the laws unchanging,
Answer to creation's riddle,
Which beneath all sound are hidden.
And we know full well the magic
Which, unseen, through space is floating,
That, as subtle as a shadow,
Through the hearing's gateway passeth,
And in beast hearts, as in human,
Love and longing and enchantment,
Madness and delirium wakens.
None the less, 'tis ours to suffer
That when cat love finds expression
In the night, in sweetest numbers,
Men accord to us but scorning,
And they brand as 'caterwauling'
All our choicest compositions.
Yet, alas! 'tis ours to suffer
That these same contemptuous mortals
Call such sounds into existence
As I have been forced to hear.
Sounds like these are, surely, garlands
Bound of briars, straw, and thistles,
Where the stinging nettle flaunteth.
And in view of yonder damsel,
Grasping yon abhorrent trumpet,
Can a man, with front unblushing,
Jeer when cats are making music?
Suffer, gallant heart within me,

Suffer! Times are surely coming
When the sapient human being
Will from us acquire the method
Of high feeling's right expression.
When the rude world, struggling upward
Toward the climax of all culture,
Will appreciate 'caterwauling'.
History, in the main, is righteous,
All injustice is atoned for."

from *The Trumpeter* (1893)

Prosper Mérimée on Cats

CHAMPFLEURY (1821–89)

I have passed some pleasant and profitable hours in talking of
cats with M. Prosper Mérimée, who loved them, and did not
consider that he degraded himself as a man by acknowledging
the intelligence of those animals. M. Mérimée would not
admit, indeed, that they had any fault except an excessive
sensitiveness. According to him, the cat proves its susceptibility
by an extreme politeness, "In that," he said, "the animal
resembles well-bred persons."

From *Les Chats*

Pussy

ANONYMOUS (*c.* 1830)

I like little pussy, her coat is so warm;
And if I don't hurt her, she'll do me no harm.
So I'll not pull her tail, nor drive her away,
But pussy and I very gently will play.
She shall sit by my side, and I'll give her some food;
And she'll love me because I am gentle and good.

I'll pat pretty pussy, and then she will purr;
And thus show her thanks for my kindness to her.
But I'll not pinch her ears, nor tread on her paw,
Lest I should provoke her to use her sharp claw.
I never will vex her, nor make her displeased –
For pussy don't like to be worried and teased.

A Dignified Cat

ANDREW LANG (1844–1912)

A regretted friend of my own, a black cat with a great deal of
retenue, never went near another cat's dish; while, if another cat
approached his dish, he instantly retired. "More food," he seemed
to say, "is not worth a wrangle." He withdrew from all forms of
competition, like a dignified Royal cat in exile. On the other
hand, many cats, and one of mine in particular, always desert their
own platter (however tempting) for that of their neighbour.

Lisy's Parting with Her Cat

JAMES THOMSON (1834–82)

The dreadful hour with leaden pace approached,
Lashed fiercely on by unrelenting fate,
When Lisy and her bosom Cat must part:
For now, to school and pensive needle doomed,
She's banished from her childhood's undashed joy,
And all the pleasing intercourse she kept
With her grey comrade, which has often soothed
Her tender moments, while the world around
Glowed with ambition, business, and vice.
Or lay dissolved in sleep's delicious arms:
And from their dewy orbs the conscious stars
Shed on their friendship influence benign.

But see where mournful Puss, advancing, stood
With outstretched tail, casts looks of anxious woe
On melting Lisy, in whose eye the tear
Stood tremulous, and thus would fain have said,
If nature had not tied her struggling tongue:
"Unkind, Oh! who shall now with fattening milk,
With flesh, with bread, and fish beloved, and meat,
Regale my taste? and at the cheerful fire,
Ah, who shall bask me in their downy lap?
Who shall invite me to the bed, and throw
The bedclothes o'er me in the winter night,
When Eurus roars? Beneath whose soothing hand
Soft shall I purr? But now, when Lisy's gone,
What is the dull officious world to me?
I loathe the thoughts of life": thus plained the Cat,
While Lisy felt, by sympathetic touch,
These anxious thoughts that in her mind revolved,
And casting on her a desponding look,
She snatched her in her arms with eager grief,
And mewing, thus began: "O Cat beloved!
Thou dear companion of my tender years!
Joy of my youth! that oft hast licked my hands
With velvet tongue ne'er stained by mouse's blood.
Oh, gentle Cat! how shall I part with thee?
How dead and heavy will the moments pass
When you are not in my delighted eye,
With Cubi playing, or your flying tail.
How harshly will the softest muslin feel,
And all the silk of schools, while I no more
Have your sleek skin to soothe my softened sense?
How shall I eat while you are not beside
To share the bit? How shall I ever sleep
While I no more your lulling murmurs hear?
Yet we must part – so rigid fate decrees –
But never shall your loved idea, dear,
Part from my soul, and when I first can mark
The embroidered figure on the snowy lawn,

Your image shall my needle keen employ.
Hark! now I'm called away! Oh direful sound!
I come – I come, but first I charge you all –
You – you – and you, particularly you,
O Mary, Mary, feed her with the best,
Repose her nightly in the warmest couch,
And be a Lisy to her!" Having said,
She sat her down, and with her head across,
Rushed to the evil which she could not shun,
While a sad mew went knelling to her heart!

The Royal Cat Wager

CHARLES H. ROSS

It is stated in a Japanese book that the tip of a Cat's nose is always cold, except on the day corresponding with our Midsummer-day. This is a question I cannot say I have gone into very deeply. I know, however, that Cats always have a warm nose when they awaken from sleep. All Cats are fond of warmth. I knew one which used to open an oven door after the kitchen fire was out; and creep into the oven. One day the servant shut the door, not noticing the cat was inside, and lighted the fire. For a long while she could not make out whence came the sounds of its crying and scratching, but fortunately made the discovery in time to save its life. A Cat's love of the sunshine is well known, and perhaps this story may not be unfamiliar to the reader:

One broiling hot summer's day Charles James Fox and the Prince of Wales were lounging up St James's Street, and Fox laid the Prince a wager that he would see more Cats than his Royal Highness during their promenade, although the Prince might choose which side of the street he thought fit. On reaching Piccadilly, it turned out that Fox had seen thirteen Cats and the Prince none. The Prince asked for an explanation of this apparent miracle.

"Your Royal Highness," said Fox, "chose, of course, the shady side of the way as most agreeable. I knew that the sunny side would be left for me, and that Cats prefer the sunshine."

from *The Book of Cats* (1868)

That Little Black Cat

D'ARCY WENTWORTH THOMPSON (1829–1902)

Who's that ringing at our door-bell?
　"I'm a little black cat and I'm not very well."
"Then rub your little nose with a little mutton fat,
　And that's the best cure for a little pussy-cat."

All Cats Together

ANDREW LANG (1844–1912)

Other cats came, with kind inquiries, to visit a puss whose leg had been hurt in a rabbit trap. One of them, having paid her visit, went out, caught a rabbit, and brought it back to the sufferer. What sportsman could do more?

C

EDWARD LEAR (1812–88)

C was Papa's grey Cat,
　Who caught a squeaky Mouse;
She pulled him by his twirly tail
　All about the house.

from *Nonsense Songs, Stories, Botany and Alphabets* (1871)

Memoir of the Cats of Greta Hall

ROBERT SOUTHEY (1774–1843)

For as much, most excellent Edith May [Southey's daughter], as
you must always feel a natural and becoming concern in
whatever relates to the house wherein you were born, and
in which the first part of your life has thus far so happily been
spent, I have for your instruction and delight composed these
Memoirs of the Cats of Greta Hall: to the end that the memory
of such worthy animals may not perish, but be held in deserved
honour by my children, and those who shall come after them.
And let me not be supposed unmindful of Beelzebub of Bath,
and Senhor Thomas de Lisboa, that I have not gone back to an
earlier period, and included them in my design. Far be it from
me to intend any injury or disrespect to their shades! Opportunity of doing justice to their virtues will not be wanting at
some future time, but for the present I must confine myself
within the limits of these precincts.

In the autumn of the year 1803, when I entered upon this
place of abode, I found the hearth in possession of two cats,
whom my nephew Hartley Coleridge (then in the seventh year
of his age) had named Lord Nelson, and Bona Marietta. The
former, as the name implies, was of the worthier gender: it is as
decidedly so in Cats, as in Grammar and in law. He was an ugly
specimen of the streaked-carroty, or Judas-coloured kind;
which is one of the ugliest varieties. But *nimium ne crede colori.*
In spite of his complexion, there was nothing treacherous about
him. He was altogether a good Cat, affectionate, vigilant and
brave; and for services performed against the Rats was deserv-
edly raised in succession to the rank of Baron, Viscount and
Earl. He lived to a good old age; and then, being quite helpless
and miserable, was in mercy thrown into the river. I had more
than once interfered to save him from this fate; but it became at
length plainly an act of compassion to consent to it. And here
let me observe that in a world wherein death is necessary, the
law of nature by which one creature preys upon another is a

law of mercy, not only because death is thus made instrumental to life, and more life exists in consequence, but also because it is better for the creatures themselves to be cut off suddenly, than to perish by disease or hunger – for these are the only alternatives.

There are still some of Lord Nelson's descendants in the town of Keswick. Two of the family were handsomer than I should have supposed any Cats of this complexion could have been; but their fur was fine, the colour a rich carrot, and the striping like that of the finest tyger or tabby kind. I named one of them William Rufus; the other Danayr le Roux, after a personage in the Romance of Gyron le Courtoys. [...]

For a considerable time afterwards, an evil fortune attended all our attempts at re-establishing a Cattery. Ovid disappeared and Virgil died of some miserable distemper. You and your cousin are answerable for these names: the reasons which I could find for them were, in the former case the satisfactory one that the same Ovid might be presumed to be a master in the Art of Love; and in the latter, the probable one that something like Ma-ro might be detected in the said Virgil's notes of courtship.

There was poor Othello: most properly named, for black he was, and jealous undoubtedly he would have been, but he in his kittenship followed Miss Wilbraham into the street, and there in all likelihood came to an untimely end. There was the Zombi – (I leave the Commentators to explain that title, and refer them to my History of Brazil to do it) – his marvellous story was recorded in a letter to Bedford – and after that adventure he vanished. There was Prester John, who turned out not to be of John's gender, and therefore had the name altered to Pope Joan. The Pope I am afraid came to a death of which other Popes have died. I suspect that some poison which the rats had turned out of their holes, proved fatal to their enemy. For some time I feared we were at the end of our Cat-a-logue: but at last Fortune as if to make amends for her late severity sent us two at once – the never-to-be-enough-praised Rumpelstilzchen, and the equally- to-be-admired Hurlybur-lybuss.

And "first for the first of these" as my huge favourite and almost namesake Robert South, says in his Sermons.

When the Midgeleys went away from the next house, they left this creature to our hospitality, cats being the least movable of all animals because of their strong local predilections; they are indeed in a domesticated state the serfs of the animal creation, and properly attached to the soil. The change was gradually and therefore easily brought about, for he was already acquainted with the children and with me; and having the same precincts to prowl in was hardly sensible of any other difference in his condition than that of obtaining a name; for when he was consigned to us he was an anonymous cat; and I having just related at breakfast with universal applause the story of Rumpelstilzchen from a German tale in Grimms' Collection, gave him that strange and magnisonant appellation; to which upon its being ascertained that he came when a kitten from a bailiff's house, I added the patronymic of Macbum. Such is his history, his character may with most propriety be introduced after the manner of Plutarch's parallels when I shall have given some previous account of his great compeer and rival Hurlyburlybuss – that name also is of Germanic and Grimmish extraction.

Whence Hurlyburlybuss came was a mystery when you departed from the Land of Lakes, and a mystery it long remained. He appeared here, as Mango Gapac did in Peru, and Quetzalcohuatl among the Aztecas, no one knew from whence. He made himself acquainted with all the philofelists of the family – attaching himself more particularly to Mrs Lovell, but he never attempted to enter the house, frequently disappeared for days, and once since my return for so long a time that he was actually believed to be dead and veritably lamented as such. The wonder was whither did he retire at such times – and to whom did he belong; for neither I in my daily walks, nor the children, nor any of the servants ever by any chance saw him anywhere except in our own domain, There was something so mysterious in this, that in old times it might have excited strong suspicion, and he would have been in danger of passing for a Witch in disguise, or a familiar. The mystery however was solved about four weeks ago, when as we were returning from a walk up the Greta, Isabel saw him on his transit across the road and the wall from Shullcrow in a direction towards the Hill. But to this day we are ignorant who has the honour to be his owner in the eye of the law; and the owner is equally ignorant of the high honour in which Hurlyburlybuss is held, of the heroic name which he has obtained, and that his fame has extended far and wide – even unto Norwich in the East, and Escott and Crediton and Kellerton in the West, yea – that with Rumpelstilzchen he has been celebrated in song, by some hitherto undiscovered poet, and that his glory will go down to future generations.

The strong enmity which unhappily subsists between these otherwise gentle and most amiable cats, is not unknown to you. Let it be imputed, as in justice it ought, not to their individual characters (for Cats have characters – and for the benefit of philosophy, as well as felisophy, this truth ought generally to be known) but to the constitution of Cat nature – an original sin, or an original necessity, which may be only another mode of expressing the same thing:

> Two stars keep not their motion in one sphere,
> Nor can one purlieu brook a double reign
> Of Hurlyburlybuss and Rumpelstilzchen.

When you left us, the result of many a fierce conflict was that Hurly remained master of the green and garden, and the whole of the out of door premises, Rumpel always upon the appearance of his victorious enemy retiring into the house as a citadel or sanctuary. The conqueror was perhaps in part indebted for this superiority to his hardier habits of life, living always in the open air, and providing for himself; while Rumpel (who though born under a bum-bailiff's roof was nevertheless kittened with a silver spoon in his mouth) passed his hours in luxurious repose beside the fire, and looked for his meals as punctually as any two-legged member of the family. Yet I believe that the advantage on Hurly's side is in a great degree constitutional also, and that his superior courage arises from a confidence in his superior strength, which as you well know is visible in his make. What Benito and Maria Rosa used to say of my poor Thomaz, that he was *muito hidalgo*, is true of Rumpelstilzchen, his countenance, deportment and behaviour being such that he is truly a gentleman-like tom-cat. Far be it from me to praise him beyond his deserts – he is not beautiful, the mixture, tabby and white, is not good (except under very favourable combinations) and the tabby is not good of its kind. Nevertheless he is a fine cat, handsome enough for his sex, large, well-made, with good features, and an intelligent countenance, and carrying a splendid tail, which in Cats and Dogs is undoubtedly the seat of honour. His eyes which are soft and expressive are of a hue between chrysolite and emerald. Hurlyburlybuss's are between chrysolite and topaz. Which may be the more esteemed shade for the *olho de gato* I am not lapidary enough to decide. You should ask my Uncle. But both are of the finest water. In all his other features Hurly must yield the palm, and in form also; he has no pretensions to elegance, his size is ordinary and his figure bad: but the character of his face and neck is so masculine, that the Chinese, who use the word "bull" as synonymous with "male", and call a boy a bull-child, might with great propriety denominate him a bull-cat. His make evinces such decided marks of strength and courage that if cat-fighting were as fashionable as cock-fighting, no cat would stand a fairer chance of winning a Welsh main. He would become as famous as the Dog Billy himself, whom I look upon as the most distinguished character that has appeared since Buonaparte.

Some weeks ago Hurlyburlybuss was manifestly emaciated and enfeebled by ill health, and Rumpelstilzchen with great magnanimity made overtures of peace. The whole progress of the treaty was seen from the parlour window. The caution with which Rumpel made his advances, the sullen dignity with which they were received, their mutual uneasiness when

Rumpel, after a slow and wary approach, seated himself whisker-to-whisker with his rival, the mutual fear which restrained not only teeth and claws, but even all tones of defiance, the mutual agitation of their tails which, though they did not expand with anger, could not be kept still for suspense, and lastly the manner in which Hurly retreated, like Ajax still keeping his face towards his old antagonist, were worthy to have been represented by that painter who was called the Rafaelle of Cats. The overture I fear was not accepted as generously as it was made; for no sooner had Hurlyburlybuss recovered strength than hostilities were recommenced with greater violence than ever, Rumple who had not abused his superiority while he possessed it, had acquired meantime a confidence which made him keep the field. Dreadful were the combats which ensued, as their ears, faces and legs bore witness. Rumpel had a wound which went through one of his feet. The result had been so far in his favour that he no longer seeks to avoid his enemy, and we are often compelled to interfere and separate them. Oh it is awful to hear the "dreadful note of preparation" with which they prelude their encounters! – the long low growl slowly rises and swells till it becomes a high sharp yowl – and then it is snapt short by a sound which seems as if they were spitting fire and venom at each other. I could half persuade myself that the word "felonious" is derived from the feline temper as displayed at such times. All means of reconciling them and making them understand how goodly a thing it is for cats to dwell together in peace, and what fools they are to quarrel and tear each other, are in vain. The proceedings of the Society for the Abolition of War are not more utterly ineffectual and hopeless.

All we can do is to act more impartially than the Gods did between Achilles and Hector, and continue to treat both with equal regard.

written for his daughter, 18 June 1824

Edwards Lear's Foss

HENRY STRACHEY

When staying at Cannes at Christmas, 1882, I was invited by Mr Lear to go over to San Remo to spend a few days with him. Mr Lear's villa was large, and the second he had built; the first became unbearable to him from a large hotel having been planted in front of it. So he put his new house in a place by the sea, where, as he said, nothing could interrupt his light unless the fishes built. The second house was exactly like the first. This, Mr Lear explained to me, was necessary or else Foss, his cat, might not have approved of the new villa. At breakfast the morning after I arrived, this much-thought of, though semi-tailed, cat jumped in at the window and ate a piece of toast from my hand. This, I found, was considered an event; when visitors stayed at the Villa Tennyson, Foss generally hid himself in the back regions; but his recognition of me was a sort of "guinea stamp" which seemed to please Mr Lear greatly, and assured him of my fitness to receive the constant acts of kindness he was showing me . . . He took from a place in his bureau a number of carefully cut-out backs of old envelopes, and on these he drew, to send to my sister, then eight years old, the delightful series of heraldic pictures of his cat. After he had done seven he said it was a great shame to caricature Foss, and laid aside the pen.

Nursery Rhymes

ANONYMOUS (19th century)

Pussy-cat, Pussy-cat, Where Are You Going?
Pussy-cat, Pussy-cat, where are you going?
"Into the meadow to see the men mowing."
If you go there you are sure to be shot,
Put in a pudding, and boiled in a pot.

Pussy-cat Mew

Pussy-cat Mew jumped over a coal,
And in her best petticoat burnt a great hole.
Pussy-cat Mew shall have no more milk
Till she has mended her gown of silk.

Ten Little Mice

Ten little mice sat down to spin;
Pussy passed by, and just looked in,
"What are you doing, my jolly ten?"
"We're making coats for gentlemen."
"Shall I come in and cut your threads?"
"No! No! Mistress Pussy – you'd bite off our heads."

Fanny and Her Cat

Come here, little Puss,
    And I'll make you quite smart,
You shall wear this gold chain,
    And I'll wear this fine heart;
And when we are drest,
    My dear Aunty shall see
Who then will look best,
    Little Pussy or me.

"Pussy-cat, Pussy-cat, Where Have You Been?"

Pussy cat, pussy cat, where have you been?
I've been to London to look at the queen.
Pussy cat, pussy cat, what did you there?
I frightened a little mouse under her chair.

A Keyboard Cat

EMILE ZOLA (1840–1902)

To win her over to his musical scheme, Lazare wished to teach
her to play on the piano. He showed her how to place her fingers
on the keys, and kept her for hours running up and down the
scales. But she discouraged him very much by her lack of

enthusiasm. She was always on the look-out for something to laugh at and make a joke of, and took great delight in making Minouche promenade along the keyboard and execute barbaric symphonies with her paws, asserting that the cat was playing the famous banishment from the Earthly Paradise, whereat the composer himself smiled. Then they broke out into boisterous fun again, she threw her arms round his neck, and he spun her round like a top, while Minouche, joining in the merriment, sprang from the table to the top of the cupboard.

from *The Joy of Life*

Nervous as a Cat

J.V. VON SCHEFFEL (1826–86)

Oh, men do us vast injustice,
And we look for thanks in vain;
They misunderstand completely
All our nature's finer strain.

Waking from a drunken slumber,
Hark, the mortal, lying flat,
Mutters, with a throbbing forehead,
"I'm as nervous as a cat!"

Nervous as a cat − O insult!
Gentle are our tones and soft;
Human cries are harsh and boist'rous,
In the streets I've heard them oft.

Ay, they do us sore injustice;
Little do their rude hearts know
All that cats can bear of anguish,
Fierce and deep, and bitter woe!

from "Songs of the Tom-cat Hiddigeigei"
in *The Trumpeter* (1893)

The Cure

GEORGE MACKAY BROWN (1921–)

Not two hundred yards from Jenny's father's croft stood the island church, and beside it the manse where the minister lived with his elderly mother Mrs Martin. It was a sad house, because poor Mrs Martin had not been at all well for years. What was wrong with her nobody knew, not even the island doctor. It was just that the kind old lady was melancholy all the time now. Her sad eyes looked out at a sad world. She didn't see the point of going out any longer, when there was nothing but sadness and vanity to be seen and heard. If she went anywhere, she reasoned, she would only intensify the existing sadness. Indoors there was little solace for her either, though her son Andrew was all considerateness and kindness. Her food tasted of nothing. The books she had loved once bored her now. Sometimes she would take up wool and knitting needles, but all she knitted was an immensely long, grey, scarf-like garment, that grew and grew and was now fifteen feet long if it was an inch.

"Mother," said the Rev. Andrew Martin one morning after breakfast (which he had prepared and set, for she wasn't interested in cooking either), "Mother, it's such a beautiful day! There are only two little clouds like white lambs in the sky. Everything is so beautiful and warm and clear. It's a shame to be indoors. You really must sit outside on a morning like this. I'll bring your chair and your shawl."

"If you like," said Mrs Martin dully. And she was sorry her words were so leaden and dispirited, for she didn't like hurting her son; and because she loved him, and because the morning through the sitting-room window was so radiant, her spirits sank lower than ever.

Andrew wrestled the huge fireside chair outside and set it just beside the door, and he arranged the cushion. Mrs Martin came out like Mary Queen of Scots approaching the scaffold. She sighed and sat down. Andrew draped the shawl about her shoulders.

"Bring my knitting," she said.

Having seen her as comfortable as possible, Andrew retired to his study to work on his Sunday sermon, and the old lady was alone.

And really, it was such a beautiful morning! A blackbird sang from the garden wall, burst after burst of purest ecstasy! The two little clouds like lambs had been joined by a third, high up in the intense blue sky, but they seemed to be too tranced with delight to move. The sea, between the two green hills, shimmered. You could almost feel the joy of the grass growing, and the teeming wild flowers. You could, if you were not Mrs Martin. She sat there, the sole blight on this happy summer world. As she sat, a tear welled in her eye – melancholy's answer to the dewdrop in the heart of the garden rose.

She took up her knitting needles, but they made an ugly "clack-clack" in the delicate web of sound that lay over the island. She dropped them again.

Just then, Mrs Martin saw a black cat on the garden wall, magnified and distorted by the unfallen tears in her eyes. Of course, it was the cat of Inquoy, Jan Thomson's croft. What was its name now – Flannel? Funnel? Mrs Martin couldn't quite remember. Some funny name like that. And it was a strange cat too. It followed the Thomson girl to school most mornings. It had (so she'd heard) attacked the coastguard's Alsatian dog – flown in his face like a black whirlwind, claws and teeth out – and sent the huge powerful dog home with his tail between his legs. And here it was now, on the garden wall of the manse. That had never happened before.

The cat seemed to be taking a friendly interest in the creature he shared the wall with – the joyous blackbird. The blackbird was too busy keeping a wary eye on the cat to sing now. It quivered on the wall, poised for flight, should that sinister shadow make one move.

Really, thought Mrs Martin, if there is to be any "nature red in tooth and claw" in this garden, I'll call Andrew to take me inside. I just *couldn't* stand that!

And then she realized that the black cat was looking at her, in a very concerned way. He looked, and looked, and then leapt softly from the wall on to the lawn, and approached her.

The blackbird resumed its song, a magnificent fount of celebration.

You would almost think the cat had some kind of message for Mrs Martin. But in the long garden there were so many distractions. First it was the butterflies. Three of them exploded silently out of the rosebush over Fankle's face. He fought with them for several seconds, but butterflies are much harder to fight against than dogs, and the butterflies separated, drifting airily each his own way. Fankle didn't seem to mind such a lyrical defeat. Once more he turned a serious regard on poor afflicted Mrs Martin.

What now – whatever was the creature doing now? He seemed to have found something in the long grass. Delicately he howked it out with a forepaw, and it was – a fragment of cherry-cake! Mrs Martin was *astonished*. The duplicity of Andrew! So this was what he did in the garden, late in the evening, after she was in bed – eat cherry-cake – slice after slice of it, she wouldn't wonder. The thing was, Andrew had become worried last winter that "he was digging his grave with his teeth". It was sweet things that he had always gone for, from his childhood up – chocolate, cream buns, meringues, honey and bread, but chiefly and most of all: *cherry-cake*. Cherry-cake was the chief villain in the thrilling drama that was going on in Andrew's body. Cherry-cake he loved passionately and devotedly – and it was cherry-cake that would finish Andrew off. So Andrew believed. It was true, he seemed to be getting fatter with every month that passed, and he was deeply worried about it. Last winter Andrew had come to a solemn decision – no more sweet things for him. He renounced them, he put them behind him. He got a diet sheet from the doctor which he studied carefully. Above all, cherry-cake, that had been his joy and delight, was to be banned for ever from the manse.

Be sure your sins will find you out! So this was what Andrew did night after night, in the garden, when he was supposed to

be studying the growth of potatoes and lettuce and strawberries
– he was wolfing down, in secret, thick slices of cherry-cake!

Mrs Martin didn't know whether to laugh or cry. If it had
been a really serious business – if Andrew was indeed cherry-
caking himself to death – there would have been cause for tears.
But the truth was, Andrew was and had always been an acute
hypochondriac, forever worrying about his health. The island
doctor had assured Mrs Martin, privately, that there was
nothing wrong with Andrew – he could eat, with safety, as
much cherry-cake as he wanted. And Mrs Martin had told the
doctor in return that stoutness ran in the family: Andrew's
father and uncle and grandfather had been even huger than
Andrew: vast men, that set the earth trembling under their feet.

It had taken this cat to discover Andrew's innocent deceit. A
fair fragment of cherry-cake Andrew must have dropped and
not found in the twilight of last night! The black cat swallowed
the cherry, his eyes melting with sheer sensuous delight.

"You *are* a strange cat," said Mrs Martin out loud. The
blackbird agreed with her, thrillingly. Fankle himself seemed to
acquiesce. He approached the invalid obliquely, across the
shallot bed.

Then, before Mrs Martin was aware of it, he pounced! He
pushed the ball of grey wool away, he parried, dancingly he
threatened it – you would think he both loved and hated it.
Then something happened: his claw got hooked in the endless
scarf that Mrs Martin was knitting, and he could not get the
paw free. He tugged, he pulled. The knitting needles fell with a
tiny clatter on the flagstones. Fankle whirled about, and that
was the worst thing he could have done, for the scarf began to
drape itself about him, and the harder the cat tugged and
struggled, the closer he was wound. The struggle to escape
went on for the duration of two blackbird songs, and at the end
of it Fankle lay there on the grass at Mrs Martin's feet like a
badly put together Egyptian mummy. Even his head was
covered – one ear only stuck out. At last, from inside the grey
swathe, emerged a tiny "miaow".

"Andrew," cried Mrs Martin.

Her stout son was there in five seconds, his pen in his hand.

"Free that cat, Andrew," said Mrs Martin.

"Good gracious!" said Andrew. "How on earth did this happen?" And then; when he had unwound Fankle and unhooked the claw, "Why, it's the Thomsons' cat – Fankle."

"Fankle, is that its name?" said Mrs Martin. "Well, Andrew, since you've been so good as to free Fankle, you can have a thick slice of cherry-cake."

At the gape of guilty astonishment Andrew gave, she began to laugh: first a slow smile, then a reluctant chuckle, then a full-throated shout of merriment. It was just like the happy Mrs Martin of seven years ago, before the melancholy had come on her. It was, to Andrew, the most beautiful sound in all that summer of music and poetry.

As for Fankle, he gathered himself together with dignity, and left the garden without another glance at Mrs Martin and the Rev. Andrew Martin. He even ignored the blackbird.

It would be wrong to say that Mrs Martin was entirely cured of her depressions from that day on. She still sighed occasionally, and thought with sadness of the emptiness of existence and the pain of life. But she could go out – a thing that had never happened for seven years. She could visit the crofts, and speak to the old women and the children. She could shop at the village store. She sat once more in her pew in the kirk on Sundays. The whole island was the better of that, because they had always liked Mrs Martin.

Every Friday afternoon a little box was delivered at the door of Inquoy croft, addressed in Mrs Martin's writing to *Fankle Thomson*. Inside was a tin of salmon, Fankle's favourite food. At tea-time on Fridays, Fankle ate with great luxury.

Rev. Andrew Martin resumed his eating of cherry-cake publicly, and grew rather fatter, but it suited him; and now he didn't mind so much, when there was laughter once more across the breakfast table at the manse.

from *Six Lives of Fankle the Cat*

REQUIESCAT

"O heaven will not ever heaven be
Unless my cats are there to welcome me."
Epitaph in a pet cemetery

Last Words to a Dumb Friend

THOMAS HARDY (1840–1928)

Pet was never mourned as you
Purrer of the spotless hue,
Plumy tail, and wistful gaze
While you humoured our queer ways,
Or outshrilled your morning call
Up the stairs and through the hall –
Foot suspended in its fall –
While expectant, you would stand
Arched to meet the stroking hand;
Till your way you chose to wend
Yonder, to your tragic end.

Never another pet for me!
Let your place all vacant be;
Better blankness day by day
Than companion torn away.
Better bid his memory fade,
Better blot each mark he made,
Selfishly escape distress
By contrived forgetfulness,
Than preserve his prints to make
Every morn and eve an ache.

From the chair whereon he sat
Sweep his fur, nor wince thereat;
Rake his little pathways out
Mid the bushes roundabout;
Smooth away his talons' mark
From the claw-worn pine-tree bark,
Where he climbed as dusk embrowned,
Waiting us who loitered round.

Strange it is this speechless thing,
Subject to our mastering,
Subject for his life and food
To our gift, and time, and mood;
Timid pensioner of us Powers,
His existence ruled by ours,
Should – by crossing at a breath
Into safe and shielded death,
By the merely taking hence
Of his insignificance –
Loom as largened to the sense,
Shape as part, above man's will,
Of the Imperturbable.

As a prisoner, flight debarred,
Exercising in a yard,
Still retain I, troubled, shaken,
Mean estate, by him forsaken;
And this home, which scarcely took
Impress from his little look,
By his faring to the Dim
Grows all eloquent of him.

Housemate, I can think you still
Bounding to the window-sill,
Over which I vaguely see
Your small mound beneath the tree,
Showing in the autumn shade
That you moulder where you played.

Calvin, the Cat

CHARLES DUDLEY WARNER (1829–1900)

Calvin is dead. His life, long to him, but short for the rest of us,
was not marked by startling adventures, but his character was so

548

uncommon and his qualities were so worthy of imitation that I have been asked by those who personally knew him to set down my recollections of his career.

His origin and ancestry were shrouded in mystery; even his age was a matter of pure conjecture. Although he was of the Maltese race, I have reason to suppose that he was American by birth as he certainly was in sympathy. Calvin was given to me eight years ago by Mrs Stowe, but she knew nothing of his age or origin. He walked into her house one day out of the great unknown and became at once at home, as if he had been always a friend of the family. He appeared to have artistic and literary tastes, and it was as if he had inquired at the door if that was the residence of the author of *Uncle Tom's Cabin*, and, upon being assured that it was, had decided to dwell there. This is, of course, fanciful, for his antecedents were wholly unknown, but in his time he could hardly have been in any household where he would not have heard *Uncle Tom's Cabin* talked about. When he came to Mrs Stowe, he was as large as he ever was, and apparently as old as he ever became. Yet there was in him no appearance of age; he was in the happy maturity of all his powers, and you would rather have said in that maturity he had found the secret of perpetual youth. And it was as difficult to believe that he would ever be aged as it was to imagine that he had ever been in immature youth. There was in him a mysterious perpetuity.

After some years, when Mrs Stowe made her winter home in Florida, Calvin came to live with us. From the first moment, he fell into the ways of the house and assumed a recognized position in the family – I say recognized, because after he became known he was always inquired for by visitors, and in the letters to the other members of the family he always received a message. Although the least obtrusive of beings, his individuality always made itself felt.

His personal appearance had much to do with this, for he was of royal mould, and had an air of high breeding. He was large, but he had nothing of the fat grossness of the celebrated Angora family; though powerful, he was exquisitely proportioned, and as graceful in every movement as a young leopard. When he stood up to open a door – he opened all the doors with old-fashioned latches – he was portentously tall, and when he stretched on the rug before the fire he seemed too long for this world – as indeed he was. His coat was the finest and softest I have ever seen, a shade of quiet Maltese; and from his throat downward, underneath, to the white tips of his feet, he wore the whitest and most delicate ermine; and no person was ever more fastidiously neat. In his finely formed head you saw something of his aristocratic character; the ears were small and cleanly cut, there was a tinge of pink in the nostrils, his face was handsome, and the expression of his countenance exceedingly intelligent – I should call it even a sweet expression if the term were not inconsistent with his look of alertness and sagacity.

It is difficult to convey a just idea of his gaiety in connection with his dignity and gravity, which his name expressed. As we know nothing of his family, of course it will be understood that Calvin was his Christian name. He had times of relaxation into utter playfulness, delighting in a ball of yarn, catching sportively at stray ribbons when his mistress was at her toilet, and pursuing his own tail, with hilarity, for lack of anything better. He could amuse himself by the hour, and he did not care for children; perhaps something in his past was present to his memory. He had absolutely no bad habits, and his disposition was perfect. I never saw him exactly angry, though I have seen his tail grow to an enormous size when a strange cat appeared upon his lawn. He disliked cats, evidently regarding them as feline and trea-cherous, and he had no association with them. Occasionally there would be heard a night concert in the shrubbery. Calvin would ask to have the door opened, and then you would hear a rush and a "Pestzt", and the concert would explode, and Calvin would quietly come in and resume his seat on the hearth. There was no trace of anger in his manner, but he wouldn't have any of that about the house. He had the rare virtue of magnanimity. Although he had fixed notions about his own rights, and extraordinary persistency in getting them, he never showed temper at a repulse; he simply and firmly persisted till he had what he wanted. His diet was one point; his idea was that of the scholars about dictionaries – to "get the best". He knew as well as anyone what was in the house, and would refuse beef if turkey was to be had; and if there were oysters, he would wait over the turkey to see if the oysters would not be forthcoming. And yet he was not a gross gourmand; he would eat bread if he saw me eating it, and thought he was not being imposed on. His habits of feeding, also, were refined; he never used a knife, and he would put up his hand and draw the fork down to his mouth as gracefully as a grown person. Unless necessity compelled, he would not eat in the kitchen, but insisted upon his meals in the dining-room, and would wait patiently, unless a stranger were present; and then he was sure to importune the visitor, hoping that the latter was ignorant of the rule of the house, and would give him something. They used to say that he preferred as his tablecloth on the floor a certain well-known Church journal; but this was said by an Episcopalian. So far as I know, he had no religious prejudices, except that he did not like the association with Romanists. He tolerated the servants, because they belonged to the house, and would sometimes linger by the kitchen stove; but the moment visitors came in he arose, opened the door, and marched into the drawing-room. Yet he enjoyed the company of his equals, and never withdrew, no matter how many callers – whom he recognized as of his society – might come into the drawing-room. Calvin was fond of company, but he wanted to choose it; and I have no doubt that his was an aristocratic fastidiousness rather than one of faith. It was so with most people.

The intelligence of Calvin was something phenomenal, in his rank of life. He established a method of communicating his wants, and even some of his sentiments; and he could help himself in many things. There was a furnace register in a retired room, where he used to go when he wished to be alone, that he always opened when he desired more heat; but never shut it, any more than he shut the door after himself. He could do almost everything but speak; and you would declare sometimes that you could see a pathetic longing to do that in his intelligent face. I have no desire to overdraw his qualities, but if there was one thing in him more noticeable than another, it was his fondness for nature. He could content himself for hours at a low window, looking into the ravine and at the great trees, noting the smallest stir there; he delighted, above all things, to accompany me walking about the garden, hearing the birds, getting the smell of the fresh earth, and rejoicing in the sunshine. He followed me and gambolled like a dog, rolling over on the turf and exhibiting his delight in a hundred ways. If I worked, he sat and watched me, or looked off over the bank, and kept his ear open to the twitter in the cherry trees. When it stormed, he was sure to sit at the window, keenly watching the rain or the snow, glancing up and down at its falling; and a winter tempest always delighted him. [...]

I hesitate to speak of his capacity for friendship and the affectionateness of his nature, for I know from his own reserve that he would not care to have it much talked about. We understood each other perfectly, but we never made any fuss about it; when I spoke his name and snapped my fingers, he came to me; when I returned home at night, he was pretty sure to be waiting for me near the gate, and would rise and saunter along the walk, as if his being there were purely accidental – so shy was he commonly of showing feeling; and when I opened the door he never rushed in, like a cat, but loitered, and lounged, as if he had had no intention of going in, but he would condescend to. And yet, the fact was, he knew dinner was ready, and he was bound to be there. He kept the run of dinner-time. It happened sometimes, during our absence in the summer, that dinner would be early, and Calvin, walking about the grounds, missed it and came in late. But he never made a mistake the second day. There was one thing he never did – he never rushed through an open doorway. He never forgot his dignity. If he had asked to have the door opened, and was eager to go out, he always went deliberately; I can see him now, standing on the sill, looking about at the sky as if he was thinking whether it were worthwhile to take an umbrella, until he was near having his tail shut in.

His friendship was rather constant than demonstrative. When we returned from an absence of nearly two years, Calvin welcomed us with evident pleasure, but showed his satisfaction rather by tranquil happiness than by fuming about. He had the faculty of making us glad to get home. It was his constancy that was so attractive. He liked companionship, but he wouldn't be petted, or fussed over, or sit in anyone's lap a moment; he always extricated himself from such familiarity with dignity and with no show of temper. If there was any petting to be done, however, he chose to do it. Often he would sit looking at me, and then, moved by a delicate affection, come and pull at my coat and sleeve until he could touch my face with his nose, and then go away contented. He had a habit of coming to my study in the morning, sitting quietly by my side or on the table for hours, watching the pen run over the paper, occasionally swinging his tail round for a blotter, and then going to sleep among the papers by the inkstand. Or, more rarely, he would watch the writing from a perch on my shoulder. Writing always interested him, and, until he understood it, he wanted to hold the pen.

He always held himself in a kind of reserve with his friend, as if he had said, "Let us respect our personality, and not make a 'mess' of friendship." He saw, with Emerson, the risk of degrading it to trivial conveniency. "Why insist on rash personal relations with your friends? Leave this touching and clawing." Yet I would not give an unfair notion of his aloofness, his fine sense of the sacredness of the me and the not-me. And, at the risk of not being believed, I will relate an incident, which was often repeated. Calvin had the practice of passing a portion of the night in the contemplation of its beauties, and would come into our chamber over the roof of the conservatory through the open window, summer and winter, and go to sleep at the foot of my bed. He would do this always exactly in this way; he never was content to stay in the chamber if we compelled him to go upstairs and through the door. He had the obstinacy of General Grant. But this is by the way. In the morning he performed his toilet and went down to breakfast with the rest of the family. Now, when the mistress was absent from home, and at no other time, Calvin would come in the morning, when the bell rang, to the head of the bed, put up his feet and look into my face, follow me about when I rose, "assist" at the dressing, and in many purring ways show his fondness, as if he had plainly said, "I know that she has gone away, but I am here." Such was Calvin in rare moments.

He had his limitations. Whatever passion he had for nature, he had no conception of art. There was sent to him once a fine and very expressive cat's head in bronze, by Frémiet. I placed it on the floor. He regarded it intently, approached it cautiously and crouchingly, touched it with his nose, perceived the fraud, turned away abruptly, and never would notice it afterward. On the whole, his life was not only a successful one, but a happy one. He never had but one fear, so far as I know: he had a mortal and a reasonable terror of plumbers. He would never stay in the house when they were here. No coaxing could quiet him. Of course, he didn't share our fear about their charges, but he must have had some dreadful experience with them in that portion of his life which is unknown to us. A plumber was to him the devil, and I have no doubt that, in his scheme, plumbers were foreordained to do him mischief.

In speaking of his worth, it has never occurred to me to estimate Calvin by the worldly standard. I know that it is customary now, when anyone dies, to ask how much he was worth, and that no obituary in the newspapers is considered complete without such an estimate. The plumbers in our house were one day overheard to say that, "They say that *she* says that *he* says that he wouldn't take a hundred dollars for him." It is unnecessary to say that I never made such a remark, and that, so far as Calvin was concerned, there was no purchase in money.

As I look back upon it, Calvin's life seems to me a fortunate one, for it was natural and unforced. He ate when he was hungry, slept when he was sleepy, and enjoyed existence to the very tips of his toes and the end of his expressive and slow-moving tail. He delighted to roam about the garden, and stroll among the trees, and to lie on the green grass and luxuriate in all the sweet influences of summer. You could never accuse him of idleness, and yet he knew the secret of repose. The poet who wrote so prettily of him that his little life was rounded with a sleep, understated his felicity; it was rounded with a good many. His conscience never seemed to interfere with his slumbers. In fact, he had good habits and a contented mind. I can see him now walk in at the study door, sit down by my chair, bring his tail artistically about his feet, and look up at me with unspeakable happiness in his handsome face. I often thought that he felt the dumb limitation which denied him the power of language. But since he was denied speech, he scorned the inarticulate mouthings of the lower animals. The vulgar mewing and yowling of the cat species was beneath him; he sometimes uttered a sort of articulate and well-bred ejaculation when he wished to call attention to something that he considered remarkable or to some want of his, but he never went whining about. He would sit for hours at a closed window, when he desired to enter, without a murmur, and when it was opened he never admitted that he had been impatient by bolting in. Though speech he had not, and the unpleasant kind of utterance given to his race he would not use, he had a mighty power of purr to express his measureless content with congenial society. There was in him a musical organ with stops of varied power and expression, upon which I have no doubt he could have performed Scarlatti's celebrated cat's fugue.

Whether Calvin died of old age, or was carried off by one of the diseases incident to youth, it is impossible to say; for his departure was as quiet as his advent was mysterious. I only know that he appeared to us in this world in his perfect stature and beauty, and that after a time, like Lohengrin, he withdrew. In his illness there was nothing more to be regretted than in all his blameless life. I suppose there never was an illness that had more dignity and sweetness and resignation in it. It came on gradually, in a kind of listlessness and want of appetite. An alarming symptom was his preference for the warmth of a furnace register to the lively sparkle of the open wood fire. Whatever pain he suffered, he bore it in silence, and seemed only anxious not to obtrude his malady. We tempted him with the delicacies of the season, but it soon became impossible for him to eat, and for two weeks he ate or drank scarcely anything. Sometimes he made an effort to take something, but it was evident that he made the effort to please us. The neighbours – and I am convinced that the advice of neighbours is never good for anything – suggested catnip. He wouldn't even smell it. We had the attendance of an amateur practitioner of medicine, whose real office was the cure of souls, but nothing touched his case. He took what was offered, but it was with the air of one to whom the time for pellets was past. He sat or lay day after day almost motionless, never once making a display of those vulgar convulsions or contortions of pain which are so disagreeable to society. His favourite place was on the brightest spot of a Smyrna rug by the conservatory, where the sunlight fell and he could hear the fountain play. If we went to him and exhibited our interest in his condition, he always purred in recognition of our sympathy. And when I spoke his name, he looked up with an expression that said, "I understand it, old fellow, but it's no use." He was to all who came to visit him a model of calmness and patience in affliction.

I was absent from home at the last, but heard by daily postal card of his failing condition; and never again saw him alive. One sunny morning he rose from his rug, went into the conservatory (he was very thin then), walked around it deliberately, looking at all the plants he knew, and then went to the bay window in the dining room, and stood a long time looking out upon the little field, now brown and sere, and towards the garden, where perhaps the happiest hours of his life had been spent. It was a last look. He turned and walked away, laid himself down upon the bright spot in the rug, and quietly died.

It is not too much to say that a little shock went through the neighbourhood when it was known that Calvin was dead, so marked was his individuality; and his friends, one after another, came in to see him. There was no sentimental nonsense about his obsequies; it was felt that any parade would have been distasteful to him. John, who acted as undertaker, prepared a candlebox for him, and I believe assumed a professional decorum; but there may have been the usual levity underneath, for I heard that he remarked in the kitchen that it was the "driest wake he ever attended". Everybody, however, felt a fondness for Calvin, and regarded him with a certain respect. Between him and Bertha there existed a great friendship, and she apprehended his nature; she used to say that sometimes she was afraid of him, he looked at her so intelligently; she was never certain that he was what he appeared to be.

When I returned, they had laid Calvin on a table in an upper chamber by an open window. It was February. He reposed in a candlebox, lined about the edge with evergreen, and at his head stood a little wineglass with flowers. He lay with his head tucked down in his arms – a favourite position of his before the fire – as if asleep in the comfort of his soft and exquisite fur. It was the involuntary exclamation of those who saw him, "How natural he looks!" As for myself, I said nothing. John buried him under the twin hawthorn trees – one white and the other pink – in a spot where Calvin was fond of lying and listening to the hum of summer insects and the twitter of birds.

Perhaps I have failed to make appear the individuality of character that was so evident to those who knew him. At any rate, I have set down nothing concerning him but the literal truth. He was always a mystery. I did not know whence he came; I do not know whither he has gone. I would not weave one spray of falsehood in the wreath I lay upon his grave.

from *My Summer in a Garden* (1882)

Lament for Tabby; or, The Cat's Coronach

ELIZABETH DRINKER

And art thou fallen, and lowly laid,
The housewife's boast, the cellar's aid,
    Great mouser of thy day!
Whose rolling eyes, and aspect dread

Whole whiskered legions oft have fled
In midnight battle fray.
There breathes no kitten of thy line
But would have given his life for thine.

Oh, could I match the peerless strain
That wailed for black Sir Roderic slain,
   Or that whose milder tone
O'er Gertrude, fall'n in beauty's prime,
The grace of Pennsylvania's clime,
   Raised the sepulchral moan!
Such strain might burst th' eternal bar,
And reach thy spirit from afar.

But thou, remote from pain and strife,
Now reap'st the meed of virtuous life
   In some Elysian grove,
Where endless streams of milk abound,
And soft valerian paints the ground
   Thy joyous footsteps rove;
With Tasso's cat by poems named,
And Whittington's, in story famed,
   Requies cat in pace.

Egyptian Cats

HERODOTUS (*c.* 480–*c.* 425 BC)

And when a fire breaks out very strange things happen to the
cats. The Egyptians stand round in a broken line, thinking more
of the cats than of quenching the burning; but the cats slip
through or leap over the men and spring into the fire. When
this happens, there is great mourning in Egypt. Dwellers in a
house where a cat has died a natural death shave their eyebrows
and no more; where a dog has so died, the head and the whole
body are shaven.

Dead cats are taken away into sacred buildings, where they
are embalmed and buried, in the town of Bubastis; bitches are
buried in sacred coffins by the townsmen, in their several
towns; and the like is done with ichneumons. Shrewmice
and hawks are taken away to Buto, ibises to the city of Hermes.
There are but few bears, and the wolves are little bigger than
foxes; both these are buried wherever they are found lying.

Atossa

MATTHEW ARNOLD (1822–88)

Poor Matthias! Wouldst thou have
More than pity? claim'st a stave?
– Friends more near us than a bird
We dismiss'd without a word.
Rover, with the good brown head,
Great Atossa, they are dead;
Dead, and neither prose nor rhyme
Tells the praises of their prime.
Thou didst know them old and grey,
Know them in their sad decay.
Thou hast seen Atossa sage
Sit for hours beside thy cage;
Thou wouldst chirp, thou foolish bird,
Flutter, chirp – she never stirr'd!
What were now these toys to her?
Down she sank amid her fur;
Eyed thee with a soul resign'd –
And thou deemedst cats were kind!
– Cruel, but composed and bland,
Dumb, inscrutable and grand,
So Tiberius might have sat,
Had Tiberius been a cat.

from "Poor Matthias"

Cat Hypnosis

W.H. HUDSON (1841–1922)

I must now return to the subject of [...] Bawcombe's cat at Doveton, who had the habit of sitting on a rail of the line which runs through the vale, and was eventually killed by a train. So strange a story – for how strange it seems that an animal of so cautious and well-balanced a mind, so capable above all others of saving itself in difficult and dangerous emergencies, should have met its end in such a way! – might very well have suggested something behind the mere fact, some mysterious weakness in the animal similar to that which Herodotus relates of the Egyptian cat in its propensity of rushing into the fire when a house was burning and thus destroying itself. Yet no such idea came into my mind: it was just a "strange fact", an accident in the life of an individual, and after telling it I passed on, thinking no more about the subject, only to find long months afterwards, by the merest chance, that I had been very near to a discovery of the greatest significance and interest in the life-history of the animal.

It came about in the following way. I was on the platform of a station on the South-Western line from Salisbury to Yeovil, waiting for my train, when a pretty little kitten came out of the stationmaster's house at the end of the platform, and I picked it up. Then a child, a wee girlie of about five, came out to claim her pet, and we got into a talk about the kitten. She was pleased at its being admired, and saying she would show me the other one, ran in and came out with a black kitten in her arms. I duly admired this one too. "But," I said, "they won't let you keep both, because then there would be too many cats."

"No – only two," she returned.

"Three, with their mother."

"No, they haven't got a mother – she was killed on the line."

I remembered the shepherd's cat, and by and by finding the stationmaster I questioned him about the cat that had been killed.

"Oh, yes," he said, "cats are always getting killed on the line
– we can never keep one long. I don't know if they try to cross
the line or how it is. One of the porters saw the last one get
killed and will tell you just how it happened."

I found the porter, and his account was that he saw the cat on
the line, standing with its forepaws on a rail when an express
train was coming. He called to the cat two or three times, then
yelled at it to frighten it off, but it never moved; it stared as if
dazed at the coming train, and was struck on the head and
knocked dead.

This story set me making inquiries at other village stations,
and at other villages where there are no stations, but close to
which the line runs in the Wylye vale and where there is a
pointsman. I was told that cats are very often found killed on
the line, in some instances crushed as if they had been lying or
sitting on a rail when the train went over them. They got
dazed, the men said, and could not save themselves.

I was also told that rabbits were sometimes killed and, more
frequently, hares. "I've had several hares from the line," one
man told me. He said that he had seen a hare running before a
train, and thought that in most cases the hare kept straight on
until it was run down and killed. But not in every case, as he
had actually seen one hare killed, and in this case the hare sat up
and remained staring at the coming train until it was struck.

It cannot be doubted, I think, that the cat is subject to this
strange weakness. It is not a case of "losing its head" like a
cyclist amidst the traffic in a thoroughfare, or of miscalculating
the speed of a coming train and attempting too late to cross the
line. The sight of the coming train paralyzes its will, or
hypnotizes it, and it cannot save itself.

Now the dog, a less well-balanced animal than the cat and
inferior in many ways, has no such failing, and is killed by a
train purely through blundering. While engaged in making
these inquiries, a Wiltshire woman told me of an adventure she
had with her dog, a fox-terrier. She had just got over the line at
a level crossing when the gates swung to, and looking for her
dog she saw him absorbed in a smell he had discovered on the

other side of the line. An express train was just coming, and screaming to her dog she saw him make a dash to get across just as the engine came abreast of her. The dog had vanished from sight, but when the whole train had passed up he jumped from between the rails where he had been crouching and bounded across to her, quite unhurt. He had dived under the train behind the engine, and waited there till it had gone by!

It is, however, a fact that not all the cats killed on the line have been hypnotized or dazed at the sight of the coming train; undoubtedly some do meet their death through attempting to cross the line before a coming train. At all events, I heard of one such case from a person who had witnessed it. It was at a spot where a small group of workmen's cottages stands close to the line at a village; here I was told that "several cats" got killed on the line every year, and as the man who gave me the information had seen a cat running across the line before a train and getting killed, it was assumed by the cottagers that it was so in all cases.

from *A Shepherd's Life* (1910)

Epitaph on a Pet Cat

JOACHIM DU BELLAY (1525–60)

My life seems dull and flat,
And, as you'll wonder what,
Magny, has made this so,
I want you first to know
It's not for rings or purse
But something so much worse:
Three days ago I lost
All that I value most,
My treasure my delight;
I cannot speak or write,
Or even think of what
Belaud, my small grey cat,

Meant to me, tiny creature,
Masterpiece of nature
In the whole world of cats –
And certain death to rats! –
Whose beauty was worthy
Of immortality.

Belaud, first let me say,
Was not entirely grey
Like cats bred here at home,
But more like those in Rome,
His fur being silver-grey
And fine and smooth as satin,
While, lying back, he'd display
A white expanse of ermine;
Small muzzle, tiny teeth;
Eyes of a tempered warmth,
Whose pupils of dark-green
Showed every colour seen
In the bow which splendidly
Arches the rainy sky.

Plump neck, short ears, height
To his head proportionate;
Beneath his ebony nostrils
His little leonine muzzle's
Prim beauty, which appeared
Fringed by the silvery beard
Which gave such waggish grace
To his young dandy's face.

His slender leg, small foot –
No lambswool scarf could be
More soft, except when he
Unsheathed and scratched with it!
His neat and downy throat,
Long monkey's tail, and coat
Diversely flecked and freckled,

In natural motley speckled;
His flank and round stomach
Under control, his back
Longish – a Syrian
If ever there was one!

This was Belaud, a gentle
Animal, whose title
To beauty was so sure
He'd no competitor!
A sad and bitter cross!
Irreparable loss!
It almost seems to me
That Death, though he must be
More ruthless than a bear,
Would, if he'd known my rare
Belaud, have felt his heart
Soften – and for my part
I would not wince and shrink
So from life's joys, I think.

But Death has never watched
Him as he jumped or scratched,
Laughed at his nimble tricks,
His many wild frolics,
Admired the sprightly grace
With which he'd turn, or race,
Or, with one whirl of cat,
Tumble, or seize a rat
And play with it – and then
Would make me laugh again
By rubbing at his jaw
With such a frisky paw
In such a dashing manner!
Or when the little monster
Leapt quietly on my bed,
Or when he took his bread

Or meat most daintily
Straight from my lips – for he
Showed in such various ways
His quaint, engaging traits!

What fun to watch him dance,
Scamper, and skate, and prance
After a ball of thread;
To see his silly head
Whirl like a spinning wheel
After his velvet tail;
Or, when he made of it
A girdle, and would sit
Solemnly on the ground,
Showing his fluffy round
Of paunch, seeming to be
Learned in theology,
The spit of some well-known
Doctor at the Sorbonne!
And how, when he was teased,
He used to fence with us –
Yet if we stopped to fuss
Was very soon appeased!

O Magny, now you see
How he diverted me,
You'll realize why I mourn –
And surely no cat born
Has ever had so nice
A style with rats and mice!

He would come unawares
Upon them in their lairs,
And not one could escape
Unless he'd thought to scrape
A second hole – no rat
Ever outran that cat!

And let me add at once
My Belaud was no dunce,
But very teachable,
Knowing how to eat at table –
When offered food, that is:
That eager paw you'd see,
Held out so flirtingly,
Might scratch you otherwise!

Belaud was well-behaved
And in no way depraved;
His only ravages
Were on an ancient cheese,
A finch, and a young linnet
Whose trillings seemed to get
On Belaud's nerves – but then
How perfect are we men?

He wasn't the sort to be
Out everlastingly
After more food to eat,
But was content to wait
Until his meals, when he
Ate without gluttony.

Also he was by nature
A well conducted creature;
For he would never spread
His traces far and wide
Like many cats, but tried
To live as a well-bred
Feline should live and be
In all his ways cleanly . . .

He was my favourite plaything;
And not for ever purring
A long and tunelessly

Grumbling litany,
But kept in his complainings
To kitten-like miaowings.

My only memory
Of him annoying me
Is that, sometimes at night
When rats began to gnaw
And rustle in my straw
Mattress, he'd waken me
Seizing most dexterously
Upon them in their flight.

Now that the cruel right hand
Of Death comes to demand
My bodyguard from me,
My sweet security
Gives way to hideous fears;
Rats come and gnaw my ears,
And mice and rats at night
Chew up the lines I write!

The gods have sympathy
For poor humanity;
An animal's death foretells
Some evil that befalls,
For heaven can speak by these
And other presages.
The day fate cruelly
Took my small dog from me –
My Peloton – the sense
Of evil influence
Filled me with utter dread;
And then I lost my cat:
What crueller storm than that
Could break upon my head!

He was my very dear
Companion everywhere
My room, my bed, my table,
Even more companionable
Than a little dog; for he
Was never one of those
Monsters that hideously
Fill the night with their miaows;
And now he can't become,
Poor little puss, a tom –
Sad loss, by which his splendid
Line is abruptly ended.

God grant to me, Belaud,
Command of speech to show
Your gentle nature forth
In words of fitting worth,
Your qualities to state
In verse as delicate,
That you may live while cats
Wage mortal war on rats.

translated by R.N. Currey

The Death of Rumpelstiltzchen

ROBERT SOUTHEY (1774–1843)

Alas, Grosvenor, this day died poor old Rumpel, after as long and happy a life as cat could wish for, if cats form wishes on that subject. His full titles were: "The most Noble the Archduke Rumpelstiltzchen, Marquis Macbum, Earl Tomlemagne, Baron Raticide, Waowhler, and Skaratch."

There should be a court mourning in Catland, and if the Dragon [Bedford's cat] wear a black ribbon round his neck, or a band of crape, *à la militaire*, on one of his forelegs, it will be but a becoming mark of respect.

As we have no catacombs here, he is to be decently interred in the orchard, and catmint planted on his grave. Poor creature, it is well that he has thus come to his end, since he had grown to be an object of pity. I believe we are, each and all, servants included, more sorry for his loss, or rather more affected by it, than any one of us would like to confess.

from a letter to Grosvenor C. Bedford

On the Death of a Favourite Cat, Drowned in a Tub of Gold Fishes

THOMAS GRAY (1716–71)

'Twas on a lofty vase's side,
Where China's gayest art had dy'd
　　The azure flowers that blow;
Demurest of the tabby kind,
The pensive Selima, reclin'd,
　　Gaz'd on the lake below.

Her conscious tail her joy declar'd;
The fair round face, the snowy beard,
　　The velvet of her paws,
Her coat, that with the tortoise vies,
Her ears of jet, and emerald eyes,
　　She saw; and purr'd applause.

Still had she gaz'd; but 'midst the tide
Two angel forms were seen to glide,
　　The Genii of the stream:
Their scaly armour's Tyrian hue
Thro' richest purple to the view
　　Betray'd a golden gleam.

The hapless Nymph with wonder saw:
A whisker first, and then a claw,

With many an ardent wish,
She stretch'd in vain to reach the prize.
What female heart can gold despise?
    What Cat's averse to fish?

Presumptuous Maid! with looks intent
Again she stretch'd, again she bent,
    Nor knew the gulf between.
(Malignant Fate sat by, and smil'd.)
The slipp'ry verge her feet beguil'd,
    She tumbled headlong in.

Eight times emerging from the flood
She mew'd to ev'ry wat'ry God,
    Some speedy aid to send.
No Dolphin came, no Nereid stirr'd:
Nor cruel *Tom*, nor *Susan* heard.
    A Fav'rite has no friend!

From hence, ye Beauties, undeceive'd,
Know, one false step is ne'er retriev'd,
    And be with caution bold.
Not all that tempts your wand'ring eyes
And heedless hearts, is lawful prize;
    Nor all that glisters, gold.

Don Pierrot de Navarre

THÉOPHILE GAUTIER (1811–72)

A cat brought from Havana by Mademoiselle Aita de la
Penuela, a young Spanish artist whose studies of white angoras
may still be seen gracing the printsellers' windows, produced
the daintiest little kitten imaginable. It was just like a swan's-
down powder-puff, and on account of its immaculate whiteness it received the name of Pierrot. When it grew big this was

lengthened to Don Pierrot de Navarre as being more grandiose and majestic.

Don Pierrot, like all animals which are spoiled and made much of, developed a charming amiability of character. He shared the life of the household with all the pleasure which cats find in the intimacy of the domestic hearth. Seated in his usual place near the fire, he really appeared to understand what was being said, and to take an interest in it.

His eyes followed the speakers, and from time to time he would utter little sounds, as though he too wanted to make remarks and give his opinion on literature, which was our usual topic of conversation. He was very fond of books, and when he found one open on a table he would lie on it, look at the page attentively, and turn over the leaves with his paw; then he would end by going to sleep, for all the world as if he were reading a fashionable novel.

Directly I took up a pen he would jump on my writing-desk and with deep attention watch the steel nib tracing black spider-legs on the expanse of white paper, and his head would turn each time I began a new line. Sometimes he tried to take part in the work, and would attempt to pull the pen out of my hand, no doubt in order to write himself, for he was an aesthetic cat, like Hoffman's Murr, and I strongly suspect him of having scribbled his memoirs at night on some house-top by the light of his phosphorescent eyes. Unfortunately these lucubrations have been lost.

Don Pierrot never went to bed until I came in. He waited for me inside the door, and as I entered the hall he would rub himself against my legs and arch his back, purring joyfully all the time. Then he proceeded to walk in front of me like a page, and if I had asked him, he would certainly have carried the candle for me. In this fashion he escorted me to my room and waited while I undressed; then he would jump on the bed, put his paws round my neck, rub noses with me, and lick me with his rasping little pink tongue, while giving vent to soft in-articulate cries, which clearly expressed how pleased he was to see me again. Then when his transports of affection had subsided, and the hour for repose had come, he would balance himself on the rail of the bedstead and sleep there like a bird perched on a bough. When I woke in the morning he would come and lie near me until it was time to get up. Twelve o'clock was the hour at which I was supposed to come in. On this subject Pierrot had all the notions of a concierge.

At that time we had instituted little evening gatherings among a few friends, and had formed a small society, which we called the Four Candles Club, the room in which we met being, as it happened, lit by four candles in silver candlesticks, which were placed at the corners of the table.

Sometimes the conversation became so lively that I forgot the time, at the risk of finding, like Cinderella, my carriage turned into a pumpkin and my coachman into a rat.

Pierrot waited for me several times until two o'clock in the morning, but in the end my conduct displeased him, and he went to bed without me. This mute protest against my innocent dissipation touched me so much that ever after I came home regularly at midnight. But it was a long time before Pierrot forgave me. He wanted to be sure that it was not a sham repentance; but when he was convinced of the sincerity of my conversion, he deigned to take me into favour again, and he resumed his nightly post in the entrance-hall. [...]

Don Pierrot de Navarre, being a native of Havana, needed a hot-house temperature. This he found indoors, but the house was surrounded by large gardens, divided up by palings through which a cat could easily slip, and planted with big trees in which hosts of birds twittered and sang; and sometimes Pierrot, taking advantage of an open door, would go out hunting of an evening and run over the dewy grass and flowers. He would then have to wait till morning to be let in again, for although he might come mewing under the windows, his appeal did not always wake the sleepers inside.

He had a delicate chest, and one colder night than usual he took a chill which soon developed into consumption. Poor Pierrot, after a year of coughing, became wasted and thin, and his coat, which formerly boasted such a snowy gloss, now put one in mind of the lustreless white of a shroud. His great limpid eyes looked enormous in his attenuated face. His pink nose had grown pale, and he would walk sadly along the sunny wall with slow steps, and watch the yellow autumn leaves whirling up in spirals. He looked as though he were reciting Millevoye's elegy. There is nothing more touching than a sick animal; it submits to suffering with such gentle, pathetic resignation. Everything possible was done to try and save Pierrot. He had a very clever doctor who sounded him and felt his pulse. He ordered him asses' milk, which the poor creature drank willingly enough out of his little china saucer. He lay for hours on my knee like the ghost of a sphinx, and I could feel the bones of his spine like the beads of a rosary under my fingers. He tried to respond to my caresses with a feeble purr which was like a death rattle.

When he was dying he lay panting on his side, but with a supreme effort he raised himself and came to me with dilated eyes in which there was a look of intense supplication. This look seemed to say: "Cannot you save me, you who are a man?" Then he staggered a short way with eyes already glazing, and fell down with such a lamentable cry, so full of despair and anguish, that I was pierced with silent horror.

He was buried at the bottom of the garden under a white rosebush which still marks his grave.

from "The White and Black Dynasties"
in *La Ménagerie Intime* translated by Lady Chance

In Memoriam Mrs Snowball Pat Paw

LOUISA M. ALCOTT (1832–88)

THE PUBLIC BEREAVEMENT

It is our painful duty to record the sudden and mysterious disappearance of our cherished friend, Mrs Snowball Pat Paw. This lovely and beloved cat was the pet of a large circle of warm and admiring friends; for her beauty attracted all eyes, her graces and virtues, endeared her to all hearts, and her loss is deeply felt by the whole community.

When last seen, she was sitting at the gate, watching the butcher's cart; and it is feared that some villain, tempted by her charms, basely stole her. Weeks have passed, but no trace of her has been discovered; and we relinquish all hope, tie a black ribbon to her basket, set aside her dish, and weep for her as one lost to us for ever.

A LAMENT

For S. B. Pat Paw

We mourn the loss of our little pet,
    And sigh o'er her hapless fate.
For never more by the fire she'll sit,
    Nor play by the old green gate.

The little grave where her infant sleeps,
    Is 'neath the chestnut tree;
But o'er *her* grave we may not weep,
    We know not where it may be.

Her empty bed, her idle ball,
    Will never see her more;
No gentle tap, no loving purr
    Is heard at the parlour door.

Another cat comes after her mice,
    A cat with a dirty face;
But she does not hunt as our darling did,
    Nor play with her airy grace.

Her stealthy paws tread the very hall
    Where Snowball used to play,

But she only spits at the dogs our pet
So gallantly drove away.

She is useful and mild, and does her best,
But she is not fair to see;
And we cannot give her your place, dear,
Nor worship her as we worship thee.

from *Little Women* (1868–9)

A Favourite Cat's Dying Soliloquy Addressed to Mrs Patton of Lichfield
ANNA SEWARD (1747–1809)

Long years beheld me *Patton*'s mansion grace,
The gentlest, fondest of the feline race;
Before her frisking thro' the garden glade,
Or at her feet, in quite slumber, laid;
Prais'd for my glossy back, of tortoise streak,
And the warm smoothness of my snowy neck;
Soft paws, that sheath'd for her the clawing nails,
The shining whisker, and meand'ring tail.
Now feeble age each glazing eye-ball dims,
And pain has stiffen'd these once supple limbs;
Fate of eight lives the forfeit gasp obtains,
And e'en the ninth creeps languid thro' my veins.

Much, sure, of good the future has in store,
When Lucy basks on *Patton*'s hearth no more,
In those blest climes where fishes oft forsake
The winding river and the glassy lake;
There as our silent-footed race behold
The spots of crimson and the fins of gold,
Venturing beyond the shielding waves to stray,
They gasp on shelving banks, our easy prey;
While birds unwing'd hop careless o'er the ground,

575

And the plump mouse incessant trots around,
Near wells of cream, which mortals never skim,
Warm marum creeping round their shallow brim;
Where green valerian tufts, luxuriant spread,
Cleanse the sleek hide, and form the fragrant bed.

Yet, stern dispenser of the final blow,
Before thou lay'st an aged Grimalkin low,
Bend to her last request a gracious ear,
Some days, some few short days to linger here!
So, to the guardian of her earthly weal
Shall softest purs these tender truths reveal:
Ne'er shall thy now expiring Puss forget
To thy kind cares her long-enduring debt;
Nor shall the joys that painless realms decree,
Efface the comforts once bestow'd by thee;
To countless mice thy chicken bones preferr'd,
Thy toast to golden fish and wingless bird:
O'er marum border and valerian bed
Thy Lucy shall decline her moping head;
Sigh that she climbs no more, with grateful glee,
Thy downy sofa and thy cradling knee;
Nay, e'en by walls of cream shall sullen swear,
Since *Patton*, her lov'd mistress, is not there.

More Egyptian Cats

DIODORUS OF SICILY (1st century BC)

When one of these animals dies they wrap it in fine linen and
then, wailing and beating their breasts, carry it off to be embalmed; and after it has been treated with cedar oil and such spices
as have the quality of imparting a pleasant odour and of preser-
ving the body for a long time, they lay it away in a consecrated
tomb. And whoever intentionally kills one of these animals is put
to death, unless it be a cat or an ibis that he kills; but if he kills one

of these, whether intentionally or unintentionally, he is certainly put to death, for the common people gather in crowds and deal with the perpetrator most cruelly, sometimes doing this without waiting for a trial. And because of their fear of such a punishment any who have caught sight of one of these animals lying dead withdraw to a great distance and shout with lamentations and protestations that they found the animal already dead. So deeply implanted also in the hearts of the common people is their superstitious regard for these animals and so unalterable are the emotions cherished by every man regarding the honour due to them that once, at the time when Ptolemy their king had not as yet been given by the Romans the appellation of "friend" and the people were exercising all zeal in courting the favour of the embassy from Italy which was then visiting Egypt and, in their fear, were intent upon giving no cause for complaint or war, when one of the Romans killed a cat and the multitude rushed in a crowd to his house, neither the officials sent by the king to beg the man off nor the fear of Rome which all the people felt were enough to save the man from punishment, even though his act had been an accident. And this incident we relate, not from hearsay, but we saw it with our own eyes on the occasion of the visit we made to Egypt.

To a Cat

IBN ALALAF ALNAHARWANY

Poor Puss is gone! 'Tis fate's decree —
Yet I must still her loss deplore,
For dearer than a child was she,
And ne'er shall I behold her more.

With many a sad presaging tear
This morn I saw her steal away,
While she went on without a fear
Except that she should miss her prey.

I saw her to the dove-house climb,
With cautious feet and slow she stept,
Resolved to balance loss of time
By eating faster than she crept.

Her subtle foes were on the watch
And mark'd her course, with fury fraught,
And while she hoped the birds to catch,
An arrow's point the huntress caught.

In fancy she had got them all,
And drunk their blood, and suck'd their breath;
Alas! she only got a fall,
And only drank the draught of death.

Why, why was pigeons' flesh so nice,
That thoughtless cats should love it thus?
Hadst thou but lived on rats and mice,
Thou hadst been living still, poor Puss.

Curst be the taste, howe'er refined,
That prompts us for such joys to wish,
And curst the dainty where we find
Destruction lurking in the dish.

                              translated by J.D. Carlyle

Bathsheba

JOHN GREENLEAF WHITTIER (1807–92)

To whom none ever said scat,
No worthier cat
Ever sat on a mat
Or caught a rat:
Requies – cat.

Dedication

GRAHAM R. TOMSON (1863–1911)

Dear Furry Shade! in regions of the Dead,
On pleasant plains, by murmurous waters, led;
What placid joys your brindled bosom swell!
While smiling virgins crowned with asphodel
Bring brimming bowls of milk in sacrifice,
And, passing plump and sleek, th' Elysian mice
Sport round your feet, and frisk, and glide away,
Captured at last – a not too facile prey.
Yet, with each earthly care and tremor stilled,
With every wish of cat-hood well fulfilled,
Still sometimes turn, with retrospective gaze,
To count the sweets of less luxurious days,
When you were wont to take your simple ease
Couched at my feet or stretched along my knees:
When never cloud our loving-kindness knew
(Though now and then, alas! I punished you),
Still were you fain, conciliating, bland,
With velvet cheek to chafe th' avenging hand.
Still would you watch, did I but chance to roam,
Supine upon the threshold of our home
Until, my brief-paced aberrations o'er,
With purrings deep you welcomed me once more.
O dearly-loved! Untimely lost! – today
An offering at your phantom feet I lay:
Purr fond applause, and take in gracious kind
This little wreath of various verses twined;
Nor, though Persephone's own Puss you be,
Let Orcus breed oblivion – of me.

Jeremy Bentham's Cat

DR BOWRING

Bentham was very fond of animals, particularly "pussies", as he called them, when they had domestic virtues, but he had no particular affection for the common race of cats. He had one, however, of which he used to boast that he had "made a man of him", and whom he was wont to invite to eat macaroni at his own table. This puss got knighted, and rejoiced in the name of Sir John Langbourne. In his early days he was a frisky, inconsiderate, and, to say the truth, somewhat profligate gentleman; and had, according to the report of his patron, the habit of seducing light and giddy young ladies, of his own race, into the garden of Queen's Square Place: but tired at last, like Solomon, of pleasures and vanities, he became sedate and thoughtful – took to the church, laid down his knightly title, and was installed as the Reverend John Langbourne. He gradually obtained a great reputation for sanctity and learning, and a Doctor's degree was conferred upon him. When I knew him, in his declining days, he bore no other name than the Reverend Doctor John Langbourne: and he was alike conspicuous for his gravity and philosophy. Great respect was invariably shown his reverence: and it was supposed that he was not far off from a mitre, when old age interfered with his hopes and honours. He departed amidst the regrets of his many friends, and was gathered to his fathers, and to eternal rest, in a cemetery in Milton's garden.

Upon a Friend's Pet Cat, Being Sick

JOHN WINSTANLEY (1678-1751)

How fickle's Health! when sickness thus
So sharp, so sudden visits *Puss*!
A warning fair, and Instance good,
To show how frail are Flesh and Blood,

That Fate has Mortals at a Call,
Men, Women, Children – Cats and all.
Nor should we fear, despair, or sorrow,
If well today, and ill tomorrow,
Grief being but a Med'cine vain,
For griping Gut, or aching Brain,
And Patience the best Cure for Pain.
How brisk and well, last Week, was *Puss!*
How sleek, and plump, as one of us:
Yet now, alack! and well-a-day!
How dull, how rough, and fall'n away.
How feintly creeps about the House!
Regardless or of Play, or Mouse;
Nor stomach has, to drink, or eat,
Of sweetest Milk, or daintiest Meat;
A grievous this, and sore Disaster
To all the House, but most his Master,
Who sadly takes it thus to heart,
As in his Pains he bore a part.
And, what increases yet his Grief,
Is, nought can cure, or give Relief,
No Doctor caring to prescribe,
Or Med'cine give, for Love, or Bribe,
Nor other Course, but to petition
Dame Nature, oft the best Physician,
The readiest too, and cheapest sure,
Since she ne'er asks a Fee for Cure
Nor ever takes a single Shilling,
As many basely do for killing.
So, for a while, snug let him lie,
As Fates decree, to live or die,
While I, in dismal dog'rel Verse,
His Beauties and his Fame rehearse.
Poor *Bob!* how have I smiled to see
Thee sitting on thy Master's Knee?
While, pleased to stroke thy Tabby-coat,
Sweet Purrings warbling in thy Throat,

He would with rapturous Hug declare,
No Voice more sweet, or Maid more fair.
No prating Poll, or Monkey bold,
Was more caress'd by Woman old,
Nor flutt'ring Fop, with Am'rous Tongue,
So much admir'd by Virgin Young.
Miss *Betty's* Bed-fellow, and Pet
(Too young to have another yet),
At Dinner, he'd beside her sit,
Fed from her Mouth with sweetest Bit;
Not Mrs L———'s so charming *Philly*
Was more familiar, fond, or silly,
Nor Mrs C———'s ugly Cur
Made more a foustre, or more stir.
Oft tir'd, and cloy'd, with being petted,
Or else by *Molly* beaten, fretted,
He'd out into the Garden run,
To sleep in th' Shade, or bask in th' Sun;
Sometimes about the Walks he'd ramble,
Or on the verdant Green would amble,
Or under the hedges sculking sit,
To catch the unwary *Wren*, or *Tit*,
Or *Sparrows* young, which Sun-beams hot
Had forc'd to quit their mansion Pot,
Then murther with relentless Claws.
Now, cruel Death, so fierce and grim,
With gaping jaws does threaten him,
While pining, he, with Sickness sore,
Oppress'd and griev'd, can hunt no more.

Now joyful Mice skip, frisk, and play,
And safely revel, Night and Day.
The Garrets, Kitchens, Stairs, and Entry,
Unguarded by that dreadful Sentry.

The Pantry now is open set,
No fear for *Puss* therein to get,

With Chicken cold to run away,
Or sip the Cream set by for Tea;
Jenny now need not watch the Door,
Or for lost Meat repine no more,
Nor *Molly* many a scolding dread
For slamming him from off the Bed;
Poor harmless Animal! now lies
As who can say, he lives or dies.
Tho' I have heard a saying that
Some three times three Lives has a Cat;
Should Death then now the Conquest gain,
And feeble *Bob*, with struggle vain,
To his resistless Fate give way,
Yet come to Life, another Day,
How will Time scratch his old bald Pate,
To see himself so *Bobb'd*, so Bit,
To find that *Bob* has eight Lives more
To lose, e'er he can him secure.
Should he however, this Bout dye,
What Pen should write his Elegy?
No living Bard is fit, not One;
Since *Addison*, and Parnel's gone;
Or such another Pen, as that
Which wrote so fine on Mountaign's Cat.

The Church Cat

GEORGE BORROW (1803–81)

As I and my family sat at tea in our parlour, an hour or two after we
had taken possession of our lodgings, the door of the room and
that of the entrance of the house being open, on account of the
fineness of the weather, a poor black cat entered hastily, sat down
on the carpet by the table, looked up towards us, and mewed
piteously. I never had seen so wretched a looking creature. It was
dreadfully attenuated, being little more than skin and bone, and

was sorely afflicted with an eruptive malady. And here I may as well relate the history of this cat previous to our arrival which I subsequently learned by bits and snatches. It had belonged to a previous vicar of Llangollen, and had been left behind at his departure. His successor brought with him dogs and cats, who, conceiving that the late vicar's cat had no business at the vicarage, drove it forth to seek another home, which, however, it could not find. Almost all the people of the suburb were Dissenters, as indeed were the generality of the people at Llangollen, and knowing the cat to be a church cat, not only would not harbour it, but did all they could to make it miserable; whilst the few who were not Dissenters, would not receive it into their houses, either because they had cats of their own, or dogs, or did not want a cat, so that the cat had no home and was dreadfully persecuted by nine-tenths of the suburb. Oh, there never was a cat so persecuted as that poor Church of England animal, and solely on account of the opinions which it was supposed to have imbibed in the house of its late master, for I never could learn that the Dissenters of the suburb, nor indeed of Llangollen in general, were in the habit of persecuting other cats; the cat was a Church of England cat, and that was enough: stone it, hang it, drown it! were the cries of almost everybody. If the workmen of the flannel factory, all of whom were Calvinistic Methodists, chanced to get a glimpse of it in the road from the windows of the building, they would sally forth in a body, and with sticks, stones, or for want of other weapons, with clots of horse-dung, of which there was always plenty on the road, would chase it up the high bank or perhaps over the Camlas – the inhabitants of a small street between our house and the factory leading from the road to the river, all of whom were Dissenters, if they saw it moving about the perllan, into which their back windows looked, would shriek and hoot at it, and fling anything of no value, which came easily to hand, at the head or body of the ecclesiastical cat. The good woman of the house, who though a very excellent person, was a bitter Dissenter, whenever she saw it upon her ground or heard it was there, would make after it, frequently attended by her maid Margaret, and her young son, a boy about nine years of age, both of whom hated the cat, and were always ready to attack it, either alone or in company, and no wonder, the maid being not only a Dissenter, but a class teacher, and the boy not only a Dissenter, but intended for the Dissenting ministry. Where it got its food, and food it sometimes must have got, for even a cat, an animal known to have nine lives, cannot live without food, was only known to itself, as was the place where it lay, for even a cat must lie down sometimes; though a labouring man who occasionally dug in the garden told me he believed that in the springtime it ate freshets, and the woman of the house once said that she believed it sometimes slept in the hedge, which hedge, by the bye, divided our perllan from the vicarage grounds, which were very extensive. Well might the cat having led this kind of life for better than two years look mere skin and bone when it made its appearance in our apartment, and have an eruptive malady, and also a bronchitic cough, for I remember it had both. How it came to make its appearance there is a mystery, for it had never entered the house before, even when there were lodgers; that it should not visit the woman, who was its declared enemy, was natural enough, but why, if it did not visit her other lodgers, did it visit us? Did instinct keep it aloof from them? Did instinct draw it towards us?

We gave it some bread-and-butter, and a little tea with milk and sugar. It ate and drank and soon began to purr. The good woman of the house was horrified when on coming in to remove the things she saw the church cat on her carpet. "What impudence!" she exclaimed, and made towards it, but on our telling her that we did not expect that it should be disturbed, she let it alone. A very remarkable circumstance was, that though the cat had hitherto been in the habit of flying not only from her face, but the very echo of her voice, it now looked her in the face with perfect composure, as much as to say, "I don't fear you, for I know that I am now safe and with my own people." It stayed with us two hours and then went away. The next morning it returned. To be short, though it went away every night, it became our own cat, and one of our family. I gave it something which cured it of its eruption, and through good treatment it soon lost its other ailments and began to look sleek and bonny.

We were at first in some perplexity with respect to the disposal of the ecclesiastical cat; it would of course not do to leave it in the garden to the tender mercies of the Calvinistic Methodists of the neighbourhood, more especially those of the flannel manufactory, and my wife and daughter could hardly carry it with them. At length we thought of applying to a young woman of sound church principles who was lately married and lived over the water on the way to the railway station, with whom we were slightly acquainted, to take charge of the animal, and she on the first intimation of our wish willingly acceded to it. So with her poor puss was left along with a trifle for its milk-money, and with her, as we subsequently learned, it continued in peace and comfort till one morning it sprang suddenly from the hearth into the air, gave a mew and died. So much for the ecclesiastical cat.

from *Wild Wales* (1862)

Epitaph

JOHN JORTIN

WORN out with age and dire disease, a cat,
Friendly to all save wicked mouse and rat,
I'm sent at last to ford the Stygian lake,
And to the infernal coast a voyage make.
Me Proserpine received, and smiling said:
"Be blessed within these mansions of the dead.
Enjoy among thy velvet-footed loves,
Elysian's sunny banks, and shady groves!"
"But if I've well deserved (O gracious Queen),
If patient under sufferings I have been,
Grant me at least one night to visit home again,
Once more to see my home and mistress dear,
And purr these grateful accents in her ear:
'Thy faithful cat, thy poor departed slave
Still loves her mistress, e'en beyond the grave.' "

Hiddigeigei's Last Song

J.V. VON SCHEFFEL (1826–86)

Soon life's thread must break and ravel,
　　Weak this arm, once strong and brave:
In the scene of all my travail,
　　In the granary, dig my grave.

Warlike glory there I won me,
　　All the fight's fierce joy was mine;
Lay my shield and lance upon me,
　　As the last of all my line.

Ay, the last! The children's merit
　　Like their sires' can never grow;
Nought they know of strife of spirit;
　　Upright are they, dull and slow.

Dull and meagre; stiffly, slowly,
　　Move their minds, of force bereft;
Few indeed will keep as holy
　　The bequest their sires have left.

Yet once more, in days far distant,
　　When at rest I long have lain,
One fierce caterwaul insistent
　　Through your ranks shall ring again:

"Flee, ye fools, from worse than ruin!"
　　Hark to Hiddigeigei's cry;
Hark, his wrathful ghostly mewing:
"Flee from mediocrity!"

　　　　　　from "Songs of the Tom-cat Hiddigeigei"
　　　　　　　　in *The Trumpeter* (1893)

Epitaph on the Duchess of Maine's Cats

FRANÇOIS DE LA MOTRE LE VAYER (1588–1672)

Puss passer-by, within this simple tomb
  Lies one whose life fell Atropos hath shred;
The happiest cat on earth hath heard her doom,
  And sleeps for ever in a marble bed.
Alas! what long delicious days I've seen!
  O cats of Egypt, my illustrious sires,
You who on altars, bound with garlands green,
  Have melted hearts, and kindled fond desires—
Hymns in your praise were paid, and offerings too,
  But I'm not jealous of those rights divine,
Since Ludovisa loved me, close and true,
  Your ancient glory was less proud than mine.
To live a simple pussy by her side
Was nobler far than to be deified.

On the Death of a Cat,
A Friend of Mine, Aged Ten Years and a Half

CHRISTIAN ROSSETTI (1830–94)

Who shall tell the lady's grief
When her Cat was past relief?
Who shall number the hot tears
Shed o'er her, beloved for years?
Who shall say the dark dismay
Which her dying caused that day?

Come, ye Muses, one and all,
Come obedient to my call.

Come and mourn, with tuneful breath,
Each one for a separate death;
And while you in numbers sigh,
I will sing her elegy.

Of a noble race she came,
And Grimalkin was her name.
Young and old full many a mouse
Felt the prowess of her house:
Weak and strong full many a rat
Cowered beneath her crushing pat:
And the birds around the place
Shrank from her too close embrace.
But one night, reft of her strength,
She laid down and died at length:
Lay a kitten by her side,
In whose life the mother died.
Spare her line and lineage,
Guard her kitten's tender age,

And that kitten's name as wide
Shall be known as hers that died.

And whoever passes by
The poor grave where Puss doth lie,
Softly, softly let him tread,
Nor disturb her narrow bed.

from *Verses* (1847)

Elegy on de Marsay

J.K. STEPHEN (1859–92)

Come cats and kittens everywhere,
What'er of cat the world contains,

From Tabby on the kitchen stair
To Tiger burning in his lair
  Unite your melancholy strains;

Weep, likewise, kindred dogs, and weep
  Domestic fowls and pigs and goats;
Weep horses, oxen, poultry, sheep,
Weep finny monsters of the deep,
  Weep foxes, badgers, weasels, stoats.

Weep more than all, exalted man
  And hardly less exalted maid;
Out-weep creation if you can
Which never yet, since time began,
  Such creditable grief displayed.

It little profiteth that we
  Go proudly up and down the land,
And drive our ships across the sea,
And babble of Eternity,
  And hold the Universe in hand;

If, when our pride is at its height,
  And glory sits upon our head,
A sudden mist can dim the light,
A voice be heard in pride's despite,
  A voice which cries: "De Marsay's dead."

De Marsay dead! and never more
  Shall I behold that silky form
Lie curled upon the conscious floor
With sinuous limbs and placid snore,
  As one who sleeps through calm and storm?

De Marsay dead! De Marsay dead!
  And are you dead, de Marsay, you?
The sun is shining overhead

With glory undiminished,
  And you are dead; let me die too!

The birds, and beasts, and fishes come,
  And people come, of all degrees;
Beat, sadly beat the funeral drum,
And let the gloomy organ hum
  With dark mysterious melodies.

And (when we've adequately moaned),
  For all the world to wonder at,
Let this great sentence be intoned:
No cat so sweet a mistress owned;
  No mistress owned so sweet a cat.

from *Lapsus Calami* (1891)

Index of Authors

Acknowledgments

Hilaire Belloc, "A Conversation with a Cat", reprinted by permission of The Peters Fraser & Dunlop Group on behalf of the Estate of Hilaire Belloc

George Mackay Brown, "The Cure", from *Six Lives of Fankle the Cat*, reprinted by permission of John Murray (Publishers) Ltd

Anton Chekhov, "Who Was to Blame?", from *The Cook's Wedding and Other Stories* translated by Constance Garnett, reprinted by permission of A.P. Watt Ltd on behalf of the Executors of the Estate of Constance Garnett

Ernest Dudley, "The White Mog", reprinted by permission of the author

Marian Evans, "The Miracle of St Simon's", reprinted by permission of the author

Geoffrey Household, "Abner of the Porch", from *The Europe That Was*, reprinted by permission of A.M. Heath Ltd

James Herriot, "Mrs Bond's Cats", from *All Things Bright and Beautiful* reprinted by permission of Michael Joseph Ltd, David Higham Associates and St Martin's Press LLC © 1973, 1974 by James Herriot

Bryan MacMahon, "The Cat in the Cornfield", from *The Red Petticoat and Other Stories*, reprinted by permission of Macmillan Ltd

Christopher Park, "The Case of the Rolls-Royce and the Flying Cat", reprinted by permission of the author

Ellis Peters, "The Trinity Cat", reprinted by permission of Deborah Owen Ltd © 1976 by Ellis Peters. First published in *Winter's Crimes 8* (Macmillan 1976)

ACKNOWLEDGMENTS

Every effort has been made to contact copyright-holders. However, the editor and publishers would be pleased to hear from any that they have been unable to trace and due acknowledgment will be made in future editions.